ASTROPHYSICS OF ACTIVE GALAXIES AND QUASI-STELLAR OBJECTS

Edited by

JOSEPH S. MILLER

Lick Observatory
University of California
Santa Cruz

University Science Books
1985

This volume is based on the
1984 SANTA CRUZ ASTROPHYSICS WORKSHOP
held in honor of
PROFESSOR DONALD E. OSTERBROCK
on his 60th Birthday

University Science Books

20 Edgehill Road, Mill Valley, CA 94941

Library of Congress Catalog Card Number: 85-050984

ISBN 0-935702-21-0

Printed in the United States of America

10   9   8   7   6   5   4   3   2   1

PREFACE

The Seventh Santa Cruz Workshop on Astrophysics was held July 16-July 27, 1984 at the University of California, Santa Cruz. The subject was "Astrophysics of Quasi-Stellar Objects and Active Galactic Nuclei" and approximately 140 scientists attended the meeting. The Organizing Committee consisted of the following individuals: Dr. George Blumenthal (University of California, Santa Cruz), Dr. Eugene Capriotti (Ohio State University), Dr. Marshall Cohen (California Institute of Technology), Dr. Holland C. Ford (Space Telescope Science Institute), Dr. William Mathews (University of California, Santa Cruz), Dr. Christopher F. McKee (University of California, Berkeley), Dr. Joseph Miller, Chairman (University of California, Santa Cruz), Dr. Daniel Weedman (Pennsylvania State University), and Dr. Ray J. Weymann (University of Arizona).

The decision to hold the 1984 Workshop in honor of Donald Osterbrock on his 60th birthday grew out of discussions between Eugene Capriotti and me. Six years had passed since the previous Santa Cruz Workshop on active galaxies and quasi-stellar objects, and the influence of Osterbrock's work, on this field of research has been extensive. Readers of this volume will see the impact of his research repreatedly throughout the book. Furthermore, Osterbrock's students (and students of these students) have made numerous important contributions to the subject of the Workshop; four of the authors of chapters in this book were his Ph.D. students.

The Organizing Committee felt it was important to publish some kind of permanent account of the material presented in the Workshop. It was decided that a proceedings including invited and contributed papers as well as transcriptions of the discussions would not be appropriate for a Workshop. Rather, a number of topics were identified as important areas of concern during the meeting, and the Organizing Committee invited participants to produce chapters on these topics. The goal was to have each chapter represent the current state of research on a topic, incorporating material presented and discussed at the Workshop. While authors were given a considerable amount of freedom in how they approached their subject material, they were strongly encouraged to attempt to present a balanced view of the subject rather than their own personal views. The result is a fair amount of variety in the approach of the various chapters, but I feel that overall they give an excellent feeling for the areas of agreement and concern that emerged during the Workshop.

It was clear to all who attended both this Workshop and the one in 1978 on the same subject that considerable progress has been made since then in most of areas treated during the meeting. It is now realized that the distinction between active galaxies and normal ones is not clear cut; in fact, there is considerable evidence that the majority of spiral galaxies show some kind of activity not directly related to stellar sources in their nuclei.

The standard idea that there are two distinct emission regions, one producing broad lines and the other narrow, is clearly a gross simplification. Furthermore, the idea that photoionization models for the broad-line region which treat it in terms of the ionization structure of a single cloud is clearly inappropriate when detailed comparisons are made with observations, and a new generation of more realistic models is required. Considerable evidence has accumulated that where the "narrow-line region" ends and the interstellar medium of the galaxy itself begins is not well defined, and active nuclei may affect substantial portions of the galaxies in which they reside. The dynamical state of the gas producing the nuclear emission lines is still an area of considerable controversy.

The overall continuum energy distribution of central objects received considerable attention, with the addition of new X-ray, ultraviolet, and infrared data furnishing new insights. It appears that much of the X-ray to infrared continuum can be understood as a powerlaw with superimposed "bumps," the bumps arising from Fe II emission and perhaps thermal emission from a disk. However, realistic models for the mechanisms which give rise to the featureless continuum do not yet exist. Similarly, the physics of compact radio sources and jets is understood only in the most general terms. There is a clear consensus that some kind of accretion process is responsible for the energy generation in QSOs and active nuclei. There is considerable evidence that there are correlations among the radio and optical properties of active nuclei which indicate that processess occurring on vastly different size scales and observed at different wavelengths are intimately related, but no detailed models have been produced which account for this.

While there is now an extensive body of data which indicates that luminous active galactic nuclei are indeed in galaxies, the nature of the host galaxies themselves is unclear. The situation for quasars is even more puzzling. Available evidence suggests that they are not in normal galaxies, and perhaps the quasar phenomenon produces or results from disruptions extending over galactic dimensions; interaction between galaxies appears to play a role in the production of nuclear activity in many cases.

So while it was clear at the Workshop that we still do not have anything like a clear, comprehensive picture of what is happening in active galaxies and QSOs, real progress has been made toward that picture and I believe that this volume provides a good perspective of the state of research on many of the topics connected with the physics of active galactive nuclei.

Joseph S. Miller
April 1985

Acknowledgements

The planning and work associated with a gathering of this type is considerable. Unless one has gone through the effort oneself, it is very difficult to appreciate the seemingly endless series of decisions, arrangements, and letters that are required. Sue Robinson, who has been extensively involved in six of the past Workshops, carried the responsibility for nearly all of the administrative duties associated with this Workshop. This included extensive correspondence with hundreds of individuals, arranging the rather complex scheduling of the rooms, making sure that facilities were in order for the meeting itself, solving people's difficult logistics problems during the meeting— the list goes on indefinitely. All of us who were at the meeting know the debt of gratitude we owe her for the excellent, dedicated job she performed, and there is no question that she played an important role in the overall success of the Workshop.

The preparation of this volume was the work of Sue Robinson and Pat Shand, who is in charge of publications at Lick Observatory. They typed all the papers into the text formatter of the Lick VAX computer, carefully corrected manuscripts in accordance with authors' suggestions, and produced the final camera-ready copy with the assistance of Lick programmer De Clarke and the Lick laser printer. The excellent overall quality of production of this volume is entirely their credit. We also wish to thank the Astrophysics Division of NASA for their grant to provide partial funding for the production of this book and Mr. Bruce Armbruster, Editor at University Science Books, for his eager willingness to publish the book on a short time scale.

Partial support for expenses associated with the Workshop were provided by grants from the Lawrence Livermore Laboratory and CALSPACE.

TABLE OF CONTENTS

LOW-LUMINOSITY ACTIVE GALACTIC NUCLEI

William C. Keel

Kitt Peak National Observatory

National Optical Astronomy Observatories*

ABSTRACT

The properties of low-luminosity active nuclei are summarized, including low-ionization nuclei (LINERs), weak Seyfert nuclei, composite objects, and starbursts. Continuities exist among all classes of objects exhibiting nonstellar energy input, implying that a similar continuity of physical processes exists. These objects are very common among "normal" galaxies, so that the presence of nonstellar activity may reflect basic and widespread galaxy properties, most likely depth of the central potential well.

Important questions remain as to the details of the relations among the classes of active nuclei, their relation to star-forming nuclei, and how these objects differ from the high-luminosity classical Seyfert nuclei, radio galaxies, and QSOs. In particular, the ionization mechanism in low-ionization objects is not well established, with reasonable arguments available supporting models of shock heating and photionization by a central power-law-like source. There is some support for the idea that various LINERs may have different dominant modes of energy input.

The relation between nuclear star formation and nonstellar activity needs to be clarified. The properties of starburst nuclei suggest that they may evolve rapidly into compact configurations of collapsed remnants, which might further collapse into massive accretors. Conversely, some luminous active nuclei show surrounding star formation, which may indicate that nuclear activity can induce star formation in its environs.

* Operated by the Association of Universities for Research in Astronomy, Inc., under contract with the National Science Foundation

I. INTRODUCTION

The discovery of such active objects as Seyfert and radio galaxies has long engendered speculation that they represent one end of a continuum of galactic nuclear activity extending all the way to the comparatively mild events in the nucleus of our galaxy or the very subtle nonstellar components of the M31 nucleus. Burbidge, Burbidge, and Sandage (1963), Ambartsumian (1971), Burbidge (1978) and Rees (1978), for example, have considered the connections suspected between normal and active nuclei, based on plausible duty cycles for activity, the number of quasar remnants to be expected now given the strong evolution seen at large redshifts, and the notion of galaxies having the potential for strong nuclear activity without necessarily manifesting it constantly. A single, unified picture for galactic nuclei is naturally attractive, but only recently have hard data supporting continuous sequences of nuclear activity become available.

This chapter deals specifically with the low- and intermediate-luminosity active nuclei that bridge the gap between "normal" nuclei and classical Seyfert and radio galaxies. No fully unified treatment is yet possible, since these levels of activity have several manifestations that are, in our present understanding, distinct. The observed continuities and differences among these will be stressed, in the hope of spurring further work on how fundamental these distinctions are.

In this discussion, I reserve the term "active nucleus" for one in which the presence of energy input not traceable to stars and their remnants (including supernovae) can be demonstrated. No clean definition of a "low-luminosity active nucleus" can be made; such objects include the intrinsically faintest conventional Seyfert nuclei, low-ionization nuclei (LINERs), and some X-ray selected nuclei. For definiteness, most of the objects discussed here have Hα luminosities below 10^{40} ergs/s, mainly because classical Seyferts are much brighter than this and most LINERs are fainter. "Starburst" nuclei, though not active in the sense adopted here, are discussed because they suffer guilt by association in some galaxies and may in fact be related to genuinely active nuclei in an evolutionary sequence.

II. RECOGNITION AND CLASSIFICATION

The taxonomy of low-level active nuclei is almost entirely observational, and in fact mostly dependent on optical spectroscopic properties. This is only partly historical in origin; in many cases optical emission lines are the most sensitive single tracers of weak nonstellar processes. Nuclear activity may be inferred from the presence of a) emission-line ratios not compatible with stellar photoionization, b) emission-line widths in excess of the velocities associated with stars in a nucleus, c) a strong nuclear X-ray source, or d) a compact radio source.

Considerable work has been done on measurement and interpretation of the emission-line ratios in "normal" galactic nuclei. It became clear quite early that the high [N II] $\lambda6583$/Hα ratio generally seen in ellipticals and early-type spirals requires very high nitrogen abundances, nonstellar ionizing agents, or both (Burbidge and Burbidge 1965). Much more recently, the availability of spectrophotometry for large numbers of nuclei has prompted systematic discrimination of object types based on combinations of emission-line intensity ratios. Heckman (1980b) defined a class of LINERs (Low-Ionization Nuclear Emission-line Regions) on the basis of the relative strengths of [O II] $\lambda3727$, [O I] $\lambda6300$, and [O III] $\lambda5007$. This original definition incorporated the conditions [O II] $>$ [O III] and [O I]/[O III] > 0.33; in addition, all the objects in Heckman's study have [O II]/H$\beta > 2.5$. Their spectra contain a wider range of ionization states and much stronger low-ionization lines ([O I],[S II]) than produced in H II regions. This form of analysis was codified by Baldwin, Phillips, and Terlevich (1981), in what has become the standard basis for emission-line classification. They show that Seyferts and LINERs can be discriminated from H II regions (and planetary nebulae) in a variety of line-ratio planes. In particular, use of the ratios [O III] $\lambda5007$/Hβ and [N II] $\lambda6583$/Hα has proven especially valuable because neither ratio is very reddening-sensitive and only about 2000 Å of spectrum need be observed. In fact, almost the same level of discrimination between H II regions and active objects is possible using [O I] $\lambda6300$ or [S II] $\lambda\lambda6717,6731$ as substitutes for [O II] $\lambda3727$ (Stauffer 1982b).

As long as either agent is dominant, pigeonholing a nucleus as photoionized by starlight or as active is in principle straightforward. As usual, the real universe introduces complications. The most severe in most of these nuclei is the fact that the emission lines are weak and are superimposed on a complex stellar continuum. In a typical LINER, the strongest emission lines have equivalent widths at the nucleus of only a few Angstroms, so that proper accounting of the underlying spectrum is crucial for accurate measurement. This can be seen from the spectrum of the representative, and in fact fairly strong, LINER NGC 4579 (Fig. 1). Several approaches to accurate line measurement are possible, and successful under appropriate conditions. For emission in elliptical-galaxy nuclei, or for spirals with relatively strong emission, an emission-free elliptical spectrum may be used as a template; in some cases spirals with very weak emission may be used in this role (Heckman, Balick, and Crane 1980; Stauffer 1982b). For objects with very weak lines or in nuclei with more recent star formation, it may be necessary to generate a synthetic population and spectrum (Keel 1983c), especially to match the Balmer absorption lines when stars earlier than about G are present. This approach is more general in applicability, but suffers from limitations in our understanding of stellar populations, particularly in untangling age and abundance effects (witness the lengthy and inconclusive literature of spectral synthesis; Gunn, Stryker, and Tinsley 1981).

Comparison of data obtained by various observers using these approaches shows that the absorption corrections for Hα and Hβ used can differ by a factor of two for a single galaxy. At

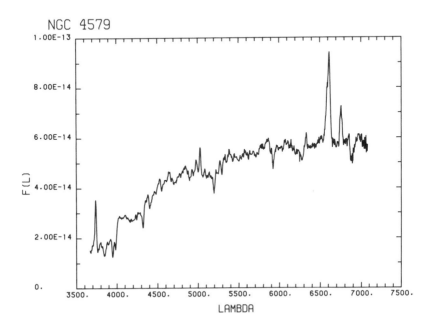

Figure 1: The optical spectrum of the LINER NGC 4579, obtained with the IIDS system at the KPNO 2.1-m. Note the strong [N II] , [S II], and [O I], with [O III] weak compared to its appearance in Seyfert nuclei. This nucleus has a weak broad component at Hα, extending over a range of about 3500 km s^{-1}.

the weakest levels, this is at present a fundamental limitation in interpreting emission spectra. Further difficulties are posed by reddening and aperture effects. Detection (though not necessarily measurement) of reddening is straightforward for strong-emission objects, and may be approached in the traditional fashion. Aperture effects can enter because the luminosities of weak active nuclei may not greatly exceed those of H II regions nearby in the galaxies, and the nonstellar-ionized gas is often spatially resolved.

These points will be further mentioned in succeeding sections.

A succinct summary of emission-line classifications may be given as follows: any nucleus with [N II] $\lambda6583$/Hα greater than 0.70 is a variety of low-level active nucleus. In addition, [O I] $\lambda6300$/Hα greater than 0.10 also qualifies, even for weak [N II]. The boundary between Seyfert and low-ionization nuclei is not well-defined, but Seyferts are usually taken to have [O III] $\lambda5007$/Hβ greater than 3.0, from linewidth considerations (Shuder and Osterbrock 1981). These criteria largely define the optical recognition of low-level activity.

Nuclei recognized as active because of X-ray emission or a compact nuclear radio source usually fall on the active side of the optical classification, when the nucleus is accessible. Narrow-line X-ray galaxies, which may be loosely defined as those examined optically as a result of unusually high X-ray luminosity, include LINERs, weak Seyferts, and luminous but obscured Seyferts. Einstein results have produced detections of optically selected LINERs and weak Seyferts, blurring another observational distinction.

Each of these classes will now be reviewed in some detail, with concluding remarks relating them to one another and to more luminous active nuclei, and highlighting some of the current outstanding questions. The bulk of the review concerns LINERs, since they are the most numerous of weakly active nuclei and present the most pressing observational and theoretical questions.

III. LINERs: IONIZING MECHANISMS

Well before the formal definition of this class (Heckman 1980b), various studies indicated their widespread occurrence and identified many of the properties basic to models of the emission regions. Noting that emission spectra of elliptical and early Hubble-type spiral nuclei, when detected, generally have [N II] $\lambda6583$/Hα greater than 1, Burbidge and Burbidge (1962,1965) considered explanations involving collisional ionization or photoionization plus very high nitrogen abundance. Somewhat more refined calculations found that pure collisional ionization cannot reproduce the observed ionization balance, as seen in the forbidden lines of O°, O^+, and O^{++} (Peimbert 1968; Alloin 1973).

In contrast, the nonuniform ionization structure in a radiative shock front can reproduce the range of ionization seen in LINERs. In a detailed study of the prototype LINER NGC 1052, Fosbury *et al.* (1978) proposed shock heating as the dominant ionizing mechanism, which conclusion has frequently been applied to LINERs as a class (Fosbury *et al.* 1977; Heckman 1980b; Stauffer 1982b). This picture is attractive in having the line emission a direct consequence of cloud motions in the nuclei. Collisions at velocities consistent with the velocity dispersions are expected, and additional shock heating could take place in instances of collimated ejection impinging on the interstellar medium.

An alternate, and equally compelling, mechanism for producing low-ionization spectra seems to have been first presented in detail by Kent and Sargent (1979). In modelling the filaments of NGC 1275, they showed that photoionization by a very dilute power-law source could produce line ratios very similar to those seen in LINERs. More recent calculations by Ferland and Netzer (1983) and Halpern and Steiner (1983) indicated that a LINER-like spectrum could result from simply reducing the luminosity of a Seyfert-like power-law continuum source by factors 10-100 without changing the gas density or volume.

Both of these pictures are still current in studies of LINERs, so a more extensive discussion is in order. In shock models, the strength of forbidden-line emission relative to that in the Balmer lines is enhanced due to the strong temperature dependence of the forbidden-line emissivity, coupled with the steep temperature gradient in the recombination zone behind the shock. The strong low-ionization lines are produced in the cooling region well behind the shock front, which has considerable geometric extent and thus gives large integrated (column) emissivities in these lines.

Calculations of the emitted spectrum of shocked interstellar matter have been published by a number of workers, usually in contexts appropriate for supernova remnants. Cox (1972) calculated a set of plane-parallel models for comparison with the Cygnus Loop, giving a reasonable match in ionization level and measured [O III] temperature. Further investigations incorporated changes in elemental abundances (Dopita 1976,1977) and ionization of preshock matter by the shock's own ultraviolet line emission (Shull and McKee 1979). The predictions of these calculations differ somewhat in absolute emergent flux, relative intensities of lines in various hydrogen series (such as Ly α/Hβ), and the exact velocity-ionization scaling, but certain basic properties of shock emission are clear.

The most telling spectroscopic indicator of shock emission is the temperature-sensitive [O III] $\lambda4363/\lambda5007$ ratio. These lines arise from decays originating in upper levels of substantially different excitation energy, so that their ratio directly reflects the populations in these levels; at low densities, it reflects the relative numbers of electrons with the requisite energies, hence the electron temperature. Since most of the [O III] emission arises close behind the shock front, this ratio is predicted to lie in the range 0.04 to 0.1 for relevant shock velocities, indicating characteristic temperatures 2×10^4 to 10^5 K (the conversion is given by Eissner *et al.* 1969). Since such temperatures are never reached by photoionized material under conditions in galactic nuclei, measurement of this line ratio has figured prominently in several studies. Reproducing the line ratios in these nuclei requires that emission be dominated by shocks in the (relatively narrow) velocity range 85-130 km s^{-1} (with the calibration of Shull and McKee 1979); because of the rapid rise in line intensity with velocity, the spatially integrated spectrum reflects the highest velocities occurring over a significant area. The high [N II]/Hα value results from the temperature effect mentioned above.

In contrast, photoionization models of LINERs use standard thermal equilibrium in dilute radiation fields of various kinds to generate the needed ionization level and range. The comparable intensities of the [O I], [O II], and [O III] lines require a continuum shape much flatter than that of a blackbody or OB star; most work has centered on power laws, largely by analogy with classical active nuclei. Ferland and Netzer (1983) examined the behavior of gas directly illuminated by the ionizing source for a wide range of ionization parameter U (ionizing photon density/particle density). They find that LINERs and Seyfert narrow-line regions can be placed along a continuum, with LINERs at $U \approx 10^{-3}$ and Seyferts at $U \approx 10^{-1}$ to 10^{-2}. A somewhat modified scheme was used by Halpern and Steiner (1983), in which the emitting clouds can be so optically thick in the Lyman continuum that the dominant source of ionization for most of the gas is in soft X-rays; this would have particular relevance in very gas-rich environments. They allow for substantial variation in the covering fraction of obscuring matter, so that LINERs might be otherwise luminous and heavily obscured Seyfert nuclei. This picture presents difficulties for the majority of LINERs, requiring an inverted luminosity function for the central source luminosities, but may be important for some objects, such as classical radio galaxies. Both sets of calculations, while single-point in character, provide good matches to observed spectra.

Both shock and photoionization models are capable of reasonable agreement with the observed strengths of the stronger emission lines in LINERs, which are usually the only ones measurable. Indeed, a striking demonstration of the similarity of such spectra is provided by comparison of the (shocked) Cygnus Loop with the (photoionized) Crab Nebula filaments (Miller 1974,1978). Aside from the high helium abundance in the Crab, the only clear difference in the spectra is the strength of the [O III] $\lambda 4363$ line, reflecting the high temperature in the O^{++} zone of the Cygnus Loop.

This feature is virtually the only optical line capable of giving a clear discrimination between shocked and photoionized gas, as long as densities above 10^5 are not important. A number of workers have addressed this point, primarily with regard to NGC 1052. Koski and Osterbrock (1976) and Fosbury *et al.* (1978) concluded that the [O III] temperature was about 2×10^4 K, implying a dominant role for shocks. However, fuller consideration of the underlying stellar continuum features led Keel and Miller (1983) and Rose and Tripicco (1984) to conclude that the $\lambda 4363$ line strength is quite uncertain and is probably consistent with photoionization. The difficulty in making this measurement arises from the position of $\lambda 4363$ in the galaxy spectrum. It lies in a crowded region, at the edge of a CN band whose strength varies from galaxy to galaxy, even among luminous ellipticals. Here, again, the interpretation of emission spectra is limited by the extent of our ignorance of details of the stellar populations.

In most nuclei, the ratios of strong lines can be accounted for either by shocks or photoionization, with appropriately chosen model parameters. However, the distribution of a number of well-observed LINERs in several line-ratio planes suggests a more important role for photoionization, as the objects lie more nearly along expected tracks of varying abundance and ionization parameter than those of shock velocity and abundance (Keel 1983c). More recent work has concentrated on producing more realistic models for the emission regions, including recent observational constraints, and on incorporating line-profile information into a picture of LINERs. Péquignot (1984) has examined the spectral components needed to produce the line spectrum of NGC 1052 by photoionization, since this nucleus has been particularly well observed for such lines as [S II] $\lambda\lambda 4069,4076$ and He II $\lambda 4686$. A substantial blackbody-like contribution (at 8×10^4 K) is required to produce enough ionizing photons without too much He^{++}. The strength of the auroral lines of [S II] and [O III] then requires emission over a very broad density range, including the high-density regime in which these lines are no longer thermometers. Strong observational evidence for such a density range comes from the correlation between linewidth and critical density seen in some strong LINERs and related nuclei (Filippenko and Halpern 1984;

Filippenko 1985). The correlation is stronger for critical density than for ionization potential, suggesting density as the fundamental quantity. In particular, lines of the same species, such as [O II], can have different widths if they originate in different upper levels (Fig. 2).

Binette (1984) has also incorporated nonuniform densities into photoionization models, with particular attention to the determination of abundances. Straightforward application of the Ferland and Netzer (1983) models indicated a large range in (N+O/H), from 0.8 to 4.7 times solar (Keel 1983c). By taking into account the weak correlation between ionization level and [N II]/Hα, Binette finds at most a range of a factor three in N/H around solar, and notes that this is still an upper limit to the actual scatter because some of the model parameters are not yet well-determined. His models suggest that LINERs are more nearly a one-parameter family than are Seyferts or other high-ionization objects.

Evidence has accumulated, from both theoretical and observational considerations, that many LINERs are powered by photoionization from a flat-spectrum radiation source similar to the very luminous ones in conventional active nuclei. However, instances may well exist of LINER-like spectra in different environments whose main source of energy is shock heating (aside from supernova remnants, which unquestionably are such cases). For example, the very extensive low-ionization region in NGC 6240 (Fosbury and Wall 1979; Fried and Schulz 1983) is best explained by shocks subsidiary to the merger of two gas-rich galaxies, particularly in view of the strong H_2 emission measured by Joseph, Wright, and Wade (1984) and by Rieke *et al.* (1984). Similarly, extended low-ionization regions away from the nuclei in some radio galaxies seem to require *in situ* ionization, perhaps as a result of a shock front between a jet and the interstellar medium (e.g., Heckman *et al.* 1982).

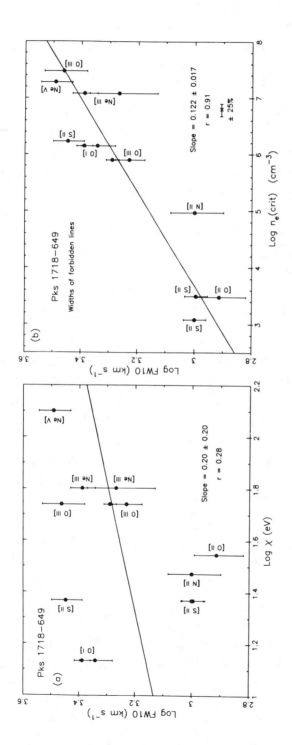

Figure 2: The relations between critical density n_e and ionization potential χ, and line width (measured at 10% of the peak intensity) Filippenko (1985). The correlation with n_e is tighter than with χ, indicating that density is the controlling quantity rather than the local radiation field. The existence of this relation shows the importance of the high-density regime in modelling these objects. Each point represents a single transition of the indicated ion; some ions appear several times due to transitions with different critical density or ionization potential.

Multiple ionization mechanisms may also be indicated in some of the extended emission regions around normal LINER nuclei. At distances up to a kiloparsec from the nucleus (Keel 1983b), very low densities (a few cm^{-3}) are required to maintain the appropriate ionization parameter for nuclear photoionization. Observation of the [S II] $\lambda\lambda6717,6731$ doublet should be able to resolve this point.

Spectra in the ultraviolet could in principle test the power-law photoionization model, since the nonthermal continuum would be much more easily detected against the weaker UV starlight. In the few cases which can be reached with IUE, the results seem to be mixed. In M81, the UV continuum is marginally consistent with a single power law extending up to the X-ray measurements (Bruzual, Peimbert, and Torres-Peimbert 1982; Elvis and van Speybroeck 1982). The UV level in NGC 1052 does not allow such a spectral shape (Fosbury *et al.* 1981), though a hot thermal contribution is allowed. The situation in M87 is marginal with regard to direct detection of the nonthermal continuum (Perola and Tarenghi 1980), while the UV spectrum of NGC 4579 seems to allow a single power law up through X-rays (Goodrich 1985). This problem is at the very limits of IUE's capacity, and is tailor-made for the Space Telescope. Definitive work will most likely await the high-quality spectra to be produced by ST, and a firmer understanding of the ultraviolet properties of the galaxies' stellar components. Note, however, that detectability of an ultraviolet nonstellar continuum is strongly affected by even modest extinction; lack of an observed continuum might be interpreted more as evidence for dust than as evidence against photoionization models.

Apart from modelling of the emission spectrum, independent evidence exists for the presence of active nuclei in LINERs, in the form of broad wings at $H\alpha$ and nuclear X-ray emission. A few LINERs were noted as having $H\alpha$ wings of 3000-4000 km s^{-1} extent by Heckman (1980b), Stauffer (1982b), and Keel (1983c). M81, with the same level of activity and spectral character, has been called a Seyfert 1 (or 1.9) on this basis, but is in fact rather typical of strong LINERs (Peimbert and Torres-Peimbert 1981, Shuder and Osterbrock 1981). It is significant that these objects have Hα emission over velocity ranges comparable to those observed in Seyferts with continuum luminosities as much as four orders of magnitude greater than those inferred for LINERs; the velocity-controlling mechanism is not strongly linked to the central source's luminosity. Further direct links between LINERs and high-luminosity active nuclei are afforded by objects with very strong broad Balmer lines and low-ionization narrow lines, such as Arp 102B (Stauffer, Schild, and Keel 1983) and NGC 7213 (Filippenko and Halpern 1984), and the many classical radio galaxies with various levels of LINER emission. Detailed studies of these have been performed by Carswell *et al.* (1984) and Filippenko (1985) for Pictor A and PKS 1718-65, both of which exhibit very strong low-ionization narrow lines; Pictor A has in addition broad Balmer lines and a featureless blue continuum.

Evidence for a general connection between LINERs and broad-line regions has been strengthened by Filippenko and Sargent (1985), in a survey for broad Hα in objects otherwise known to harbor strong LINERs. Of 75 bright galaxies examined, broad Hα was measured in about 1/3, and suspected in more than half. While a complete sample has not yet been observed, comparison of their sample with samples that are magnitude-limited suggests that about 10% of luminous disk systems have broad Hα at easily detectable levels. It seems clear, also, that a large fraction of LINERs harbor weak active nuclei, independent of the details of ionization of the narrow-line region. In a number of these objects, in fact, various authors classify the same system as a Seyfert or LINER based on the broad or narrow lines; Phillips *et al.* (1984) have used "LINER 1.9" to refer to such objects, by analogy with the Seyfert 1.9 class (e.g. Osterbrock 1984), which applies strictly to similar objects with high-ionization narrow lines. For some purposes, it may be useful to preserve the distinction between low- and high-ionization narrow lines, whether or not a broad-line region is observed. It should be stressed, however, that there is continuity in the properties of narrow-line regions between LINERs and Seyfert nuclei. With regard to gas densiy, total mass, filling factor, and spatial extent, the extended emission regions of LINERs are essentially identical to the narrow-line regions of most Seyferts, needing only the higher level of ionization for a match in physical properties.

IV. LINERs: OCCURRENCE AND SYSTEMATICS

Spectroscopic surveys by Heckman, Balick, and Crane (1980), Stauffer (1982a), and Keel (1983a), have resulted in the detection of LINERs (and their discrimination from Seyfert nuclei and H II regions) for a large number of galaxies, mostly disk systems. From the parts of these surveys comprising complete (magnitude-limited) samples, the occurrence of low-ionization emission may be derived as a function of Hubble type and galaxy absolute magnitude. The strongest result (hardly a new one; see Burbidge and Burbidge 1965) is the clear preference of LINERs for early-type galaxies. About 80% of nuclei in types Sa-Sb have detectable LINERs, while they are seen in only 20% of Sc nuclei. These objects are obviously very common, with a space density almost two orders of magnitude above that of classical Seyfert nuclei. Together with the luminosity function of LINERs, this means that the most common type of active nucleus is the weak low-ionization object, in which the only strong emission line is [N II] $\lambda6584$ (a "one-LINER"). Ellipticals have until recently received less attention in the crucial $H\alpha/$[N II] region, because their emission is generally even weaker than that in spirals; new surveys (e.g., Phillips 1984) show that at least 50% of elliptical and S0 nuclei have emission apparently indicating LINERs.

In the case of spirals, in which nuclear H II regions may contribute to the emission, these fractions are lower limits. A number of objects with H II-dominated spectra at relatively large apertures are shown to be composite objects including LINERs when examined at higher resolution. Further work will be required to determine how much of the Sb/Sc dichotomy results from such composite nuclei.

No significant difference in LINER occurrence is seen in galaxies with and without strong bars (Heckman 1980c). This, and the morphological type distribution of LINERs, parallel the properties of galaxies with classical Seyfert nuclei (Adams 1977, Heckman 1978). The similarity suggests that the same extranuclear conditions can give rise to both classical Seyfert nuclei and LINERs.

The integrated luminosity of the host galaxy affects both the probability of occurrence and the emission-line luminosity of LINERs at a given morphological type. The median Hα luminosity increases to brighter absolute magnitudes, by about 0.15 dex per magnitude; this is a weaker dependence than that found for nuclear continuum luminosity (Keel 1983a). In addition, for late morphological types (Sc), the fraction of LINERs grows toward high galaxy luminosities. Examination of a small group of very large and luminous Sc's (Keel 1984b) suggests that most or all Sc's brighter than, for example, M101 have LINERs or Seyfert nuclei.

The scatter in these relations precludes a direct control mechanism, but suggests that depth of the central potential well and stellar mass available for gas supply are factors influencing the occurrence and luminosity of LINERs. A comparison with Seyferts is again suggestive. The fraction of galaxies with Seyfert nuclei climbs rapidly for brighter galaxies (see Meurs and Wilson 1984); this is true even after correction for the contribution of the nuclei to the integrated magnitudes of very active systems.

Observations of LINERs at non-optical wavelengths are still few. Heckman (1980b) found that they frequently, but not exclusively, correspond to compact nuclear radio sources. More detailed mapping has shown extended radio emission on scales comparable to that of the emission region, at a few hundred parsecs (e.g., van der Hulst, Crane, and Keel 1981). Infrared measurements show excess nonstellar emission from 10-20μ, probably due to dust heated in a different way than seen in star-forming regions (Lawrence *et al.* 1984). These data also suggest complex structure in many of these nuclei, with significant roles for extended gas and dust.

Detailed observations of a few very nearby galaxies, recently available, suggest that a considerably more complex picture than the simple shock vs. photoionization scheme may apply. An outstanding set of emission-line images of the nuclear region of M31 has been produced by Jacoby, Ford, and Ciardullo (1985), showing an extensive set of ionized-gas filaments over an area of diameter 800 parsecs. The existence of ionized gas near the nucleus had been shown by Munch (1961), who found it extended and with velocities suggesting expansion. Spectra by Rubin and Ford (1971) had shown the emission near the nucleus to have the high [N II]/Hα(≈ 2) indicating LINER-like emission; it is noteworthy that this emission is extremely weak or absent at the nucleus itself. Jacoby and collaborators favor shock ionization for the filaments on morphological grounds; limits on a UV source in the M31 nucleus are uncomfortably low for photoionization models.

The nucleus of M51 is more typical of luminous LINERs, and has been thought a bridge to Seyfert nuclei on the bases of line ratios, gradients, and profiles (Rose and Searle 1982; Rose and Cecil 1983). New data at high spatial resolution show a complex structure, with evidence of energy deposition and mass motions as far as 800 parsecs from the nucleus. Optical and radio imaging by Ford *et al.* (1985) and echelle spectroscopy by Goad and Gallagher (1985) are in accord as regards the existence of an expanding "bubble" near the nucleus, with such high velocity dispersion as to exceed the nuclear linewidth of ≈ 1800 km s^{-1} at zero intensity. The images suggest emission on the working surfaces of paired jets, which blow huge bubbles in the local interstellar medium. This picture is much like that worked out for the radio structures of

Seyfert nuclei by Wilson and Ulvestad (1982) and Ulvestad and
Wilson (1983). The velocity field, however, shows no evidence of
the gas entrainment expected in simple jet schemes. Goad and
Gallagher interpret their spectra as showing an expanding shell
of gas south of the nucleus, with line ratios similar to those in
the nucleus itself; the mode of ionization of this gas is not clearly
determined. The velocity structure indicates that these fireworks
occur within the disk of M51 rather than being ejection out of the
galactic plane. If jets are responsible for these structures, they
differ from those seen in classical radio galaxies, even on similar
linear scales, in having essentially no radio emission; the observed
consequences of such jets are nearly indistinguishable from those
of point sources of energy (and matter) away from the nucleus.

Detailed study of NGC 1052 has shown it to be no more
representative than most prototype objects. The electron density over most of the emitting region is rather low for nuclear gas
(around 300 cm^{-3}). The gas kinematics suggest the presence of
a rotating disk (Davies and Illingworth 1984). Evidence for nuclear activity is found in the radio, from variability of the central
flat-spectrum source (Heeschen and Conklin 1975; Heeschen and
Puschell 1983), and in the infrared, from detection of a polarized nonthermal continuum (Rieke, Lebofsky, and Kemp 1982).
The continuum level in the IR, if extrapolated as a power law,
falls short by about an order of magnitude of producing enough
ionizing photons for the observed emission region. This has led
Péquignot (1984) to postulate a blackbody-like component giving additional ionizing flux with little optical or IR contribution.
Such a component might be needed to account for other LINERs,
but only NGC 1052 has been studied so far in sufficient spectroscopic detail for realistic modelling. The extent of the emission
region (kiloparsecs) suggests that multiple ionizing agents may be
at work here.

From the complexities seen in nearby objects, it is clear
that even an average nucleus may show kinematic and ionization
phenomena not at all expected from static notions of nuclei. Mass

ejection and energy transport are not confined to radio and Seyfert galaxies, but are present in a significant fraction of "normal" galaxies.

V. LOW-LUMINOSITY SEYFERT NUCLEI

The Seyfert-nucleus luminosity function, like that of QSOs, rises steeply toward low luminosities (measured in emission lines, the continuum, or X-rays), over the range traditionally associated with active nuclei (Véron 1979; Meurs and Wilson 1984). This implies the existence of a population of objects resembling classical Seyfert nuclei in all but luminosity, even given the presence of a turnover in the luminosity function. Such nuclei appear in spectroscopic and deep X-ray surveys. Among nearby galaxies, the Stauffer (1982a) and Keel (1983a) samples completed the tally of weak Seyferts (in practice, Seyfert 2s) among bright disk galaxies in the northern sky. From a more extensive set of 666 galaxies described by Sandage (1978), Phillips, Charles, and Baldwin (1983) examined the objects described as having high-excitation emission lines. They concluded that these objects represent the low end of a continuum of Seyfert activity and are transitional to more normal nuclei. Taken together, these studies indicate that about 5% of luminous disk systems contain a Seyfert nucleus, as diagnosed by highly (power-law) ionized gas. This figure does not include low-ionization objects with broad Hα; they would raise the fraction to at least 15%. These nuclei are generally more like type 2 than type 1 Seyferts. As Phillips, Charles, and Baldwin note, these nuclei frequently fall outside the linewidth and color ranges defined for luminous Seyferts, but have line ratios clearly indicating photoionization by a power-law source extending to at least 100 eV (to produce Fe VII and Ne V).

For many of these objects, X-ray measures are available (Phillips, Charles, and Baldwin 1983; Charles and Phillips 1982; Maccacaro, Perola, and Elvis 1981; Kriss, Canizares, and Ricker 1980; Forman *et al.* 1979). Comparison of the X-ray fluxes with those of optical emission lines indicates a continuum shape near that seen in more luminous Seyferts. These objects thus appear to represent a direct lower continuation of the Seyfert class.

VI. NARROW-LINE X-RAY GALAXIES

A class of objects has been frequently discussed in the literature which seems to be defined mostly by being first found to be active through X-ray identification. Aside from classical Seyfert nuclei discovered this way in some abundance (e.g. Margon, Chanan, and Downes 1982; Reichert *et al.* 1982), the narrow-line X-ray galaxies comprise most of the (optically defined) classes of low-luminosity AGNs. Optical spectroscopy of X-ray selected galaxies by Ward *et al.* (1978), Shuder (1980), Véron *et al.* (1980,1981), and Elvis *et al.* (1981) shows a range of properties, including nuclei otherwise classifiable as Seyferts, of types 2 and 1.9, LINERs strong and weak, and composite nuclei. M82 shows a pure starburst spectrum optically, but is of low X-ray luminosity compared to the other examples and may be so dusty as to preclude optical observations of the actual nucleus.

While this group is very heterogeneous, certain properties occur often enough to warrant notice. A high proportion of X-ray selected nuclei reside in galaxies viewed nearly edge-on, and it has been suggested that they represent Seyferts viewed through the strong absorption of a galactic disk (Lawrence and Elvis 1982; Véron *et al.* 1980). In a few cases, weak broad Hα and high narrow-line Balmer decrements support this contention, but radio mapping indicates that this is not the whole story (Ulvestad and Wilson 1984). In any case, the narrow-line X-ray galaxies now seem to be the extreme tail of a broad distribution of optical-to-X-ray luminosity ratio, since numerous optically-selected LINERs and even starbursts have been found in the X-ray using the sensitivity possible with the Einstein Observatory.

VII. STARBURST NUCLEI

Star formation has long been recognized in galactic nuclei, both from its excitation of emission spectra and its effect on the integrated stellar component of the nuclear spectrum (Turnrose 1976). The normal range in star-forming rate gives rise to a variety of nuclear morphologies and spectral properties (e.g., Heckman 1980a), including many of the "hot-spot" galaxies identified by Morgan (1958) and by Sersic and Pastoriza (1965,1967). The most extreme examples of nuclear star formation have been termed "starburst nuclei" by Weedman *et al.* (1981), who find that their line luminosities, colors, and radio and X-ray properties may be consistently understood as resulting from a recent burst of star formation encompassing $\approx 10^7$ solar masses of O stars in an area a few hundred parsecs in diameter. These objects are common among Markarian galaxies (Balzano 1983) and among those selected from other objective-prism searches (MacAlpine, Smith, and Lewis 1977; Wasilewski 1983). They also are common among faint blue objects (below B=19) and cause confusion in deep color surveys for QSOs, being easily detected to z=0.4. The spectrum of an example, PG 0119+229, is shown in Figure 3. Note the strong emission lines and weakness of the forbidden lines of low-ionization species.

These objects may have emission-line luminosities as high as those of many Seyferts (L(Hα) $\approx 10^{42}$ ergs/s). They have attracted considerable attention due to the energetics of such assemblages of massive stars, supernovae, and stellar remnants, and to a suspected connection with active nuclei. The emission-line widths for many of these nuclei are as low as $\sigma = 68$ km s^{-1} (Feldman *et al.* 1982), well below representative stellar velocity dispersions for similar galaxies. Weedman (1983) has argued that remnants of massive stars formed from this gas would sink into a compact configuration at the nucleus as a dynamically distinct entity, perhaps even coalescing to form the single massive black hole often favored as the central engine for active nuclei. Even the large collection of

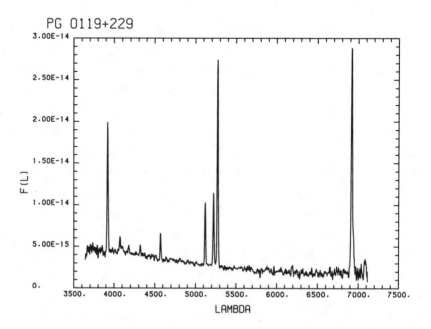

Figure 3: The optical spectrum of the starburst nucleus of PG 0119+229, obtained as in Figure 1. The emission-line ratios are essentially as seen in individual H II regions, with a continuum shape consistent with a recent burst of star formation (OB-stars dominating the light).

individual remnants in a small volume could account for the properties of some classes of active nuclei. In this view, starbursts can be precursors of Seyfert galaxies. Note that the central mass concentration would be present after a single starburst, so that any subsequent ones would coexist with it and probably appear as a composite nucleus (§VIII); the timescale for collection of remnants is fast enough that an active nucleus so formed might even coexist with its parent starburst (Weedman 1983).

An alternate connection between starbursts and active

nuclei has nuclear activity inducing extensive star formation in its neighborhood. This would proceed via shocks inducing collapse in pre-existing clouds, perhaps involving jets (e.g., Norman and May 1984). Much work remains to be done before this possibility can be evaluated. However, there are many active objects with unusual star-forming properties that suggest that such a connection can operate, even if it is rare compared to "spontaneous" starbursts (see §VIII for a discussion of individual objects). The interpretation of an observed connection will be complicated by the fact that deep potential wells are favorable sites for recurrent bursts of star formation, which may or may not eventually form compact remnant configurations, depending on the bursts IMF and dynamics of the surrounding bulge (Loose, Kruger, and Tutukov 1982; Kruger, Tutukov, and Loose 1983)

The mechanisms responsible for producing nuclear starbursts are essentially unknown; their presence and luminosity do not depend strongly on galaxy luminosity (Balzano 1983), though they are more common among spirals of late Hubble type and blue compact galaxies. They may occur more often in interacting systems than in the field (Balzano 1983; Keel *et al.* 1985). There are systems in which the starburst extends over large areas of the galaxy, such as M82 (Rieke *et al.* 1980), NGC 3690/IC 694 (Gehrz, Sramek, and Weedman 1983), and Arp 220 (Rieke *et al.* 1984). This may indicate that most of the conditions needed for starbursts do not require the privileged position of a nucleus (though accumulation of a compact array of stellar remnants or a single massive black hole can occur only at the center of the nuclear potential well).

Processes associated with starbursts can give rise to processes similar in some ways to those seen in active nuclei. There is clear evidence for nonthermal radio radiation, indicating particle acceleration most likely traceable to supernova remnants (Weedman *et al.* 1981). X-ray images suggest that starbursts can drive asymmetric mass flows, producing ejection, though much less collimated than in jets (Fabbiano and Trinchieri 1984; Trinchieri, Fabbiano, and Palumbo 1985). Such flows would produce an envelope of shocked gas, which might resemble LINER emission for the appropriate velocity range; this may be observed in NGC 253, in which the gas seen optically shows outflow (Ulrich 1978).

Some clues to conditions in starburst nuclei can be found from ionization analysis of their emission spectra. The characteristically high [O III] $\lambda5007$/Hβ could indicate either lower metallicity than normally seen in nuclei of luminous galaxies or a mass function relatively rich in massive and very hot stars. The analysis of French (1980) indicates that the abundances of O and N are about half solar in NGC 3690 and 7714, whereas for galaxies of their luminosities abundances somewhat above solar are usual. A role may still be played by the mass function, but these results suggest transport of gas from the disk into the nucleus (or possibly from companions) as a means of reducing the gas metallicity and (perhaps) inducing star formation through associated turbulence or shocks.

Starburst nuclei represent, at least in part, extreme examples of the nuclear H II regions normally found in late-type galaxies (e.g., Heckman 1980a). Some starbursts do occur in very small and low-continuum-luminosity systems (Balzano 1983); the luminosity function of Hα for nuclear H II regions in luminous spirals is nearly flat (Keel 1983a), so starbursts in dwarf galaxies are a significant fraction of the total. These are unlikely to be related to active nuclei simply because of the shallow potential well associated with such objects; further work on any differences in the properties of starbursts in galaxies of a wide range of luminosity will be needed to resolve this point.

The relation between properties of starburst and other star-forming nuclei depends greatly on the exact definition adopted for a starburst. Clearly, a starburst must represent an increased rate of star formation, but different criteria for the base rate can be used; both the average over the galaxy's history or the immediate pre-burst rate might be appropriate in different physical contexts. The time average gives a more conservative distinction between starburst and "simply star-forming" nuclei, since the rate of star formation in most nuclei seems to have dropped significantly with time (e.g., Bushouse and Gallagher 1984). Further work including gas-phase abundances may help clarify any physical distinction between these classes, and thus whether the starbursts represent a separate process or the high end of a continuum including a large fraction of all nuclei.

VIII. COMPOSITE NUCLEI

As more objects have been studied in some detail, it has become clear that many nuclei exist in which both H II regions and nonstellar ionizing sources are present. In some cases, one or the other dominates the integrated emission spectrum sufficiently that spectra with the apertures typically used would result in classification as a single type of nucleus. Detailed studies with high spatial or spectral resolution are usually needed to discern the different components. For example, the dual nature of the NGC 1365 nucleus became clear only when a slit was placed across the position of the weak Seyfert nucleus, which appears among a number of H II regions with larger $H\alpha$ luminosities (Edmunds and Pagel 1982). This is also the case in NGC 1808 (Véron-Cetty and Véron 1985); similar situations in NGC 7496 and 7582 prompted Véron *et al.* (1981) to consider the problem of finding an active nucleus hidden by giant H II regions; decomposition of line profiles in search of distinct regions in velocity space was found effective, as in several later studies. Heckman *et al.* (1983) used this procedure to identify composite nuclei in a radio-selected group, including IC 4553, NGC 2782, and NGC 3504. From a similar and overlapping sample, Keel (1984a) found evidence of composite nuclei from spatially integrated line ratios (NGC 253,3504).

As in the case of luminous starbursts, these nuclei motivate consideration of direct links between star formation and nuclear activity. In some cases, intense star formation is seen near classical Seyfert nuclei. Alloin *et al.* (1983) have mapped the velocity and ionization structure of the inner disk of NGC 1068, finding a substantial amount of gas ionized by starlight and sharing the quiet disk kinematics. A similar mix is found from infrared measurements in NGC 7469 (Cutri *et al.* 1984). While limits on young populations in nearby Seyferts indicate that such circumnuclear star formation is not universal (Malkan and Filippenko 1983), the strength of the nonthermal continuum is such that considerable star formation would be difficult to detect in many luminous Seyferts. There is clear evidence of massive recent star formation in at least one powerful radio galaxy, 3C 459 (Miller 1981). Unless the young stars contribute at least half the optical flux through the relevant aperture, their effects are very difficult to distinguish from those of varying the relative contributions of an old population and a nonstellar blue continuum (Goodrich and Osterbrock 1983), so that spatial information is crucial to a proper attack on the problem.

Spectral and spatial resolution are central to the major methods that have been used to identify composite nuclei. In the simplest cases, the various regions are completely distinct at available resolutions. These are nearby objects, in which resolutions of 50-100 pc are possible. As an example, Figure 4 shows an image in Hα+[N II] of NGC 1097. The central emission region is a high-ionization LINER or low-ionization Seyfert 2, while the surrounding H II regions have much higher emission-line luminosities and would dominate the integrated spectrum through a large aperture. For more distant objects, and those in which the emission regions are more intimately mixed, other ways of finding distinct regions are needed. Véron *et al.* (1981) and Heckman *et al.* (1983) have used the fact that narrow-line regions of active nuclei have line widths far in excess of those in giant H II regions or starburst nuclei to decompose observed profiles into H II and active components; this also yields line ratios for each component, strengthening physical interpretation of the spectra.

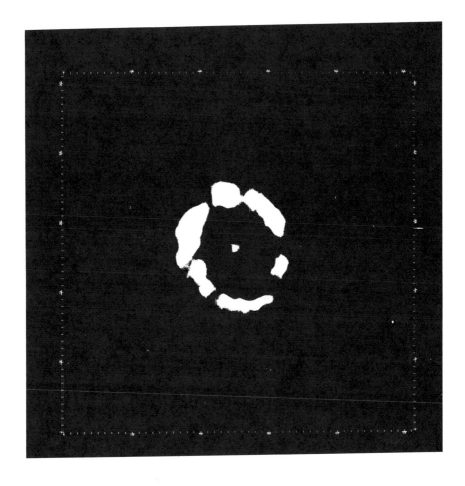

Figure 4: Image in Hα +[N II] of the composite nucleus of NGC 1097. The central (LINER or weak Seyfert) nucleus is surrounded by a ring of very luminous H II regions of diameter about 3 kpc. Similar configurations are seen in a number of additional galaxies, but seldom so well resolved due to linear size or distance.

In other cases, an active object may be found from a compact, flat-spectrum radio source (or X-ray source) in a nucleus optically dominated by star formation (Keel 1984a). This is analogous to the apparent dichotomy between optical and infrared interpretations of some composite nuclei, in which the IR measurements are much more sensitive to dust heated by stars than to the non-thermal activity, leading to disparate classifications from different wavelength regimes. Infrared observations are useful in this regard for finding evidence of star formation in more luminous systems than possible optically, because of this strong sensitivity to star-heated dust (and the ability to distinguish it from dust heated in other ways through temperature measurements).

Much further work clearly remains on composite nuclei. Larger samples and more detailed work on nearby objects are both necessary if an understanding of the relations between the various nuclear phenomena are to be understood. Higher spatial resolution at all wavelengths and spectroscopy at high spectral resolution are crucial tools for this problem.

IX. CONNECTIONS, PROBLEMS, AND PROSPECTS

From the diverse classes of objects included here, and those of higher luminosity, certain patterns suggest themselves as guides to further work and a preliminary understanding of the systematics of active nuclei. For example, a two-dimensional scheme involving ionization level and dominance of the broad-line component may be constructed. In this case, the four "corners" of such a classification contain Seyfert 2 and 1 nuclei, with high narrow-line ionization and little or much broad-line component, respectively, and various subspecies of LINERs, with low-ionization narrow-lines and various levels of broad Balmer emission. It is also significant that all of the intermediate stages in this scheme are actually observed. A continuum along the Seyfert sequence is well-known (Osterbrock 1977), and LINERs are known which form a some-what analogous sequence of increasing broad-line strength. Note also that in each extreme objects are seen with narrow-line ratios in a regime intermediate between the normal levels of Seyferts and LINERS (such as NGC 1097 and 4501 without a BLR, and PKS 0521-36 with strong, broad Hα). In principle, these connections might be interpreted as variations in accretion rate of a central massive object and differences in surrounding gas distributions, perhaps with temporal variations moving a single nucleus from one class to another.

There are two basic astrophysical points at issue in dealing with low-luminosity active nuclei. First, how frequent are massive compact accretors in galactic nuclei, and what masses are involved? Second, what is the role of and what are the controlling factors governing the flow of gas in galactic nuclei? If central massive objects are in fact ubiquitous, it is surprising that more nuclei are not very active, unless special conditions are required for an observable accretion rate. The fate of gas near a galactic nucleus is still unclear theoretically; most of the material liberated by stellar mass loss essentially disappears quietly, perhaps in a form of wind. The rate of accretion needed to drive most LINERs and weak Seyferts is a small fraction of the total mass-loss rate of stars in a typical bulge; in these cases, exotic processes such as tidal disruption of stars or radiative disturbances of their atmospheres (Mathews 1983) are neither likely nor required.

An accurate reflection of the true relations between the various classes of weakly active nuclei will, of course, be quite complex. It appears from radio morphology that Seyfert 1s and 2s require at least 10^6 years for a complete transition, if indeed such transitions are common (de Bruyn and Wilson 1978). The gas distributions and kinematics of the narrow-line region and transition zone of higher density differ in Seyferts and LINERs (De Robertis and Osterbrock 1984), so there might well be some hereditary differences among objects hosting one or the other. The presence of broad-line regions in many LINERs indicates that any such basic differences may affect the luminosity of the central source, but not its occurrence. However, since photoionization models indicate that a LINER could become much like a Seyfert 1 or 1.5 merely by increasing the ionizing-continuum luminosity, the notion that objects could change their apparent nature across this boundary is worthy of closer investigation.

With regard to the importance of galaxy properties in determining the level or presence of nuclear activity, studies of the properties of the host galaxies are basic to any attempt to sort out the trends from individual peculiarities. Such an approach to "active galaxies as galaxies" has been advocated for luminous systems by Balick and Heckman (1982), and is likely to be even more fruitful (as well as less complicated by the nuclei themselves) in the low-luminosity objects. The large fractions of some Hubble types hosting low-level AGNs (in particular LINERs) means that it is more meaningful to compare level of activity (for example, emission-line luminosity) than its mere presence or absence among galaxies, since it is almost the case that (active galaxy)=(galaxy) at these levels. For these types of systems (Sa-Sb, and probably ellipticals) the presence of at least a mildly active nucleus is almost unavoidable, and must be a clue to basic results of galaxy formation and evolution.

The greatest need for immediate work on low-luminosity nuclei seems to be a clear indication of exactly how LINERs relate to conventional active nuclei; are they shocked, photoionized, or a combination? Models of physically mixed systems are appropriate; a start has been made by Contini and Aldrovandi (1983, Aldrovandi and Contini 1985) in modelling the structure of gas filaments exposed to a power-law continuum and moving through an interstellar medium, generating shocks in a gas already photoionized. They find that for most reasonable parameters, one or the other process will dominate the emitted spectrum. This may suggest that a real continuum of LINER properties is present, with both shocks and photoionization represented as dominant agents.

Further theoretical work should take into account the evidence for a wide range of density in the emitting clouds, as has been done by Filippenko and Halpern (1984) and Binette (1984). The fact that one-zone models give reasonable fits to the integrated emission spectra of LINERs might be fortuitous, indicating that many of them are more or less ionization-bounded, so that the ensemble ionization balance is close to that given by a single-point model of similar effective ionization parameter.

On the observational side, attempts to detect the hypothetical nonstellar continuum in low-ionization nuclei need to be extended to typical spiral nuclei. These will be much more difficult than the strong-lined radio galaxies in which the ionizing continuum has been detected (Filippenko 1985), but are more representative of the class and would yield more generally applicable conclusions. Wholesale searches of this kind will require UV spectroscopy with the Space Telescope. Higher sensitivity in the X-ray will allow measurement of any high-energy continuum, such as has been detected from several LINERS using Einstein. Images in emission lines at high angular resolution might show whether structures identifiable as large-scale shocks appear. Improved understanding of the integrated spectra of galaxies would allow measurement of weaker lines than so far possible, and hence tighter constraints on the relevant physical processes, from the ultraviolet to infrared bands. Further information on the velocity fields is important, and can be gained with present techniques. The presence of high-velocity-dispersion components in the emission from some ions suggests motions controlled by a central mass concentration, and deserves more detailed study in a variety of representative objects.

The relations, if any, between starbursts and active nuclei need to be clarified. High-resolution data on the coexistence of both kinds of phenomena could show a statistical connection; detailed studies of individual cases will be needed to determine the physics involved. Such an understanding would allow meaningful models of the behavior of stellar remnants in a nucleus, and of the probability of forming one or a few central massive objects. Since the statistics of star formation in luminous disk galaxies indicate that most of them have undergone a nuclear starburst (Balzano 1983), the results of such events could play an important role in the properties of normal nuclei.

There are many suggestions at our present stage of understanding that there is in fact a common thread connecting all the manifestations of nuclear activity in galaxies. We do not yet know the details of their connections, but current research trends show promise of resolving some of the current questions in the near future.

REFERENCES

Aldrovandi, S.M.V., and Contini, M. 1985, *Astr. Ap.*, submitted,

Ambartsumian, V.A. 1971, in *Nuclei of Galaxies*, D.J.K. O'Connell, ed., (North-Holland-Elsevier: New York), p. 9.

Adams, T.F. 1977, *Ap.J. Suppl.*, **33**, 19.

Alloin, D. 1973, *Astr. Ap.*, **27**, 433.

Alloin, D., Pelat, D., Boksenberg, A., and Sargent, W.L.W. 1983, *Ap.J.*, **275**, 493.

Baldwin, J.A., Phillips, M.M., and Terlevich, R. 1981, *Pub. A.S.P.*, **93**, 5.

Balick, B., and Heckman, T.M. 1982, *Ann. Rev. Astr. Ap.*, **20**, 431.

Balzano, V.A. 1983, *Ap.J.*, **268**, 602.

Binette, L. 1984, *Astr. Ap.* submitted.

Bruzual A.G., Peimbert, M., and Torres-Peimbert, S. 1982, *Ap.J.*, **260**, 495.

Burbidge, E.M., and Burbidge, G.R. 1962, *Ap.J.*, **135**, 694.

_____. 1965, *Ap.J.*, **142**, 634.

Burbidge, G.R. 1978, I.A.U. Sym. 77,227.

Burbidge, G.R., Burbidge, E.M., and Sandage, A.R. 1963, *Rev. Mod. Phys.*, **35**, 947.

Bushouse, H.A., and Gallagher, J.S. 1984, *Pub. A.S.P.*, **96**, 273.

Carswell, R.F., Baldwin, J.A., Atwood, B., and Phillips, M.M. 1984, *Ap.J.*, **286**, in press.

Charles, P.A., and Phillips, M.M. 1982, *M.N.R.A.S.*, **200**, 263.

Contini, M., and Aldrovandi, S.M.V. 1983, *Astr. Ap.*, **127**, 15.

Cox, D.P. 1972, *Ap.J.*, **178**, 143.

Cutri, R.M., Rudy, R.J., Rieke, G.H., Tokunaga, A.T., and Willner, S.P. 1984, *Ap.J.*, **280**, 521

Davies, R.L., and Illingworth, G.D. 1984, in preparation.

de Bruyn, A.G., and Wilson, A.S. 1978, *Astr. Ap.*, **64**, 433.

De Robertis, M.M., and Osterbrock, D.E. 1984, preprint.

Dopita, M.A. 1976, *Ap.J.*, **209**, 395.

_____. 1977, *Ap.J. Suppl.*, **33**, 437.

Edmunds, M.G., and Pagel, B.E.J 1982, *M.N.R.A.S.*, **198**, 1089.

Eissner, W., Martins, P. de A., Nussbaumer, H., Seraph, H.E., and Seaton, M.J. 1969, *M.N.R.A.S.*, **146**, 63.

Elvis, M., Schreier, E.J., Tonry, J., Davis, M., and Huchra, J.P. 1981, *Ap.J.*, **246**, 20.

Elvis, M., and van Speybroeck, L.P. 1982, *Ap.J. (Lett.)*, **257**, L51.

Fabbiano, G., and Trinchieri, G. 1984, *Ap.J.*, **286**, in press.

Feldman, F.R., Weedman, D.W., Balzano, V.A., and Ramsey, L.R. 1982, *Ap.J.*, **245**, 427.

Ferland, G.J., and Netzer, H. 1983, *Ap.J.*, **264**, 105.

Filippenko, A.V. 1985, *Ap.J.*, **289**, in press.

Filippenko, A.V., and Halpern, J.E. 1984, *Ap.J.*, **285**, 458.

Filippenko, A.V., and Sargent, W.L.W.S. 1985, *Ap.J. Suppl.*, **57**, in press.

Ford, H.C., Crane, P., Jacoby, G.H., Lawrie, D.G., and van der Hulst, J.M. 1985, *Ap.J.*, submitted.

Forman, W., Schwarz, J., Jones, C., Liller, W., and Fabian, A.C. 1979, *Ap.J. (Lett.)*, **234**, L27.

Fosbury, R.A.E., Mebold, U., Goss, W.M., and Dopita, M.A. 1978, *M.N.R.A.S.*, **183**, 549.

Fosbury, R.A.E., Mebold, U., Goss, W.M., and van Woerden,H. 1977, *M.N.R.A.S.*, **179**, 89.

Fosbury, R.A.E., Snijders, M.A.J., Boksenberg, A., and Penston, M.V. 1981, *M.N.R.A.S.*, **197**, 235.

Fosbury, R.A.E., and Wall, J.V. 1979, *M.N.R.A.S.*, **189**, 79.

French, H.B. 1980, *Ap.J.*, **240**, 41.

Fried, J.W., and Schulz, H. 1983, *Astr. Ap.*, **118**, 166.

Gehrz, R.D., Sramek, R.A., and Weedman, D.W. 1983, *Ap.J.*, **267**, 551.

Goad, J.W., and Gallagher, J.S. 1985, *Ap. J.*, submitted.

Goodrich, R.W. 1985, in preparation.

Goodrich, R.W., and Osterbrock, D.E. 1983, *Ap.J.*, **269**, 416.

Gunn, J.E., Stryker, L.L., and Tinsley, B.M. 1981, *Ap. J.*, **249**, 48.

Halpern, J.P., and Steiner, J.E. 1983, *Ap.J. (Lett.)*, **269**, L37.

Heckman, T.M. 1978, *Pub. A.S.P.*, **90**, 241.

_____.1980a, *Astr. Ap.*, **87**, 142.

_____.1980b, *Astr. Ap.*, **87**, 152.

_____.1980c, *Astr. Ap.*, **88**, 365.

Heckman, T.M., Balick, B., and Crane, P.C. 1980, *Astr. Ap. Suppl.*, **40**, 295.

Heckman, T.M., Miley, G.K., Balick, B., van Breugel, W.J.M., and Butcher, H.R. 1982, *Ap.J.*, **262**, 529.

Heckman, T.M., van Breugel, W.J.M., Miley, G.K, and Butcher, H.R. 1983, *A.J.*, **88**, 1077.

Heeschen, D.S., and Conklin, E.K. 1975, *Ap.J.*, **196**, 347.

Heeschen, D.S., and Puschell, J.J. 1983, *Ap.J. (Lett.)*, **267**, L11.

Jacoby, G.H., Ford, H., and Ciardullo, R. 1985, *290*, i, npress.

Joseph, R.D., Wright, G.S., and Wade, R. 1984, *Nature*, **311**, 132.

Keel, W.C. 1983a, *Ap.J. Suppl.*, **52**, 229.

_____ . 1983b, *Ap.J.*, **268**, 632.

_____ . 1983c, *Ap.J.*, **269**, 466.

_____ . 1984a, *Ap.J.*, **282**, 75.

_____ . 1984b, in preparation.

Keel, W.C., Kennicutt, R.C., Jr., Hummel, E., and van der Hulst, J.M. 1985, A.J., *Ap. J.*, **90**, in press.

Keel, W.C., and Miller, J.S. 1983, *Ap. J. (Lett.)*, **266**, L89.

Kent, S.M., and Sargent, W.L.W.S. 1979, *Ap. J.*, **230**, 607.

Koski, A.T., and Osterbrock, D.E. 1976, *Ap. J. (Lett.)*, **203**, L49.

Kriss, G.A., Canizares, C.R., and Ricker, G.R. 1980, *Ap.J.*, **242**, 492.

Kruger, E., Tutukov, A.V., and Loose, H.H. 1983, *Astr. Ap.*, **124**, 89.

Lawrence, A., and Elvis, M. 1982, *Ap.J.*, **256**, 410.

Lawrence, A., Ward, M., Elvis, M., Fabbiano, G., Willner, S.P., Carleton, N.P., and Longmore, A. 1984, Ap.J., submitted.

Loose, H.H., Kruger, E., and Tutukov, A.V. 1982, *Astr. Ap.*, **105**, 342.

MacAlpine, G.W., Smith, S.B., and Lewis, D.W. 1977, *Ap.J.Suppl.*, **34**, 95.

Maccacaro, T., Perola, G.C., and Elvis, M. 1981, *Space Sci. Rev.*, **30**, 61.

Margon, B., Chanan, G.A., and Downes, R.A. 1982, *Ap.J. (Lett.)*, **253**, L7.

Mathews, W.G. 1983, *Ap.J.*, **272**, 390.

Meurs, E.J.A., and Wilson, A.S. 1984, *Astr. Ap.*, **136**, 206.

Malkan, M.M., and Filippenko, A.V. 1983, *Ap.J.*, **275**, 477.

Miller, J.S. 1974, *Ap.J.*, **189**, 239.

_____. 1978, *Ap.J.*, **220**, 490.

_____. 1981, *Pub. A.S.P.*, **93**, 681.

Morgan, W.W. 1958, *Pub. A.S.P.*, **70**, 364.

Munch, G. 1961, *Ap.J.*, **131**, 250.

Norman, C., and May, A. 1984, preprint.

Osterbrock, D.E. 1977, *Ap.J.*, **215**, 733.

_____. 1984, *Q.J.R.A.S.*, **25**, 1.

Peimbert, M. 1968, *Ap. J.*, **154**, 33.

Peimbert, M., and Torres-Peimbert, S. 1981, *Ap. J.*, **245**, 845.

Péquignot, D. 1984, *Astr. Ap.*, **131**, 159.

Perola, G.C., and Tarenghi, M. 1980, *Ap.J.*, **240**, 447.

Phillips, M.M. 1984, private communication.

Phillips, M.M., Charles, P.A., and Baldwin, J.A. 1983, *Ap.J.*, **266**, 485.

Phillips, M.M., Pagel, B.E.J., Edmunds, M.G., and Díaz, A. 1984, preprint.

Rees, M.J. 1978, , , I.A.U. Sym. 77, 237.

Reichert, G.A., Mason, K.O., Thorstenson, J.R., and Bowyer, S. 1982, *Ap.J.*, **260**, 437.

Rieke, G.H., Lebofsky, M.J., Thompson, R.I., Low, F.J., and Tokunaga, A.T. 1980, *Ap.J.*, **238**, 24.

Rieke, G.H., Cutri, R., Black, J.H., Kayley, W.F., McAlary, C.W., Lebofsky, M.J., and Elston, R. 1984, Ap.J., submitted.

Rieke, G.H., Lebofsky, M.J., and Kemp, J.C. 1982, *Ap.J. (Lett.)*, **252**, L53.

Rose, J.A., and Cecil, G. 1983, *Ap.J.*, **266**, 531.

Rose, J.A., and Searle, L. 1982, *Ap.J.*, **253**, 556.

Rose, J.A., and Tripicco, M.J. 1984, *Ap.J.*, **285**, in press.

Rubin, V.C., and Ford, W.K., Jr. 1971, *Ap.J.*, **170**, 25.

Sandage, A. 1978, *A.J.*, **83**, 904.

Sersic, J.L, and Pastoriza, M. 1965, *Pub. A.S.P.*, **77**, 287.

_____.1967, *Pub. A.S.P.*, **79**, 152.

Shuder, J.M. 1980, *Ap.J.*, **240**, 32.

Shuder, J.M., and Osterbrock, D.E. 1981, *Ap. J.*, **250**, 55.

Shull, J.M., and McKee, C.F. 1979, *Ap.J.*, **227**, 131.

Stauffer, J.R. 1982a, *Ap. J. Suppl.*, **50**, 517.

_____. 1982b, *Ap. J.*, **262**, 66.

Stauffer, J.R., Schild, R., and Keel, W.C. 1983, *Ap.J.*, **256**, 465.

Trinchieri, G., Fabbiano, G., and Palumbo, G.G.C. 1985, *Ap.J.*, **289**, in press.

Turnrose, B.E. 1976, *Ap.J.*, **210**, 33.

Ulrich, M.-H. 1978, *Ap.J.*, **219**, 424.

Ulvestad, J.S., and Wilson, A.S. 1983, *Ap.J.*, **275**, 8.

_____. 1984, *Ap.J.*, submitted.

van der Hulst, J.M., Crane, P.C., and Keel, W.C. 1981, *A.J.*, **86**, 1175.

Véron, P. 1979, *Astr. Ap.*, **78**, 46.

Véron, P., Lindblad, P.O., Zuiderwijk, E.J., Véron, M.P., and Adam, G. 1980, *Astr. Ap.*, **87**, 245.

Véron, P., Véron, M.P., Bergeron, J., and Zuiderwijk, E.J. 1981, *Astr. Ap.*, **97**, 71.

Véron-Cetty, M.-P., and Véron, P. 1985, Astr. Ap., submitted.

Ward, M.J., Wilson, A.S., Penston, M.V., Elvis, M., Maccacaro, T., and Tritton, K.P. 1978, *Ap.J.*, **223**, 788.

Wasilewski, A.J. 1983, *Ap.J.*, **272**, 68.

Weedman, D.W. 1983, *Ap.J.*, **266**, 479.

Weedman, D.W., Feldman, F.R., Balzano, V.A., Ramsey, L.W., Sramek, R.A., and Wu, C.-C. 1981, *Ap.J.*, **248**, 105.

Willner, S.P., Ward, M., Longmore, A., Lawrence, A., Fabbiano, G., and Elvis, M. 1984, *Pub. A.S.P.*, **96**, 143.

Wilson, A.S., and Ulvestad, J.S. 1982, *Ap.J.*, **263**, 576.

THE NARROW LINE REGION
AND ASSOCIATED RADIO EMISSION
IN ACTIVE GALACTIC NUCLEI

A.S. Wilson

and

T.M. Heckman*

Astronomy Program, University of Maryland,
College Park, MD

ABSTRACT

In this paper, we consider the kinematics of line emitting gas and the properties of synchrotron radio emission on scales of tens of pc to tens of kpc. Detailed investigations of the profile of the [O III] λ5007 line have shown strong asymmetries, with a preference for extended wings to the blue, more prominent wings than in Gaussian functions, and redshift differences from the systemic velocity. The width of this line is correlated with the stellar velocity dispersion of the galaxy bulge, suggesting gravitational accelerations play an important role in line broadening. The line widths are similar in quasi-stellar objects (QSOs), Seyfert galaxies and LINERs, but are smaller in galaxies undergoing nuclear starbursts. The widths of the broad and narrow lines seem to be correlated in objects with a broad line region, but there are no systematic differences between the narrow line kinematics of active galaxies and QSOs. The kinematics of the narrow line region do not seem to correlate with the rate of emission of energy by the nucleus, but are related to the rate at which the narrow line region intercepts this energy.

Studies of many ion species in several Seyfert 1 galaxies and LINERs have revealed correlations between line width and

---

*   Alfred P. Sloan Foundation Fellow and Visiting Assistant Professor in the Department of Physics and Astronomy, The Johns Hopkins University, Baltimore, MD 21218 ionization potential and/or critical density. *This work reveals important stratification in the narrow line region and a blending into the broad line region, but it is not yet known whether the primary correlation is the same in both Seyfert galaxies and LINERs. The connection of these results with recent gravitational infall and hot wind outflow models is briefly discussed.*

The spatially extended, high ionization nebulosities often seen in Seyfert galaxies are probably photoionized by a central power law source. Interpretation of their kinematics generally requires radial motions, most observers preferring outflow. In a few cases, the location of the broadest lines is slightly displaced from the continuum peak. Low ionization rotating disks, photoionized by hot young stars, are also seen in some Seyferts.

Radio emission from the kpc scale is intimately connected with the narrow line region. The mean radio power increases through the sequence Seyfert type 1, type 1.2–1.8, type 2, and the radio power is strongly correlated with both the luminosity and width of the [O III] $\lambda5007$ line. The rate of increase of [O III] width with both [O III] luminosity and kpc scale radio power seems to slow at high values of these parameters (i.e., for QSOs and radio galaxies with kpc scale cores, respectively). Probable connections between the radio power and the mass of the galaxy bulge are emphasized. When well resolved, most Seyfert galaxies show "linear" radio structures presumably ejected from the active nuclei. Radio source size and power are well correlated in nearby Seyferts; this relation may extend to higher radio powers (radio galaxies and QSOs with kpc scale cores). The radio ejection axis seems unrelated to the rotation axis of the galaxy disk, but is probably correlated with the major axis of the narrow line cloud complex and the direction of the optical continuum polarization vector. Galaxies observed to have linear radio sources tend to show stubby, steep-sided [O III] $\lambda5007$ profiles (Whittle). Promising ideas in this area include anisotropic escape of ionizing photons from the central source and acceleration of clouds by radio jets. Nonthermal radio emission from starbursts around

Seyfert nuclei has been identified. We summarize the properties of weak kpc scale radio emission in nearby elliptical/SO galaxies. The association between line emitting gas and synchrotron emitting plasma in the kpc scale cores of radio galaxies is discussed and the continuity with Seyferts emphasized. The data indicate that these sources reflect powerful radio jets propagating through a dense interstellar medium.

I. INTRODUCTION

This review deals with phenomena occurring on scales of $\sim 10 - 10^4$ pc around active galactic nuclei (AGNs) and quasi-stellar objects (QSOs). The great bulk of information concerning this region has come from optical spectroscopic investigation of ionized gas (the so-called Narrow Line Region, or NLR) and from radio investigation of synchrotron emitting relativistic plasma. Accordingly, we will heavily emphasize these two "windows," attempting (where appropriate) to summarize evidence that the thermal (optical) and relativistic (radio) media interact with each other. Others in this volume will deal more explicitly with photoionization models of the optically-emitting gas (Shields), with the role of dust (MacAlpine), and with the relationship of the ionized gas in "classical" active nuclei to other interesting nuclei such as LINERs and starbursts (Keel). Accordingly, we will review primarily the kinematics/dynamics of the NLR gas and the nature of the nonthermal radio emission on similar scales. (We will henceforth refer to this entire region as the NLR.)

Investigation of the NLR in AGNs and QSOs is important for a number of reasons. This region connects on its inner side with the more compact emitting regions which, while more intimately related than the NLR to the nuclear "engine" or "monster," are spatially unresolved (except in the radio) and occur in very unfamiliar surroundings. By contrast, the outer boundary of the NLR not only encompasses part of the galaxy's interstellar medium, but can often be well resolved spatially at optical wavelengths. Thus, the NLR provides a bridge from the familiar and relatively well understood to the exotic and poorly known. We will try throughout this review to highlight the way in which study of the NLR is helping to elucidate other phenomenological aspects of AGNs and QSOs (such as the Broad line Region - BLR - and the powerful, large scale radio jets).

We begin (§II) with a description of the global kinematic properties of the NLR gas, as drawn from extensive studies of the [O III] λ5007 profiles and from complementary investigations of multi-species emission line profiles. Available information on the spatially resolved properties of the NLR gas is also summarized. Next (§III), we will review the body of data concerning the non-thermal radio sources found in Seyferts, and will then briefly discuss the related classes of weak kpc scale sources in elliptical/SO galaxies and the much more powerful kpc scale radio sources found in a growing number of radio galaxies and QSOs. The review ends (§IV) with an attempt to synthesize these various data into a coherent (though largely empirical) picture of this fascinating region. Throughout the paper we use a Hubble constant $H_o = 75$ km s^{-1} Mpc^{-1}.

II. EMISSION LINE GAS

a) [O III] Global Profiles

i) Preamble

The study of the kinematics of emission line gas in AGNs and QSOs provides crucial information on the dynamical interaction between the active nucleus and its surroundings. Because the angular size of the bright core of the NLR is typically only several arc sec, even in the most nearby AGNs (e.g., Walker 1968), most of our knowledge concerning NLR kinematics has come from global (i.e., spatially unresolved) profiles of bright emission lines. Most attention has been paid to [O III] λ5007, not only because it is nearly always the brightest optical line from the NLR (e.g.,

Koski 1978), but also because it is not blended with any other lines of even moderate strength. Some bright objects have been studied in detail (e.g., Walker 1968; Glaspey *et al.* 1976; Pelat and Alloin 1980), but until recently too few galaxies were investigated for systematic trends to be discovered. The situation has changed dramatically in the last several years with the publication of a number of large surveys of the [O III] λ5007 emission line profiles, obtained with resolutions of 20–180 km s^{-1} (Heckman *et al.* 1981 [HMBB]; Véron 1981; Miley and Heckman 1982 [MH]; Feldman *et al.* 1982; Vrtilek 1983; Phillips, Charles and Baldwin 1983; Heckman, Miley and Green 1984 [HMG]; Whittle 1984a, b [W1, W2]). These investigations have uncovered various potentially important systematic properties of the NLR kinematics.

ii) Definitions of Line Parameters

The various surveys listed above have sometimes used slightly different schemes to parameterize the line profiles. We will primarily follow the system defined by HMBB, since it encompasses the largest amount of published data (see W1 for a discussion of the relative merits of various parameterizations). The primary line profile parameters of interest are the center velocity, the width, the asymmetry, and a "peakiness" parameter related to the kurtosis of the line. HMBB have published information on the line center and width at flux levels of 20%, 50%, and 80% relative to line peak (C20, C50, C80; W20, W50, W80). They also defined an "asymmetry index" $AI_{20} = (WL20 - WR20)/(WL20 + WR20)$, where WL20 and WR20 are the half-widths of the line at 20% of the peak intensity to the left and right (respectively) of the line center defined at the 80% intensity level (C80). Note that $AI_{20} > 0$ for lines which are asymmetric to the blue (blue side of the profile falls off more slowly in intensity). Finally, HMG published a "kurtosis parameter" $R_{20/50} = W20/W50$ (ratio of line widths at 20% and 50% of the peak intensity). For a Gaussian profile shape $R_{20/50} = 1.52$.

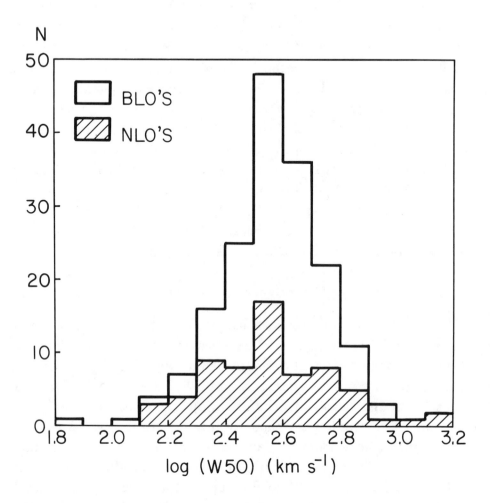

Figure 1: Histogram of the log of the [O III] λ5007 profile width at the 50% intensity level (log W50, W50 in km s⁻¹) for Narrow Line Objects (NLOs, hatched) comprising Seyfert 2s and Narrow Line Radio Galaxies, and for Broad Line Objects (BLOs, no hatching) comprising Seyfert 1s, Broad Line Radio Galaxies and QSOs. The overall distribution is well fit by a Gaussian with a mean of 2.56 (= 365 km s⁻¹) and a standard deviation of 0.20. There is no evidence for a systematic difference in W50 between NLOs and BLOs. References for the line widths are given in the text.

iii) Distributions of Line Profile Parameters

We will first summarize the available information concerning the general properties of the [O III] λ5007 emission line profiles, and will then discuss their relationship to other properties of the activity and/or the "host" galaxy.

(a) Line Widths

In Figure 1 we show histograms of the [O III] line widths (W50) taken from the combined surveys listed above (175 objects in total). The distribution of log (W50) is well fit by a Gaussian with a mean 2.56 (365 km s^{-1}) and standard deviation 0.20 ($^{+210}_{-135}$ km s^{-1}) (cf. W1). In contrast to earlier investigations of smaller samples, there now appears to be no evidence for systematic differences in the profile widths between objects with a BLR (broad line objects — BLOs — 110 in Fig. 1) and without (narrow line objects — NLOs — 65 in Fig. 1), in agreement with W2. Note that BLOs comprise Seyfert 1s, QSOs and Broad Line Radio Galaxies, while NLOs comprise Seyfert 2s and Narrow Line Radio Galaxies.

The emission line widths (usually quoted as W50) are often similar to the widths of stellar absorption lines (usually quoted as σ_{stars}) in the bulges of early type spirals of similar luminosity to the Seyferts (Meurs and Wilson 1984 [MW]; W2). Figure 2 shows a plot of log σ_{stars} against log W50$_{gas}$ for all Seyferts and LINERs with measurements of both parameters. Despite considerable scatter (due, in part, to measurement errors), statistically significant correlations are found for the sample as a whole (>99.95% significance level) and probably for the Seyferts and LINERs separately (99.7% confidence level for each). This link between the emission line widths and the gravitational potential on the kpc scale is encouraging, but there are various problems with interpreting the gas velocities as purely gravitationally bound motion. First, the slope of the best fit straight line is below unity – the points with

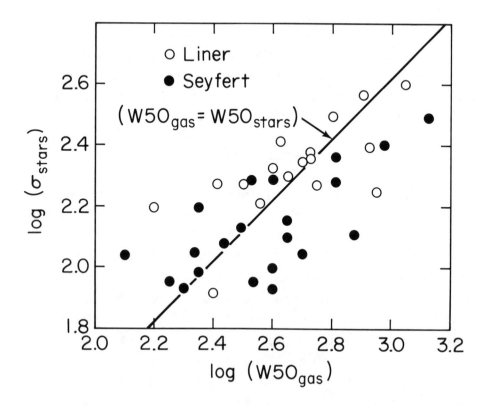

Figure 2: The log of the stellar velocity dispersion in km s^{-1} (log σ_{stars}) plotted against the log of the [O III] emission line width at the 50% intensity level (log W50) for Seyfert nuclei (filled circles) and LINERs (open circles). The diagonal line represents (for reference only) the situation in which W50 for the emission line gas = W50 for the stars (assuming a Gaussian line of sight stellar velocity profile). References for the emission line data are Heckman, Balick, and Crane (1980), Keel (1983), Stauffer (1982), Heckman *et al.* (1982, 1985a), HMG, Phillips, Charles, and Baldwin (1983), van Breugel *et al.* (1984a), Vrtilek (1983), W1, Feldman *et al.* (1982), and Heckman, Wilson and Illingworth (work in progress). References for the stellar data are Tonry and Davis (1981), Schechter (1983), Davies *et al.* (1983), Dressler and Sandage (1983), Heckman *et al.* (1985a), Whitmore, Kirshner and Schechter (1979), Whitmore and Kirshner (1981), Kormendy and Illingworth (1983), and Heckman, Wilson and Illingworth (work in progress).

the highest values of $W50_{gas}$ have $W50_{stars} < W50_{gas}$. While there is no reason to suppose that the gas and stars sample the same gravitational potential (significant amounts of [O III] $\lambda5007$ may be emitted from scales below several tens of pc), it is intriguing that most of the galaxies with high values of W50 are strong radio sources (radio galaxies or radio bright Seyferts). The relation between radio power and gaseous line width is discussed later in § III. Second, rotation or turbulence dominated models of the NLR are ruled out by systematic line asymmetries (see below). Third, the emission line profiles show more extensive wings than do Gaussians (see below), with velocity ranges of 1000–2000 km s^{-1} – much larger than expected from gravitationally induced motions on the hundreds of pc to kpc scale. Other hints of connections between the gravitational potential and kpc scale properties will be noted in this review. We are currently engaged in an observational project to provide more values of σ_{stars} for Seyfert galaxies and thus extend the relation suggested by Figure 2.

(b) Line Asymmetries

Perhaps the single most interesting result to emerge from the [O III] surveys is that this line profile is systematically asymmetric to the blue ($AI_{20}>0$). This can be clearly seen in Figure 3, in which the blue asymmetric profiles outnumber the red by a 3.3:1 margin. W1 showed that this preponderance is even stronger when the asymmmetry is measured nearer the line base. It is worth emphasizing though that strongly red-asymmetric profiles do sometimes occur (see, for example, NGC 4388 in HMG). So far, only one class of QSO/AGN has been found *not* to exhibit this preferential blue asymmetry (see below). Models involving radial flow plus dust obscuration (e.g., HMBB; Peterson, Foltz, and Byard 1981) or radial flow plus light travel time effects (Capriotti and Foltz 1982) are then suggested for the NLR (i.e., rotation or turbulence dominated models are ruled out).

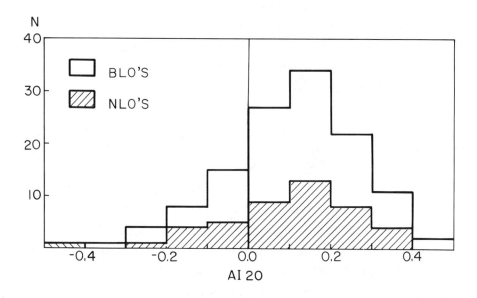

Figure 3: Histogram of AI_{20}, the "Asymmetry Index" of the [O III] $\lambda5007$ line profile at the 20% peak intensity level (see text for definition). $AI_{20} > 0$ corresponds to profiles with enhanced blue "wings." The symbols for NLOs vs. BLOs are as in Figure 1. Note the strong preference for blue asymmetries in both BLOs and NLOs. References for AI_{20} values are given in the text.

(c) Line Shifts Relative to Systemic Velocity

The physical meaning of the above profile asymmetry is highly ambiguous without information regarding the location of the galaxy systemic velocity in the line profile (i.e., a profile with asymmetric wings to the blue can be produced by "eating away" at either the blue side of the line near the peak or the red side of the line near the base). An accurate (~ 30 km s^{-1}) value for V_{sys} can be determined by a number of methods, but none is ideal. Single dish H I 21 cm profiles may be distorted by interactions with close companion galaxies and emission line rotation curves influenced by non-circular motions, while stellar velocities are difficult to measure in the presence of strong emission lines and nonthermal continua. Nevertheless, HMBB, Vrtilek (1983) and W1 have combined all these approaches, and V_{sys} is now known for 37 AGNs with well-resolved [O III] profiles.

Because the emission line profiles are asymmetric, a comparison between the [O III] velocities and V_{sys} must be conducted at a specified intensity level of the profile. Figures 4a and b plot histograms of $(C50 - V_{sys})$ and $(V_{peak} - V_{sys})$ respectively, where

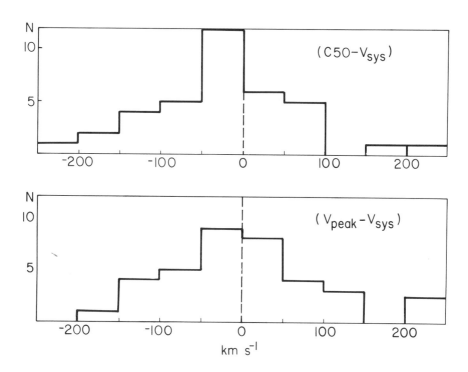

Figures 4a and 4b: Histogram (top) of the difference between the velocity of the midpoint of the [O III] $\lambda5007$ profile at the 50% intensity level (C50) and the galaxy systemic velocity (V_{sys}). Histogram (bottom) of the difference between the velocity at the peak of the [O III] $\lambda5007$ profile (V_{peak}) and V_{sys}. Note that there is no evidence for an average (systematic) offset between V_{peak} and V_{sys}, although large offsets (blueshift or redshift) are common. There is an excess of negative values for C50-V_{sys} (line midpoint blueshifted relative to V_{sys}). References for velocities given in the text.

V_{peak} is the velocity near the peak (upper 20%) of the [O III] profile. The combined data set shows a weak trend for C50 to be blueshifted with respect to V_{sys}: mean (C50 $-$ V_{sys}) = -25 $\pm$ 16 km s^{-1} (no significant difference between NLOs and BLOs). If we conservatively take (C50 $-$ V_{sys}) to be significantly different from zero only if it exceeds twice the estimated uncertainty in its value (as quoted by Vrtilek 1983 and W1), then 15 (8) galaxies exhibit a significant blueshift (redshift) of C50 relative to V_{sys}. Mirabel and Wilson (1984) found a significant excess of blueshifts of [O III] relative to the 21 cm H I velocity for a somewhat different sample of Seyferts with lower quality optical velocities. There is *no* evidence for any systematic offset between V_{peak} and V_{sys}: mean $(V_{peak} - V_{sys})$ = +1 $\pm$ 16 km s^{-1}.

If confirmed by larger samples, this agreement (in the mean) between V_{peak} and V_{sys} would indicate that: 1) all other estimators of [O III] velocity (such as C20 or the mean) must be statistically *blueshifted* with respect to systemic. It also suggests that: 2) the blue asymmetry is a consequence of repression of the red base of the line by dust obscuration, as long as the lines would be statistically symmetric and centered at the systemic velocity in the absence of dust.

Despite the absence of any *systematic* difference between V_{peak} and V_{sys}, rather large offsets (to both blue and red) between V_{sys} and the emission line velocity (however defined) are, on the face of it, very common. For example, mean $|C50 - V_{sys}|$ = 72 $\pm$ 12 km s^{-1} and mean $|V_{peak} - V_{sys}|$ = 67 $\pm$ 10 km s^{-1} (these shifts are $\sim$ 20% of the typical W50 values). About 62% of the [O III] profiles have C50 significantly displaced with respect to V_{sys} ($|C50 - V_{sys}|$ > twice the estimated uncertainty) and about 25% show shifts $\geq$ 100 km s^{-1}. For V_{peak}, the analogous percentages are 50% and 28%. We conclude that NLR models must be capable of generating profiles which are systematically asymmetric to the blue, [O III] velocities (both C50 and V_{peak}) which are significantly different from systemic (to red *or* blue), but probable statistical trends for the averages of V_{peak} and V_{sys} to coincide and for other estimators of [O III] velocity to be, on average, *below* V_{sys}.

(d) Kurtosis

A histogram of the kurtosis parameter $R_{20/50}$ is shown in Figure 5. The most interesting result to be gleaned from this figure

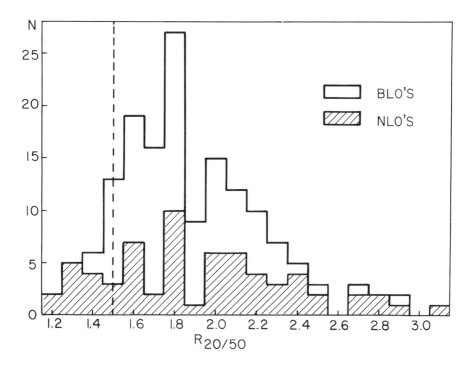

Figure 5: Histogram of the kurtosis parameter $R_{20/50}$ (ratio of the [O III] $\lambda5007$ line widths at the 20% and 50% intensity levels) for NLOs (hatching) and BLOs (no hatching). The fiducial line at $R_{20/50} = 1.52$ is appropriate to a Gaussian line profile. Most [O III] line profiles are more peaked than are Gaussians, but a significant fraction of NLOs exhibit "boxlike" profile shapes.

is that the great majority of [O III] $\lambda5007$ profiles are more "peaky" than a Gaussian (i.e., $R_{20/50} > 1.52$ for 92% of the profiles). As noted by HMG, W1, and De Robertis and Osterbrock (1984) the NLR profiles share this property with BLR profiles, but in neither case does this strongly imply any particular dynamical model.

(e) Profile "Lumpiness"

By "lumpiness" we mean the departure from smooth quasi-Gaussian or quasi-logarithmic profile shapes that may indicate large-scale structure in the NLR. A "lumpiness" parameter has not been quantitatively defined in any of the above surveys (Fourier techniques might be the best approach here). Most of the published profiles with high signal-to-noise appear rather smooth, but a significant minority ($\sim$ 10–20%) do show large lumps and/or double peaks (see for example 3C33, 0211-479, and 0518-458 in HMG and Tol 0109-383 and Mkn 509 in W1). A physical interpretation of these profile anomalies is not yet clear.

iv) Correlations with Other Properties

(a) Seyferts vs. LINERs vs. Starbursts

As first noted by Heckman (1980), and subsequently better established by W1, LINERs have a rather similar distribution in emission line widths to Seyferts. The Seyfert line widths seem to be related to the gravitational potential (see above). Since the LINER galaxies are rather similar to the Seyfert galaxies in Hubble type and absolute magnitude, the similarity in line widths is then perhaps not surprising. Data on detailed profile shapes in a large sample of LINERs are not available, so it is not yet known whether LINERs (like Seyferts) have systematically blue asymmetric profiles, exhibit significant offsets between emission line and systemic velocity, or have lines that are more "peaky" than Gaussians.

A significant amount of data on line profiles in starburst (H II region like) nuclei is also available (Véron 1981; Balzano 1983; Feldman *et al.* 1982; Heckman *et al.* 1983b; W1). These nuclei produce lines which are significantly narrower than those in LINERs or Seyferts (see also Shuder and Osterbrock 1981; Phillips, Charles and Baldwin 1983): typical widths are $\sim$ 80–200 km s^{-1} compared to 200–600 km s^{-1} for LINERs/Seyferts. These narrow lines may be related to the tendency (e.g., Heckman *et al.* 1983b) for starburst nuclei to reside in galaxies of later Hubble type (smaller bulge, implying smaller velocity dispersion). However, Weedman (1983) and W1 maintain that the gas velocities in starburst nuclei are likely to be *below* those of material in gravitational equilibrium. Data on the stellar velocity dispersions in these galaxies would be difficult to obtain, but would be quite valuable. The [O III] profiles in starburst nuclei show no evidence for systematic blue asymmetry, so the dynamical state of the gas in these nuclei seems to be fundamentally different from that in Seyferts. This is interesting in its own right, and offers an additional empirical criterion for discriminating between starburst and Seyfert nuclei.

(b) The Broad Line Region (BLR)

The establishment of any links between the NLR and BLR is important for many reasons, most obviously because the NLR can be spatially resolved (in great detail by Space Telescope!) and its structure may provide important clues to the structure of the BLR (which will remain spatially unresolved for the foreseeable future). It is also important to understand the relationship between objects with a BLR (BLOs) and those without (NLOs). Are BLOs and NLOs fundamentally similar objects? Over what timescale do objects migrate (if at all) between the two classes? Hence, we will also consider whether there is any evidence for kinematic differences in the NLR (dynamical timescale $\sim 10^6$ years) between NLOs and BLOs.

As noted earlier (§IIa and Fig. 1), there now appears to be no evidence for systematic differences between BLOs and NLOs in the profile widths (W50). Moreover, neither HMBB nor W2 find any difference in the tendency for blue asymmetric profiles between BLOs and NLOs (Fig. 3). As we will discuss below, however, BLOs do exhibit a stronger inverse correlation between line asymmetry and the average ionization state of the NLR than do the NLOs. Another possible kinematic difference between NLOs and BLOs is that a significant fraction of NLOs (17%) exhibit stubby steep-sided ("box-like") [O III] profiles ($R_{20/50} < 1.52$), while such profiles are almost unknown in BLOs ($\sim 2\%$). As discussed later (§III), stubby, steep-sided [O III] profiles may be related to the presence of "linear" (double, triple or jet-like) radio emission on kpc scales (W2) and such radio sources are more commonly seen in Seyfert 2s than in Seyfert 1s. It is, therefore, not yet clear how [O III] line shape, radio morphology and the presence of a BLR are interrelated (i.e., which are the primary and which are the secondarily induced correlations).

As first discovered by Cohen (1983) and later confirmed by HMG and W2, there is a significant correlation (albeit with considerable scatter) between the NLR ([O III]) and BLR (Balmer) line widths in BLOs. This establishes a kinematic link between the two regions, but it is not yet known whether this link relates intrinsic flow velocities or is instead an aspect angle effect in a shared non-spherically symmetric flow pattern (e.g., disk or jet). The growing body of evidence suggesting that the NLR and BLR may smoothly merge (see §IIb) favors a true dynamical link between the two regions. Despite this, W2 found no evidence that the profile *shapes* (kurtosi or asymmetries) in the NLR and BLR are statistically related.

Gaskell (talk at this conference) finds additional evidence that the NLR and BLR "know about" each other; the equivalent width of the [O III] line in low redshift QSOs is on average three times larger in objects with weak BLR Fe II optical emission than in objects with strong Fe II. Of course, it has long been known (see most recently Shuder 1981 and Osterbrock 1978) that the equivalent widths of the [O III] lines are much smaller in BLOs compared to NLOs, suggesting that the BLR may "shadow" the

NLR in some way. The strong Fe II emitters may do this shadowing exceptionally well.

(c) QSOs vs. AGNs

The quantitative continuity and qualitative similarity between Seyfert 1s and QSOs has long been recognized (e.g., Weedman 1976, 1977). As summarized by HMG, there is no evidence for systematic differences in the NLR kinematics (based on [O III] profile properties of width, asymmetry, and kurtosis) between QSOs and AGNs with BLRs.

(d) Radio Properties

We will consider the kpc scale radio sources in AGNs and QSOs in detail below (§III). Here we are concerned with the relationship of the NLR kinematics to the radio emission on *all* scales.

HMG have demonstrated that QSOs/AGNs associated with large scale ($\sim 10^2$ kpc) radio sources are the only class *not* to show a strong preference for blue asymmetric [O III] profiles. HMG concluded that either the global kinematic structure of the NLR, or the geometric relation between the NLR gas and dust must be different in objects capable of producing powerful, large scale radio jets. Available data suggest that rotation (about the radio ejection axis) may be important in the NLR in this radio class (Simkin 1979; Heckman *et al.* 1985a).

There are strong correlations of both W50 and [O III] luminosity ($L_{[OIII]}$) with the radio power of the *kpc scale* radio emission in Seyferts, as is discussed later in §IIIa.

(e) NLR and Nonthermal Luminosities

There is a good correlation between $L_{[OIII]}$ and W50 (Phillips, Charles and Baldwin 1983; W2), but interpretation of this result is hampered by the similarly good correlations between kpc scale radio power and both W50 and $L_{[OIII]}$. It is nevertheless interesting that the total rate at which the NLR gas is heated should be related to the magnitude of the characteristic velocities in the NLR. The rate of increase of W50 with $L_{[OIII]}$ seems to slow at high values of $L_{[OIII]}$ (i.e., for QSOs). Neither line asymmetry nor kurtosis is correlated with [O III] luminosity (W2).

LINERSs do *not* obey the same relation between $L_{[OIII]}$ and W50 as Seyferts and QSOs (LINERs have far less luminous NLRs than Seyferts, but have, on average, equally wide lines). This is a potentially important clue to the problem of the relationship between LINERs and Seyferts (see review by Keel in this volume).

Despite the strong correlation between $L_{[OIII]}$ and W50, there is no significant correlation between W50 (or asymmetry or kurtosis) and the nuclear "nonthermal" luminosity (HMBB, HMG, W2), as measured in the IR, optical, or X-ray spectral regions. Thus the NLR kinematics appear ignorant of the rate at which the nucleus produces luminous energy, but are highly cognizant of *the rate at which the NLR intercepts it*, as measured by $L_{[OIII]}$ and P_{21cm}.

v) Dust

HMBB found a possible correlation between [O III] asymmetry index and the $H\alpha/H\beta$ flux ratio, suggesting that the dust responsible for profile asymmetries also causes the steep Balmer decrements. However, W2 has reexamined this potentially important result with a much larger sample than available to HMBB and finds no correlation between these quantities. This may imply that the dust responsible for the steep decrements lies in an "external screen." If the dust causing the [O III] asymmetries is *internal* to the narrow line clouds, then infall models are the most natural way to explain the blue asymmetries and the blueshift of the profile wings relative to V_{sys}. On the other hand, if the dust is associated with the medium *enveloping* the clouds (so clouds on the far side of the nucleus are preferentially hidden), outflow models are preferred. When IRAS data for a large sample of Seyferts has been analyzed, it may be possible to identify thermal dust emission from the narrow line clouds themselves and investigate anew the relation between far infrared emission, line asymmetry and Balmer decrement. Capriotti and Foltz (1982) have proposed a quite different type of model in which the [0 III] line profile asymmetries do not result from a combination of radial flow and obscuration, but rather from a combination of radial flow and light travel time effects, with a variable ionizing continuum source.

vi) Physical Conditions in the NLR

In §IIb below we will consider how analysis of multi-species emission line profiles allows us to probe the stratification of physical conditions in the NLR. Here we consider whether the global [O III] profile properties are related to the *average* physical properties of the NLR.

For example, HMBB and W2 find no correlation between any [O III] λ5007 line profile parameter and the global ratio of either [O III] λ4363 to λ5007 (a temperature diagnostic for densities $\ll 10^6$ cm^{-3}, and a temperature/density diagnostic for higher densities), or of [S II] λ6717 to λ6731 (a density diagnostic for densities $<10^4$ cm^{-3}). On the other hand, both HMBB and W2 find, for BLOs, an *inverse* correlation between the average ionization state of the NLR gas (as judged by the intensity ratios of [O III]λ5007/[O II]λ3727, [O III]λ5007/[O I]λ6300, and [Ne III]λ3869/ [O II]λ3727) and the asymmetry of the [O III] λ5007 line. However, this correlation is much weaker or even absent for the NLOs. It would appear then that dusty NLRs are less highly ionized (on average), at least in BLOs. To interpret the significance of this result will require knowledge as to the location of the asymmetry producing dust relative to the emission line clouds.

vii) Galaxy Orientation

HMBB and W2 find no correlation between the widths, asymmetries, or kurtosi of the [O III] lines and the galaxy inclination. W2 finds that either the NLR is not in a disk co-aligned with the galaxy, or that the NLR velocity field must contain at least a 50% contribution from turbulence. He also concludes that either high gas velocities perpendicular to the galaxy plane must occur, or that the NLR clouds have a sufficiently large covering fraction that dust scattered line radiation from inflow can cause the extended blue wings in the [O III] profiles.

b) Multi-Species Studies

Early work (e.g., Phillips 1976, 1977, 1978; Grandi 1977; Koski 1978; Feldman and MacAlpine 1978) revealed differences of redshift between different lines in several Seyfert and radio galaxies. The high ionization forbidden lines, such as [O III] and [Ne III], were generally found to be blueshifted with respect to the low ionization ones and/or the Balmer lines. Grandi (1978) noted that the [Fe XI] $\lambda 7892$ line is blueshifted in Seyferts in comparison with low ionization species and, in two cases, is significantly broader than the other forbidden lines. He suggested that this blueshift might reflect an expanding high ionization nebulosity plus absorbing dust close to the central continuum source. [Fe X] $\lambda 6374$ in Seyferts is also both blueshifted with respect to and broader than lines of lower ionization species (Wilson 1979; Penston et al. 1984). The mean blueshift of the [Fe X] line is 120 km s^{-1} (with respect to [O I] $\lambda 6300$) and its mean W50 is 580 km s^{-1}, much broader than [O I] $\lambda 6300$. The data hint that [Fe X] *may* be broader than [O III] $\lambda 5007$, but because of both the weakness of the [Fe X] line and the small number of objects with

[Fe X] measurements, further observations are needed to check this. Wilson (1979) and Pelat, Alloin and Fosbury (1981) also pointed out a strong correlation between line width and the ionization potential of the species in the type 1 Seyfert galaxy NGC 3783 (cf. Atwood, Baldwin and Carswell 1982). The lines of highly ionized species tend to have higher transition probabilities than the low ionization lines and consequently can be emitted from higher density regions, since collisional deexcitation will be less important. In many photoionization models, the more highly ionized species are formed closer to the central ionizing source. Thus, the most straightforward explanation of these observations of NGC 3783 invokes a systematic decrease in density and velocity spread with increasing distance from the central object. In a general way, the NGC 3783 data suggest that near ($\sim 0.1 - 1$ pc) to the central object is found the BLR ($N_e \sim 10^9$ cm^{-3} $\Delta V \simeq 10^4$ km s^{-1}), further away (a few pc to tens of pc) are emitted the highly ionized species ($\Delta V \leq 10^3$ km s^{-1}) while the species of low ionization are found on a much larger scale (tens to hundreds of pc) from filaments with low velocities ($\Delta V \sim 300$ km s^{-1}) and density ($N_e \sim 10^{2-4}$ cm^{-3}). Correlations between broad and narrow line widths in samples of Seyfert 1 galaxies (§IIa) support the idea of a continuity in properties between the conventional broad and narrow line regions.

Osterbrock (1981) found a similar correlation between line width and ionization potential in his very detailed study of the high ionization Seyfert 1 galaxy III Zw 77. The lines in this remarkable galaxy range between very low (e.g., [O I]) and very

high ([Fe X] λ6374, [Fe XI]λ7892 and probably [Fe XIV] λ5303*)
ionization species. Studies of the line profiles of various species in
Mrk 704 and MCG 8-11-11 have been made by Cohen and Marcy
(1983).

The most recent contributions in this area are those by De
Robertis and Osterbrock (1984), Filippenko and Halpern (1984)
and Filippenko (1985). De Robertis and Osterbrock (1984) obtained narrow line profiles covering a wide range of ionization in
12 high ionization Seyferts. They find a good correlation between
line width and ionization potential for several, but not all, objects.
For some galaxies, a correlation is evident between line width and
the critical density for collisional deexcitation of the upper level,

$$N_{e,cr}(i) = \sum_{j<i} A_{ij} / \sum_{j\neq i} q_{ij}$$

where A_{ij} is the radiative transition probability between upper
level i and lower level j and $N_e q_{ij}$ is the collisional transition rate
from level i to level j per atom in level i. De Robertis and Osterbrock fit these correlations by empirical functions of the forms:
W33 = aχ + b and W33 = clog $N_{e,cr}$ + d, with χ representing the

---

* There are no currently accessible temperature diagnostics
for these coronal iron lines so they can be generated by photo or
collisional ionization. However, their widths are consistent with
W50 vs. ionization potential/critical density relationships. Also
their strengths are strongly correlated with other lines in the high
ionization zone (Grandi 1978; Osterbrock 1981; Penston *et al.*
1984) such as [Fe VII], for which temperature determinations generally give $1 - 6 \times 10^4$K (e.g., Boksenberg *et al.* 1975; Osterbrock
1981; Fosbury and Sansom 1983; Ward and Morris 1984). These
results favor photoionization as the input mechanism, even to the
regions of highest ionization, or else if the lines are collisionally ionized in a high temperature medium, its properties are very closely
linked with the photoionization source (Osterbrock 1981; Penston
et al. 1984).

ionization potential. The constants a, b, c and d show considerable variation from galaxy to galaxy.

Filippenko and Halpern (1984, FH) have described a detailed study of the LINER NGC 7213, the nuclear spectrum of which resembles a Seyfert 1. They argue that the spectral characteristics are more consistent with photoionization by a nonstellar continuum with a low ionization parameter than with shock heating. A crucial point is that the low [O III] ratio $R[O\ III] = I(\lambda5007 + \lambda4959)/I(\lambda4363)$ cannot be achieved at any reasonable temperature unless $N_e > 10^{5.5}$ cm^{-3}. A high temperature is then not necessarily implied, eliminating the chief argument in favor of collisional ionization in this object. In fact [O III] $\lambda4363$ ($N_{e,cr} \simeq 3 \times 10^7$ cm^{-3}) is broader than the nebular [O III] lines ($N_{e,cr} \simeq 8 \times 10^5$ cm^{-3}) and probably arises in denser clouds. There are other examples of different line widths for lines from the same species, but with different critical densities. For the nebular lines [O II] $\lambda\lambda3726, 3729$ ($N_{e,cr} \simeq 3 \times 10^3$ cm^{-3}), W50 $\simeq$ 300 km s^{-1}, but for the auroral pair [O II] $\lambda\lambda7319, 7330$ ($N_{e,cr} \simeq 6 \times 10^6$ cm^{-3}), W50 $\simeq$ 1000 km s^{-1}. Similar effects are seen for the nebular and transauroral lines of [S II]. The auroral and transauroral lines are slightly blueshifted with respect to systemic while the nebular lines are not. These observations demonstrate convincingly that linewidth is related to density rather than ionization state in this galaxy (Figs. 6, 7).

For an ion with a single excited level, the luminosity of the collisionally excited line radiation from all the gas in the nucleus with electron, ion densities N_e, N_1 and radial velocity V is (Osterbrock 1974): $L_c(N_e, N_1, V) = N_e N_1 q_{12} h\nu_{21} \Gamma(N_e, N_1, V)$, for $N_e \ll N_{e,cr}$ and $L_c(N_e, N_1, V) = N_1 \frac{\omega_2}{\omega_1} e^{-E/kT} A_{21} h\nu_{21} \Gamma(N_1, V)$, for $N_e \gg N_{e,cr}$. The symbols have their usual meanings, with the addition of $\Gamma(N_e, N_1, V) dN_e dN_1 dV$, which is the volume occupied by clouds with electron density, ion density and radial velocity in

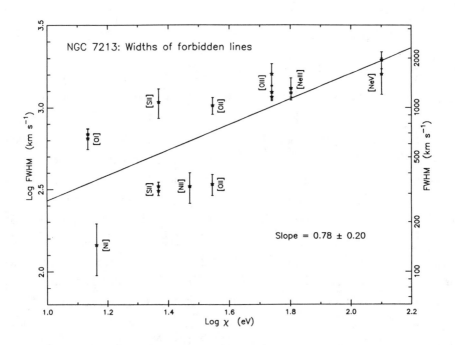

Figure 6: (from Filippenko and Halpern 1984) - Log W50 is plotted against Log χ for each forbidden line in the LINER NGC 7213, where χ is the ionization potential of the corresponding species. An unweighted linear least-squares fit formally indicates the presence of a correlation (correlation coefficient $r = 0.73$). Several lines from the same species but with markedly different widths (e.g., [O II], [S II]), however, demonstrate that *the correlation is not of fundamental significance*, and that χ is at most a secondary parameter.

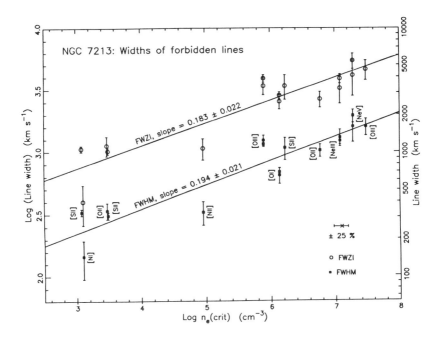

Figure 7: (from Filippenko and Halpern 1984) - Log W50 (filled squares) and log FWZI (open circles) are plotted against log $N_{e,cr}$ for each forbidden line in the LINER NGC 7213, where $N_{e,cr}$ is the critical density of the upper level from which the corresponding transition occurs. Uncertainties in theoretically calculated critical densities may be of order $\pm 25\%$. Unlike Figure 6, in which there is considerable scatter, the least-squares fits indicate high correlation coefficients ($r \approx 0.92$). Note that lines from the same species but with markedly different widths strengthen the correlation, so clouds with *different* bulk motions and densities must exist in the narrow line region.

the ranges N_e to N_e+dN_e, N_1 to N_1+dN_1 and V to V+dV. The net emission at a given V is then obtained by summing the values of L_c for all densities contributing significant line emission. Thus the contribution of gas with density N_e to a given observed line profile cannot be obtained from the observations without an ionization model (to relate N_e and N_1) and a dynamical model describing the formation and evolution of the clouds (to give $\Gamma(N_e, N_1, V)$. If $N_e \propto N_1$ and, for example, $\Gamma \propto N_e^{-2}$, then $L_c = $ const (for $N_e < N_{e,cr}$) or $L_c \propto N_e^{-1}$ (for $N_e > N_{e,cr}$). While it is clear that emission from lines with high critical densities will be weighted towards high density regions, the common assumption that the emission is *dominated* by gas near the critical density should be treated with caution. In any case, FH find the empirical relation W50 or WO $\propto N_{e,cr}^{1/5}$ for NGC 7213. An extrapolation of this trend (Fig. 7) is consistent with the Balmer line widths if $N_{e,cr} \simeq 10^9$ cm^{-3} is assumed for them. It may be possible, under simplifying assumptions, to invert the above argument and derive $\Gamma(N_e)$ if the data *do* indicate dominance of observed emission lines by gas near $N_{e,cr}$.

Similarly small R[O III] values and correlations between line width and critical density (W $\propto N_{e,cr}^{0.1-0.2}$) are found for the radio galaxies PKS1718-649 (a classic LINER) and Pic A (a type 1 Seyfert with features of LINERs) and the quasar MR2251-178 (Filippenko 1985; Carswell *et al.* 1984). This correlation may be present in a significant fraction ($\sim$ 1/3) of LINERs and low luminosity Seyfert nuclei (Filippenko and Sargent 1984). Péquignot (1984) has successfully accounted for the spectrum of the classical "shock ionized" galaxy NGC 1052 (e.g., Fosbury *et al.* 1978; Keel and Miller 1983) in terms of photoionization of gas with a wide range of densities by the radiation of a hot ($\sim 8 \times 10^4$K) black body prolonged by a flat soft X-ray continuum (see also Rose and Tripicco 1984). Thus the evidence that LINERs have a wide range of densities in their NLRs is very strong.

Further observational work in this area should address whether the correlations (W vs. χ; W vs. $N_{e,cr}$) differ for Seyfert 1s and 2s (almost all objects with reported correlations have a BLR) and whether Seyferts differ from LINERs. A medium dispersion red survey currently underway (ASW) should provide line widths and redshifts for [O I] $\lambda\lambda$6300, 6363, Hα, [N III], $\lambda\lambda$6548, 6584 and

[S II] $\lambda\lambda6717$, 6731 in about 50 Seyferts.

Commensurate with the rapid improvement in observational material, a number of theoretical studies specific to the dynamics of the NLR have recently been made. Some models have envisaged clouds falling (under gravity) into the nucleus through a hot outflowing wind (Smith 1984; Carroll and Kwan 1983 [CK]; cf. also Contini and Aldrovandi 1983). Smith (1984) distinguishes clouds which continue to fall into the nucleus from those which are small enough to be "catapulted" out through the wind's ram pressure, which is also responsible for cloud confinement. Smith is currently deriving the line profiles expected in his model. CK concluded that a two density component NLR (cf. Netzer 1982) is needed to fit the integrated line intensities of Seyferts and quasars, independent of any profile information. In their model, the high ionization lines are formed at high nucleon density ($N \geq 10^6$ cm^{-3}, needed to match R[O III] and [O III] $\lambda5007$/Hβ) and the low ionization ones at low density ($N \sim 10^{3.5}$ cm^{-3}, needed to match the [S II] $\lambda6716$/$\lambda6731$ ratio). In the CK model (cf. Kwan and Carroll 1982), clouds in a distant "reservoir" are perturbed into highly eccentric orbits which feed into the BLR. A hot intercloud medium (which generates an expanding wind) is responsible for confining and compressing the infalling clouds. Both the density and velocity increase towards the center of activity ($N \propto r^{-2}$, so the ionization parameter $U = L/Nr^2$ remains constant; $V \propto r^{-1/2}$) and this intermediate zone, between the reservoir and the BLR proper, constitutes the high density NLR. The model includes a return leg after the clouds reach periquasar, but the forbidden line emission is negligible since the clouds expand and become optically thin to the Lyman continuum. Assessing the emission line profiles from the low density reservoir and the high density clouds separately, CK calculate model profiles which confirm the intuitively expected correlation between line width and critical density. Further, any kinematic model with Keplerian orbits and constant ionization parameter and central ionizing luminosity produces $W \propto N^{1/4}$, in reasonable agreement with FH's and Filippenko's (1985) findings.

If the clouds contain dust, the infalling clouds on the far side of the continuum source are seen preferentially, giving a blue asymmetry to the line profile. These gravitational infall models seem promising and deserve further attention from both observers and theoreticians.

Krolik and Vrtilek (1984) consider a model in which the narrow lines are due to entrainment of the emitting clouds in a hot wind flowing out of the center of the galaxy. The dynamics of the hot gas are analyzed assuming steady state, spherical symmetry, a logarithmic gravitational potential, adiabatic flow and an absence of sources or sinks in the region under study. Non-adiabatic effects, such as heating by a nuclear X-ray continuum, are simulated in the context of these simplified models with an adiabatic index $\gamma < 1$. Line profiles are predicted by assuming cloud velocities are identical to the wind velocity (in contrast to the Smith [1984] model), a constant number flux of clouds and a dust optical depth of unity across the radius of the region. Depending on the γ chosen, the flow can either accelerate or decelerate. Other important effects, such as radiative acceleration, deceleration of the wind by friction with an ambient interstellar medium and an evolutionary model for the clouds themselves, need to be included before such models can be realistically confronted with observed line profiles.

c) Extended Nebulosities in Seyfert Galaxies

A substantial fraction of nearby Seyfert galaxies have spatially resolved regions of high ionization gas around their nuclei. The scales of these nebulosities range from a few hundred pc to ~10 kpc. Examples which have been studied spectroscopically include NGC 1068 (e.g., Walker 1968; Balick and Heckman 1979, 1985; Aloin *et al.* 1983), NGC 1365 (Phillips et al. 1983a), NGC 2110 and NGC 5506 (Wilson, Baldwin, and Ulvestad 1985), NGC 3227 (Rubin and Ford 1968), NGC 3516 (Ulrich and Péquignot 1980), NGC 4151 (Ulrich 1973; Anderson 1974; Fricke and Reinhardt 1974; HMBB; Heckman and Balick 1983), NGC 4507 (Adney, Wilson and Baldwin 1984), NGC 5643 and NGC 7582 (Morris *et al.* 1984), NGC 7469 (Ulrich 1972; Anderson 1973; Wilson and Baldwin, in preparation; Axon *et al.* 1984), Mark 1 and 3 (Balick and Heckman 1979), Mark 78 (Adams 1973; Boksenberg 1977), Mark 509 (Phillips *et al.* 1983b) and 3C120 (Balick and Heckman 1979; Baldwin *et al.* 1980). In reviewing this material, we were impressed by the range in morphology and kinematic behavior exhibited by the gas, making firm, general conclusions difficult. This diversity is not surprising since: i) the study of these nebulosities is limited by seeing to scales of hundreds of pc or more; ii) a given observed velocity field can often be interpreted in terms of several plausible 3-d models; iii) expanding or contracting gas in the NLR can be projected onto, and confused by, normally rotating disk gas; and, iv) parts of the nebulosity can be obscured by dust. Hopefully, spatially resolved studies of the *inner* part (< 100pc) of the NLR by ST will suffer less from confusion by H II regions and other normally rotating disk gas.

On the basis of the usual line ratios (e.g., Baldwin, Phillips and Terlevich 1981), it has been argued that the high ionization nebulosities are photoionized by a nonstellar, nuclear continuum source (e.g., Balick and Heckman 1979; Ulrich and Péquignot 1980; Baldwin *et al.* 1980; Phillips *et al.* 1983a,b; Wilson, Baldwin and Ulvestad 1985). In a few cases, extrapolation of the uv continuum observed by IUE can be shown to provide enough ionizing photons to power the whole nebulosity. The kinematics have sometimes been interpreted in terms of a few large clouds, each with a high bulk motion and internal velocity dispersion (hundreds of km s^{-1}). Walker (1968) and Ulrich (1973, 1972) mapped out four kinematically distinct clouds in the inner few arc secs of each of NGC 1068 and NGC 4151 and two clouds in NGC 7469. The kinematics of the gas in NGC 1068 are particularly complex; Figure 8

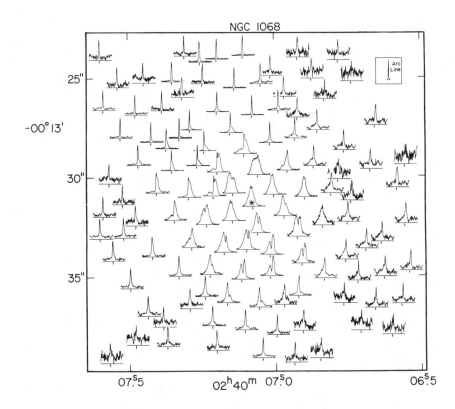

Figure 8: (from A.S. Wilson and J.A. Baldwin, in preparation) - Profiles of [O III] λ5007 in the central 16 " x 16 " of NGC 1068. Each profile is normalized so that the difference between the maximum and minimum fluxes over the range of wavelengths plotted is the same physical height. The vertical arrow under each profile indicates 1107 km s^{-1}, the heliocentric systemic velocity given by Walker (1968). The range of velocities plotted is 4300 km s^{-1} for each profile. The profiles generally refer to an area of 1".5 × 1".65 centered at the tip of the arrow. The arc line shows the instrumental profile. R.A. and dec. have been added using the accurate nuclear position given by Clements (1981). The position of the nucleus is indicated by an *.

shows the distribution of profiles of [O III] $\lambda5007$ over the inner 16 arc sec of this galaxy. This diagram represents the central section of a rather extensive study of the kinematics of NGC 1068 (Wilson and J.A. Baldwin, in preparation). Mark 78 shows two clouds, one on each side of the nucleus, with a separation of 3 arc sec and a velocity difference of 900 km s^{-1} (Adams 1973; Boksenberg 1977). For the high ionization component in NGC 1365, Phillips *et al.* (1983a) favored ejection of gas from the nucleus into the halo of the galaxy or rotation of a tilted disk. The high ionization gas forms an expanding shell in Mark 509 (Phillips *et al.* 1983b), while one interpretation of the observations of NGC 5506 invokes radial motion in a wide cone with axis roughly perpendicular to the galaxy disk (Wilson, Baldwin and Ulvestad 1985). In NGC 2110, the large scale bulk motion of the high ionization gas reflects rotation (Wilson, Baldwin and Ulvestad 1985), while in 3C120 it is mainly chaotic, but with a component of rotation (Baldwin *et al.* 1980).

As a general rule, the line widths decrease going away from the nuclei (peak of continuum light). This effect may be a simple continuation of the trend implied by the multi-species studies (§IIb). In a few cases (NGC 2110 and NGC 5643, refs. given above; 3C305, Heckman *et al.* 1982; M51, Ford *et al.* 1984), the location of the broadest lines is displaced an arc sec or a few from the peak of continuum light. Broad off-nuclear lines could result through a superposition of two or more independent high velocity clouds, through effects of dust scattering/obscuration, or through acceleration and entrainment of interstellar gas by nuclear ejecta (e.g., radio jets etc.) For example, the broadest lines could be physically associated with the continuum nucleus, but obscured in that direction and rendered visible in another by scattering from an offset concentration of dust. In M51 and 3C305, however, and perhaps NGC 2110 and NGC 5643, the cloud emitting the broad off-nuclear lines is associated with one side of a "linear" radio feature, which is apparently an effect of the nuclear activity. The offset broad lines in these galaxies may then represent ambient interstellar gas entrained in jets, plasmoids or expanding bubbles fuelled by the active nucleus. Such a scenario may also be applicable to NGC 1068, as further discussed in §III.

Low ionization gas, apparently ionized by hot young stars, is sometimes seen (e.g., NGC 1068, NGC 1365, NGC 7469, NGC 7582, Mark 509), in addition to the high ionization component. The kinematics of the low ionization gas are generally found to conform to rotation in a disk; in NGC 1068, NGC 1365 and NGC 7582 at least, the kinematic line of nodes is coincident with the photometric major axis of the galaxy, indicating the starburst lies in the galaxy disk. CO (Scoville, Young and Lucy 1983), far uv (Snijders, Briggs and Boksenberg 1982), far infrared (Telesco *et al.* 1984) and radio continuum (Wilson and Ulvestad 1982b) observations of the disk of NGC 1068 all testify to the existence of a massive starburst. The existence of a circumnuclear starburst in NGC 7469 is also indicated by measurement of the spatial extent of the 3.3 μm dust emission feature by Cutri *et al.* (1984), and by long-slit optical spectroscopy (Wilson and Baldwin, in preparation). In most, if not all, of these galaxies, the high ionization gas shows a completely different kinematical behavior to the low, almost certainly involving radial motions.

III) RADIO EMISSION

a) Seyfert Galaxies

i) Radio Surveys

In comparison with radio galaxies and radio-loud quasars, Seyfert galaxies are relatively inconspicuous at radio wavelengths. Early centimetric or decimetric wavelength surveys of classical Seyferts (Wade 1968; van der Kruit 1971) and of Markarian galaxies (Sramek and Tovmassian 1975; Sulentic 1976; Kojoian *et al.* 1976; Bieging *et al.* 1977; Biermann *et al.* 1980) led to the detection of roughly 20 Seyfert galaxies. McCutcheon and Gregory (1978) observed some 40 Seyfert and broad/narrow line radio galaxies at 2.8 and 1.3 cm and detected about 15 of the Seyferts, many of which were also seen in the longer wavelength surveys. A survey covering a range of radio wavelengths has also been conducted with the RATAN-600 telescope (Sanamyan and Kandalian 1978, 1979, 1980; Sanamyan, Kandalian and Oganyan 1983). The most extensive radio survey of Seyfert galaxies is currently the one performed with the Westerbork telescope in 21 cm continuum radiation (van der Kruit 1971; de Bruyn and Wilson 1976; Meurs and Wilson 1981; Wilson and Meurs 1982). 140 Seyfert, Seyfert-like and related galaxies were observed to a typical flux limit of 3 or 4 mJy (3σ) and 89 were detected. Technology has now advanced to the state that Ulvestad and Wilson (1984b) were able to detect *all* galaxies in a distance limited sample of nearby Seyferts by using the VLA at 6 and 20 cm. Continuum surveys at meter (e.g., Artyukh *et al.* 1982) and millimeter (e.g., Blitz, Mathieu and Bally 1984) wavelengths have detected only a small fraction of the galaxies surveyed because of limitations of sensitivity imposed by source confusion and/or present instrumentation.

ii) Integrated Radio Properties

Observed monochromatic radio powers at 21 cm for Seyferts cover the range $P_{21cm} \sim 10^{19.8} - 10^{24.9}$ W Hz^{-1}. With a typical power law spectrum of index $\alpha = 0.75$ ($S \propto \nu^{-\alpha}$), the total power emitted in the radio band is $\sim 10^{37} - 10^{42}$ erg s^{-1}, which is usually a tiny fraction of the total electromagnetic luminosity. The distribution of spectral index is bimodal: most galaxies have steep radio spectra ($\alpha \simeq 0.4 - 1.1$), but a small fraction show flat spectrum, apparently self-absorbed cores. There seem to be no systematic differences in the distributions of spectral index between types 1 and 2 (de Bruyn and Wilson 1978; Meurs 1984). Generally, no radio polarization is detectable at 21 cm. The radio emission is generally dominated by nuclear (size < a few kpc), rather than disk, emission.

One of the more interesting results to emerge from the radio surveys is the tendency for Seyfert 2s to be more luminous radio sources than Seyfert 1s. This difference is found in surveys of both Markarian selected Seyferts (Sramek and Tovmassian 1975; de Bruyn and Wilson 1978; Osterbrock 1979; Ulvestad and Wilson 1984a; MW) and a distance limited sample (Ulvestad and Wilson 1984b). In fact, the average radio power decreases continuously through the sequence type 2, intermediate type (1.2-1.9), type 1 (Osterbrock 1984; MW), indicating a correlation with the relative prominence of the NLR compared with the BLR. The radio luminosity function for Markarian Seyfert 2s lies above that for Seyfert 1s over the power range $10^{22.4} - 10^{23.6}$ W Hz^{-1} (Meurs 1982; MW) and the Seyfert 2s appear to cover a narrower range of radio powers than the Seyfert 1s. Because Seyfert 1s show greater nonstellar, nuclear continuum emission than the Seyfert 2s in most other wavebands, the difference in their radio powers is usually *increased* if the radio powers are compared at a given level of some other indicator of nonstellar luminosity. Thus, type 2 Seyferts are 40-100 times more efficient than Seyfert 1s at generating radio emission for a given nonstellar optical luminosity (Ulvestad and Wilson 1984a). Qualitatively similar results pertain if the overall photographic magnitude (Osterbrock 1984), the 2-10 keV luminosity, or (probably) the power at 10 μ are used instead of the nonstellar optical luminosity.

A connection between the radio emission and the NLR in Seyferts is also implied by correlations between P_{21cm} and [O III] luminosity $L_{[OIII]}$ (de Bruyn and Wilson 1978; W2) and between P_{21cm} and [O III] $\lambda 5007$ line width, W50 (Wilson and Willis 1980; HMBB: W2). The first of these is broadly consistent with a linear relation $P_{21cm} \propto L_{[OIII]}$. Power law fits to the second, $P_{21cm} \propto \text{W50}^{\beta}$ have obtained $\beta = 2.2 \pm 0.6$ (MW) or $\beta = 8.0$ (W2) for rather heterogeneous samples of *radio detected* Seyferts (upper limits ignored) and $\beta = 3.5 \pm 0.7$ for a smaller sample of Seyfert galaxies known to possess "linear" radio structures. These correlations appear to apply to both Seyfert 1s and 2s, although segregation of the two types is apparent in the P_{21cm} vs. $L_{[OIII]}$ relation (the Seyfert 2s have a higher P_{21cm} for a given $L_{[OIII]}$ than do Seyfert 1s, see W2). As noted in §IIa, $L_{[OIII]}$ and W50 are also correlated for Seyferts. From a partial correlation analysis, Whittle (W2) has concluded that the P_{21cm} vs. W50 and $L_{[OIII]}$ vs. W50 correlations are equally fundamental; neither appears to be caused indirectly by the other. As for the $L_{[OIII]}$ vs. W50 relation (§IIa), however, the rate of increase of W50 with P_{21cm} seems to slow or even stop at very high powers (i.e., for radio galaxies with kpc scale cores - see §IIIc).

The physical basis of these correlations is not entirely clear. Suggestions made to account for the P_{21cm} vs. $L_{[OIII]}$ relation include: 1) a pressure equilibrium between relativistic and thermal material (de Bruyn and Wilson 1978), and, 2) that the conditions under which radio plasma and ionizing photons can escape from the central sources to the NLR are the same, or at least strongly correlated (Osterbrock 1979, 1984). Osterbrock (1979) identifies the BLR as the entity which "soaks up" the radio plasma and ionizing ultraviolet light in type 1s and prevents their escape to excite the NLR.

For the P_{21cm} vs. W50 relation, one suggestion is that the narrow line clouds power the radio emission by acceleration of particles in shocks and amplification of magnetic field (Wilson and Willis 1980; HMBB). Another invokes acceleration of narrow line clouds by the jets or plasmoids presumed to power the linear radio sources (Wilson 1981, 1982; Booler *et al.* 1982). The simplest models of the latter type would give $\beta = 3$. Yet another possibility is that the relationship is not fundamental but a consequence of a dependence of each parameter on a third one. As noted in §II, the correlation of gaseous and stellar velocity dispersions, the preference of Seyfert nuclei for early-type spirals and the similarity of the line widths in Seyferts, LINERs and QSOs suggest a relation between the nuclear activity and the gravitational potential of the galaxy bulge. MW point out that the radio emission may also be related to bulge mass because: a) the relation $P_{21cm} \propto W50^{\beta}$, with $\beta \simeq 3.5$, may be similar in form to that between the bulge luminosity (L_B) or spirals and ellipticals and their stellar velocity dispersion (σ), $L_B \propto \sigma^n$ with n = 4 (Faber and Jackson 1976) or n = 5.4 $^{+0.9}_{-0.7}$ (Kormendy and Illingworth 1983). If the L_B vs. σ relation applies to the bulges of Seyferts, the P_{21cm} vs. W50 relation could indicate that P_{21cm} is correlated with L_B (or total bulge mass) and W50 is correlated with σ (cf. Figure 2). Indeed, there is some evidence for a correlation between P_{21cm} and absolute optical magnitude in type 2s (cf. MW; Kandalian 1982). To investigate this idea further, more multiaperture photometry and direct imaging of Seyferts are needed to separate nuclear, bulge and disk light. b) Hummel (1981) has shown that the power of the central radio source in normal spirals is, on average, at least a factor of 10 stronger in the early type than in the late type galaxies (cf. van der Hulst, Crane and Keel 1981). A continuity in properties between the central radio sources in Seyferts and those in early-type spirals is suggested by the possible relation of their radio luminosity functions (MW).

iii) Radio Structures – Statistical Properties

Recently, Ulvestad and Wilson (1984a,b) have mapped two distinct samples of Seyferts with the VLA, mainly in "A" (the maximum baseline) configuration. The first comprises the 29 Seyferts in the first nine lists of Markarian with 21 cm continuum flux densities above 10 mJy ("flux limited" sample). The second consists of 24 out of the 25 Seyferts and "relatively narrow line X-ray galaxies" (NLXGs) known (as of mid-1982) with recession velocities < 3100 km s^{-1} with respect to the centroid of the Local Group and $\delta > -45°$ ("distance limited" sample, selected from Huchra 1982). Despite the quite different methods used in the initial optical selection of these samples and the bias towards high radio powers in the flux limited sample, the results of the radio surveys are quite compatible, as we now summarize.

a) The radio structure of each galaxy may be classified into one of five categories: L ("linear"), D ("diffuse"), A ("ambiguous"), S ("slightly resolved") or U ("unresolved"). The breakdown of the two samples into these structure classes is given in Table 1. As may be seen, $\sim 60\%$ of the flux limited sample and $\sim 50\%$ of the distance limited sample have nuclear radio sources too compact to be well mapped with the VLA at λ 6 cm (classes S and U). Of the remainder, at least 60% show structures in the "linear" (L) class; these are doubles which straddle the optical continuum nucleus, triples (doubles plus a radio source associated with the nucleus) or jet-like radio sources. A small fraction of the galaxies have "diffuse" (D) radio emission, where the source is "blob-like" and shows no evidence for linear structure.

TABLE 1

Structure Class	Number of Galaxies in Flux Limited Sample	Number of Galaxies in Distance Limited Sample
L	8	7 or 8
D	1	2
A	2	3 or 2
S	12	7
U	6	5

b) Source sizes range between ~ 20 pc and ~ 7 kpc. The "linear" sources are rarely well resolved transverse to their major axes. Class L sources viewed end-on will, therefore, appear as class S or U; the D sources are too large to be end-on class L sources.

c) The best interpretation of the "linear" sources invokes collimated ejection from the inner nucleus in the form of oppositely directed pairs of jets, plasmoids or bubbles. Apart from the question of radio size (and power, see below), there is no *qualitative* difference between the S and the well resolved (L or D) sources. For example, essentially all S and many U galaxies have steep radio spectra. The simplest interpretation of the S and many U sources is that they represent a simple continuity of the well resolved sources to smaller linear sizes. Some of the class U sources, especially in the distance limited sample, have flat spectra and are presumably dominated by ultracompact ($\lesssim$ pc), self-absorbed cores.

d) Wilson and Willis (1980) suggest that the dense interstellar medium of the spiral galaxy provides ram pressure to confine the radio components to the inner part of the galaxy. Sanders (1984), on the other hand, argues that the Seyfert radio sources are less extensive than the 10-100 kpc jets in radio galaxies because the Seyfert phase is shortlived ($<10^6$ years). It is likely that *both* of these effects contribute to the small sizes of Seyfert radio sources. It is improbable that the *observed* radio components are as old as 10^8 years – the minimum *overall* lifetime of Seyfert activity in a particular galaxy, as derived from the fact that a few percent of galaxies contain Seyfert nuclei (Woltjer 1959). This timescale is roughly factors of $\sim$ 100 larger than the dynamical timescale of the NLR, $\sim$ 20 larger than the rotation period of disk gas (which would distort the linear sources) and 100-1000 times larger than the synchrotron/inverse Compton loss times of the relativistic electrons radiating at GHz frequencies. An important constraint is the observation that almost all Seyferts contain radio sources on the hundreds of pc scale, implying that the lifetime of the radio emission cannot be much less than the lifetime of a Seyfert "episode." Normal early-type spirals (i.e., potentially "switched off" Seyferts) do not, in general, show radio emission as powerful as the Seyferts, suggesting that the radio emission of Seyferts has a comparable lifetime to that of their defining characteristics (broad emission lines, nonthermal continuum etc.) Nonetheless, a search for faint "relic" linear radio sources in non Seyferts would be interesting.

There is clear evidence for interaction between the radio jets, lobes and the interstellar medium in the detailed maps of some Seyferts – such as NGC 1068 (Wilson and Ulvestad 1982b, 1983) – and in very powerful kpc scale sources (see §IIIc below) – such as 3C305 (Heckman *et al.* 1982). The minimum magnetic plus cosmic ray presure in the lobes is often comparable to both the ram pressure of the rotating interstellar gas and the thermal pressure of the warm NLR clouds. Thus the age of the radio sources is probably $<10^6$ years *and* interactions between the outwardly moving radio components and the interstellar gas are instrumental in determining the size and structure of the source.

   e) The radio sources in Seyfert 2s and probably NLXGs tend to be larger, as well as more powerful than those in Seyfert 1s. This result implies that type 2 Seyferts and probably NLXGs cannot be merely type 1 Seyferts with central regions heavily obscured by dust. Such differences in large scale properties between Seyfert 1s and 2s also constrain models invoking an evolutionary link between them, in which type 2s are type 1s with the continuum source temporarily off (see, for example, Penston and Perez 1984 for a recent dicussion). In the distance limited sample, Seyfert 1s have typical radio source sizes of 60-130 pc, while the other galaxies have a median radio size of 400 pc. Radio powers and sizes are well correlated both for this sample as a whole and for the Seyfert 2s and NLXGs together (Fig. 9); this correlation may extend to both lower power radio sources associated with less active galactic nuclei and to higher power radio galaxies (Fig. 9) or radio-weak quasars (Rudnick, Sitko and Stein 1984) with kpc scale cores. It may also be noted that "linear" sources seem to appear preferentially in Seyfert 2s over Seyfert 1s (also noticed by W2). We believe this is merely a resolution effect, due to the small linear and angular sizes of the radio sources in Seyfert 1s.

   The difference in sizes between the radio sources in Seyfert 1s and 2s may be interpreted in a number of ways. Intrinsically more energetic ejections in Seyfert 2s should travel further out into the galaxy in the face of interstellar ram pressure, as well as generating more radio emission. Alternatively, the gas clouds in the BLR, which can exert a tremendous ram pressure ($\rho V^2 \sim$ 10 dyne cm^{-2}) could easily block or disrupt the jets or plasmoids in the Seyfert 1s. Note that even a hot intercloud medium, in pressure equilibrium with the warm BLR clouds, may retard the relatively weak radio ejecta in Seyferts.

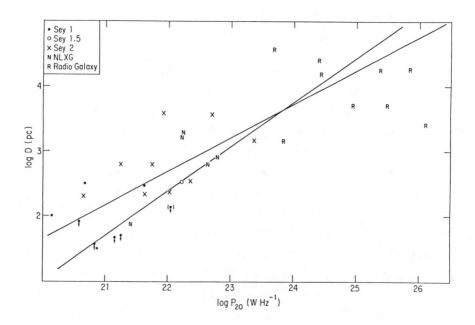

Figure 9: (from Ulvestad and Wilson 1984b) - Logarithmic plot of radio size, D (pc), against monochromatic radio power at 20 cm, P_{20} (W Hz^{-1}). Note that these scales are appropriate to $H_o = 50$ km s^{-1} Mpc^{-1}. For $H_o = 75$ km s^{-1} Mpc^{-1} (used in this paper), reduced log D by 0.18 and log P_{20} by 0.35. Different types of objects are distinguished by different symbols. The two straight lines are the least squares fits discussed in Ulvestad and Wilson (1984b). The radio galaxy points were omitted in this fitting.

f) It might be expected that the radio components would be ejected along the rotation axis of the galaxy disk. As shown in Figure 10, which is a histogram of the difference in position angle (ΔPA) between the radio source major axes and the galaxy-scale optical continuum major axes for Seyferts, this is *not* the case. Ejection close to the disk rotation axis would produce a clustering near $\Delta PA = 90°$, ejection in the plane of the galaxy would result in a broad distribution peaking at $\Delta PA = 0°$, while ejection in completely random directions would give a flat distribution

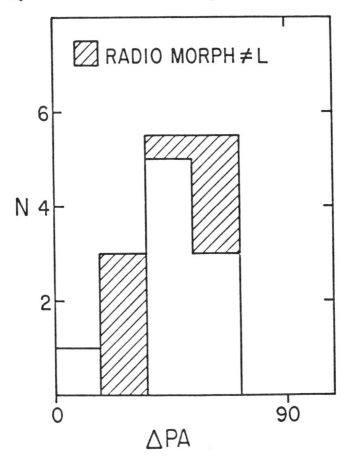

Figure 10: (from Ulvestad and Wilson 1984b) - Histogram of the difference in position angles (ΔPA) between the radio source major axes and the galaxy-scale optical continuum major axes of the Seyfert galaxies. Objects with uncertain values of ΔPA are omitted, and objects whose radio sources are not definitely classified as type L are shown hatched.

between $\Delta PA = 0°$ and 90°. There are curious deficits in this figure near $\Delta PA = 0°$ and 90°. The "hole" near $\Delta PA = 90°$

would be filled in to some extent if three highly inclined galaxies (NGC 3079, NGC 4438 and NGC 6500) with LINER-type nuclear spectra and radio features roughly perpendicular to the optical major axes (Hummel, van Gorkom, and Kotanyi 1983; Duric *et al.* 1983) were included in the sample. Galaxies with central radio source axes parallel to the major axes of the galaxy disks have been studied by Condon *et al.* (1982). These galaxies are not Seyferts; their radio emission is presumably generated by a disk population (perhaps supernova remnants) and not by nuclear activity (see Heckman *et al.* 1983b and Ulvestad and Wilson 1984b for further discussion of these issues).

From Figure 10, we can say that on a scale of ~ 1 kpc or less, there is no evidence that the radio axes in Seyferts have any knowledge of the large-scale structure of the galaxy. Thus the disks which collimate the radio ejecta (BLR?) must be tipped and may be randomly oriented with respect to the disks of the host galaxies. A tipped BLR is also suggested by the absence of any correlation between broad line width and galaxy axial ratio (Su and Simkin 1980; Keel 1980) and by theoretical arguments related to the settling of gas disks in tumbling, barlike, potential wells (Tohline and Osterbrock 1982).

g) An interesting correlation seems to exist between the major axes of the linear radio sources and the major axes of the NLR cloud complexes (Ulvestad, Wilson and Sramek 1981; and Table 2). Sometimes the association between line emitting clouds and radio components is very good (e.g., Mark 78; Adams 1973; Ulvestad, Wilson and Sramek 1981) but on other occasions the spatial scales of the radio and NLR complexes are somewhat different. If confirmed by high resolution ST imaging, this correlation has deep consequences for the nature of the NLR. One possibility is that the radio ejecta play a role in exciting and/or forming the clouds "in situ" (e.g., Heckman *et al.* 1982). In Seyferts, excitation and/or acceleration of the line emitting clouds by a jet implies low jet efficiencies for the production of radio emission, because the observed radio powers are small compared with the jet powers needed to accelerate the clouds or the power emitted as line

TABLE 2

Alignment of Linear Radio Sources
with Narrow Line Cloud Complexes

(1) Source	(2) P.A. Radio Axis (°)	(3) P.A. High Excitation NLR (ref) (°)	(4) Col.(2) − Col.(3) (°)
NGC 1068	33	40 (1)	-7
NGC 2110	1	353 (2)	8
NGC 4151	84	45 (3)	39
NGC 5548	160	152 (4)	8
NGC 5643	87	95 (5)	-8
NGC 5728	307	317 (6)	-10
Mark 3	85	113 (7)	-28
Mark 78	90	90 (8)	0

(1) Walker (1968)

(2) Wilson, Baldwin and Ulvestad (1985)

(3) Ulrich (1973)

(4) Present authors, Wu, Baldwin and Balick (unpublished)

(5) Morris *et al.* (1984)

(6) M.M. Phillips *et al.* (in preparation)

(7) Weedman (1973)

(8) Adams (1973)

radiation (e.g., Wilson 1982). Whittle (see W2) finds that Seyfert galaxies known to have linear radio sources tend to have steeper-sided, stubbier [O III] profiles than do galaxies without observed linear sources, as if the NLR gas associated with each side of the jet were radiating with opposite Doppler shifts relative to the line center velocity. The possibility that these stubby [O III] profiles are related to rotational motion should, however, also be borne in mind. "In situ" *ionization* of the clouds by a jet would, however, conflict with the conventional (and well founded) belief that the NLR is photoionized by the non-stellar ultraviolet continuum of the central object. A second possibility, which allows the central source photoionization scheme to be retained, invokes preferential escape of ionizing photons along or around the axis of the inner disk which collimates the radio emission (Osterbrock 1983, 1984). The disk would be optically thick to ionizing continuum in and near the equatorial plane. This idea is promising and ties in with an easier escape of radio plasma and ionizing photons in type 2s than type 1s, if the latter have thicker or "better developed" collimating disks (BLRs?).

h) Antonucci (1983) has suggested that the radio axes tend to be aligned with the polarization vector of the nuclear optical continuum radiation in type 1 Seyferts and be perpendicular to it in type 2s. The physical interpretation of this effect depends on the currently unknown mechanism generating the optical polarization (see discussions in Stockman, Angel, and Miley 1979; Schmidt and Miller 1980; Ulvestad, Wilson, and Sramek 1981; Antonucci 1982, 1983; Ulvestad and Wilson 1984a; Antonucci and Miller 1985).

i) Tests have been made to check whether the radio emission of Seyfert galaxies is enhanced by the presence of a companion galaxy, as is known to be the case for the central radio sources in spiral galaxies (Stocke 1978; Hummel 1981; Condon *et al.* 1982). Such an effect may be present in the flux limited sample of Markarian Seyferts (Ulvestad and Wilson 1984a), but in the distance limited sample no noticeable trend in this sense was found. This last conclusion is rather uncertain, since few nearby Seyferts appear to be truly isolated.

j) The above discussion [parts c) through i)] refers primarily to the "linear" sources, which comprise the majority of the well resolved radio structures. "Diffuse" (D) type sources are found in NGC 1068 (the disk emission, not the nuclear source: see Wilson and Ulvestad 1982b and Becklin, Scoville, and Wynn-Williams 1984), NGC 1365 (Sandqvist, Jorsäter, and Lindblad 1982), NGC 7469 and Mark 315 (Ulvestad, Wilson, and Sramek 1981) and probably NGC 7582 (Ulvestad and Wilson 1984b). While rather few examples of this type of source are known in Seyferts, there is a virtually 100% overlap between these galaxies and those known to possess circumnuclear *low ionization* gas disks apparently ionized by hot young stars (§IIc). The radio emission of these "diffuse" sources probably results from many supernovae and supernova remnants generated in the circumnuclear starbursts and is not directly related to the nuclear activity.* If this is so, detection of these radio sources may be used to identify Seyferts with prominent circumnuclear starbursts. Further, if the relation between radio power and starburst properties can be quantified (cf. Ulvestad 1982), reliable constraints on the fraction of Seyferts currently undergoing starbursts greater than a given "strength" could be obtained. This result could, in turn, be used to constrain models in which starbursts and Seyfert activity are connected in an evolutionary sense (e.g., Weedman 1983).

iv) Radio Structures – Individual Galaxies

Along with the statistical work, detailed radio studies of individual galaxies have been made with the VLA and MERLIN instruments and with VLBI techniques. Here we summarize some of the results on the better studied galaxies.

NGC 1068 shows radio emission on a wide range of scales (Fig. 11). There is: a) a bent triple source of extent 0$\overset{\prime\prime}{.}$7, the central

---

* Some of these galaxies also contain a compact weak source associated with the Seyfert nucleus itself (e.g., NGC 7469, NGC 7582, refs above; NGC 1365 (Sandqvist, private communication).

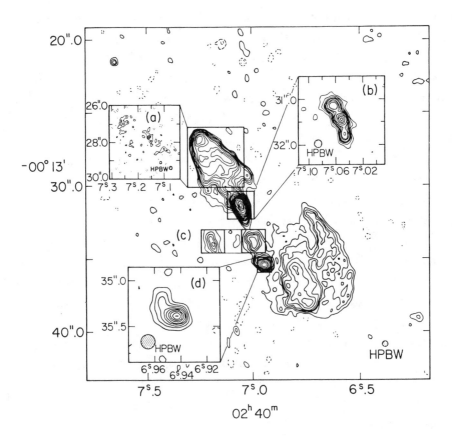

Figure 11: (from Wilson and Ulvestad 1983) - VLA maps of the central region of NGC 1068 (a type 2 Seyfert galaxy). The main map is at 4.9 GHz with resolution $0\rlap{.}''4 \times 0\rlap{.}''4$ and the optical nucleus coincides with its brightest part. Insets (a), (b) and (d) show details of the brighter regions at 15.0 GHz with resolution $0\rlap{.}''15 \times 0\rlap{.}''15$, while inset (c) shows 4.9 GHz contours of the region immediately to the SW of the nucleus with slightly better resolution than the main map. 1 " corresponds to 73 pc. See original paper for further details.

component of which is probably associated with the true nucleus (van der Hulst, Hummel, and Dickey 1982; Wilson and Ulvestad 1983). b) an intricate "linear" source, containing jets and lobes on a scale of 13" (Wilson and Ulvestad 1982b, 1983; Pedlar *et al.* 1983). The NE lobe of this source may represent a bow shock or blast wave driven into the interstellar medium of NGC 1068. Wilson and Ulvestad (1983) suggest that the spatially extended, broad emission lines (Fig. 8) represent interstellar gas entrained into such a shock at the boundary of each rapidly expanding radio lobe (see also Pedlar, Dyson, and Unger 1985). The lobes themselves are fuelled by radio jets or plasmoids emitted from the nucleus. The double emission lines seen on both the NE and SW sides of the nucleus are then interpreted as emission from the near (approaching) and far (receding) sides of the radio lobe with which they coincide (compare Figs. 8 and 11). The radio source may also have suffered ram pressure bending by the normally rotating interstellar gas (Wilson and Ulvestad 1982b). Free-free absorption by the NLR probably causes the low radio frequency spectral turnover of the nucleus (Pedlar *et al.* 1983). c) a large scale ($\sim 2''$) source associated with the starburst in the disk of the galaxy (Wilson and Ulvestad 1982a; Becklin, Scoville and Wynn-Williams 1984).

NGC 1365. Sandqvist and Lindblad (talk given at this conference) detect diffuse radio emission plus a number of compact radio sources in this galaxy. Although there is no clear cut correspondence between the compact radio sources and the optical "hot spot" H II regions, Sandqvist, Jorsäter and Lindblad (1982) suggest that the radio sources may be regions where a burst of formation of O and B stars has led to a large number of supernova remnants (~ 500 remnants per radio source). Remarkably, some of these compact radio sources are smaller than 10×25 pc (Sandqvist and Lindblad, this conference).

NGC 4151 shows a jet-like linear source (Figure 12; Johnston *et al.* 1982; Booler *et al.* 1982; Wilson and Ulvestad 1982b), the shape of which may reflect precession of the jet nozzle or ram pressure sweeping of the jets by the rotating gas disk. The spatially resol-

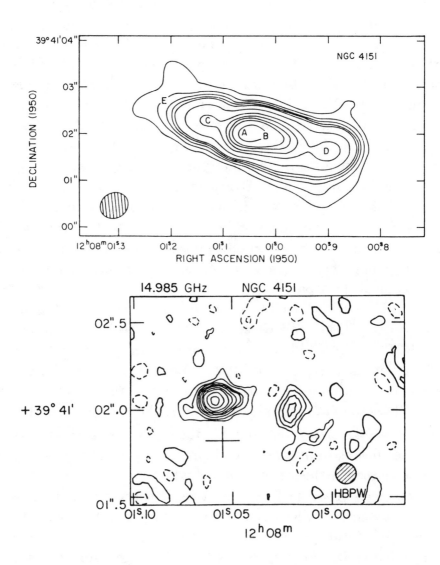

Figure 12: VLA maps of NGC 4151 (a type 1.5 Seyfert galaxy). Top (from Johnston *et al.* 1982) - Map at λ6 cm. Bottom (from Wilson and Ulvestad 1982b) - Map at λ2 cm, showing central double source (components A and B in top diagram). 1″ corresponds to 65 pc. See original papers for further details.

ved narrow line clouds seem to be related to the radio source (see Booler *et al.* 1982; Wilson 1983). The nuclear radio source of NGC 4151 has been detected by VLBI techniques (Preuss and Fosbury 1983).

NGC 5548 contains two weak extended radio lobes flanking the optical continuum nucleus plus an unresolved radio component coincident with it (Wilson and Ulvestad 1982a). There are also other radio sources further out, whose relationship to NGC 5548 is unclear.

Mark 3. A jet-like radio source is found in this galaxy (Pedlar, Unger and Booler 1984), which has also been detected by VLBI (Preuss and Fosbury 1983). As with NGC 1068, a low frequency turnover in the radio spectrum may be due to free-free absorption by ionized gas in the NLR (Pedlar, Unger and Booler 1984).

Mark 348. Neff and de Bruyn (1983) and Unger *et al.* (1984) find a variable core with an inverted spectrum plus optically thin extensions (jets?) straddling it to north and south.

James G. Peters
v)-Concluding Remarks

One of the most intriguing aspects of the radio sources seen in Seyfert galaxies is whether their relatively small $(10-10^4$ pc) sizes are related more directly to their relatively low radio power or to their location in the relatively dense interstellar media of disk galaxies. This issue is, of course, closely connected with the great puzzle of why the radio properties of active disk galaxies differ dramatically from those of active elliptical galaxies. In the next two sections, we will summarize recent data on two classes of kpc scale radio sources which not only blur the distinctions between radio emission in elliptical vs. disk galaxies, but also raise new issues concerning the role of the environment in the determination of radio source properties. These classes comprise first, the weak kpc scale emission which is associated with flat spectrum (compact) radio cores in optically bright E and SO galaxies (non Seyferts) and second, the very powerful kpc scale "steep spectrum core" radio sources found in many radio galaxies and QSOs.

b) Weak kpc Scale Sources in Elliptical/SO Galaxies

It has long been known that many nearby, optically bright elliptical and SO galaxies exhibit compact radio sources with flat or complex (synchrotron self absorbed) spectra (e.g., Heeschen 1970a,b; Dressel and Condon 1978; Hummel 1980). These weak ($\leq 10^{40}$ erg s^{-1}), compact radio cores appear to be related to the far more powerful pc scale sources seen in many radio galaxies, QSOs and BL Lac objects (see review by Phinney in this volume, and Kellermann and Pauliny-Toth 1981).

More recently, Wrobel and Heeschen (1984) have searched for and mapped radio emission on scales of $\sim 10^2 - 10^5$ pc in optically bright elliptical/SO galaxies with known compact radio cores. If we consider "kpc scale" emission to encompass the range $10^2 - 10^4$ pc, then 9 of the 11 galaxies studied exhibit kpc scale radio sources. Some of the other important properties of these kpc scale sources are:

1. Radio powers of the kpc scale emission at 1.4 GHz are typically 10^{22} watts Hz^{-1} ($L_{radio} \sim 10^{39}$ erg s^{-1}), with a range of about an order of magnitude. This is similar to the power of typical kpc scale sources in Seyferts.

2. The radio emission may be related to optical emission line gas on similar size scales, since about 75% of the galaxies with kpc scale radio sources are known to exhibit optical emission lines. There is, however, little or no information on the morphology of the emission line gas in these galaxies. Note that Ekers and Ekers (1973) and O'Connell and Dressel (1978) found that weak compact radio emission in E/SO galaxies is statistically related to the presence of optical emission lines, which Heckman (1980) concluded could almost invariably be classified as those of a LINER.

3. The radio morphology and polarization strongly suggest ejection from the nucleus, rather than radio emission from multiple

supernovae in a "starburst." About half the sources show one-sided, sometimes jet-like, features while the emission is two-sided in the others. The radio emission is frequently curved or distorted. A map of the kpc scale radio emission in NGC 1052 is shown in Figure 13.

4. The kpc scale radio sources show no preference for the projected optical major or minor axes of the parent galaxies.

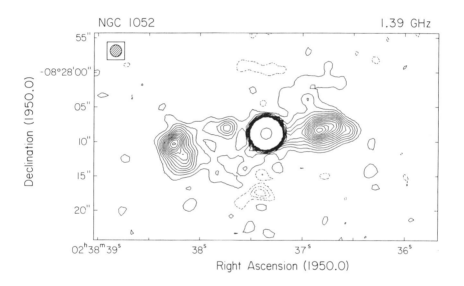

Figure 13: (from Wrobel 1984) - A total intensity map of the nucleus of NGC 1052 (a nearby elliptical galaxy) with resolution 1.″75 (FWHM). 1″ corresponds to 93 pc. See original paper for further details.

Clearly, many of these properties are quite similar to those of the Seyfert radio sources, with the biggest difference in the radio being the association of the kpc scale radio emission with a strong, compact, flat spectrum, radio core (usually weak or absent in Seyferts). This radio class may suggest that a combination of both relatively low jet power and dense ambient interstellar material (seen prominently in the LINER type emission) may be able to thwart the development of large-scale ($>10^4$ pc) radio emission in E and SO galaxies (as we have argued may be the case in Seyfert galaxies, which are typically of later Hubble/de Vaucouleurs type).

c) Powerful kpc Scale Radio Sources

The conventional classification scheme for the powerful radio sources which populate radio flux limited samples, such as the 3CR catalog, has long consisted of two primary classes: 1) extended radio sources with steep radio spectra (optically thin synchrotron emission) and typical sizes ≥ 10 kpc and, 2) compact nuclear radio sources with flat or complex radio spectra (optically thick synchrotron emission) and typical sizes ≤ 10 pc. However, during the last few years a third class of powerful radio source has been discovered with a characteristic size scale similar to that of the NLR (Bridle and Fomalont 1978; Miley 1980; Kapahi 1981; Peacock and Wall 1982; van Breugel, Miley and Heckman 1984; Fanti *et al.* 1984). These sources, christened SSCs (Steep Spectrum Cores) or CSSs (Compact Steep Spectrum sources) appear to be qualitatively similar to the sources seen in Seyfert galaxies, but are very much more powerful (typical radio luminosities integrated over $10^7 - 10^{11}$ Hz are 10^{42} to 10^{46} erg s^{-1}).

The most detailed studies of these SSCs to date are the VLA survey at λ 2 cm and λ 6 cm of 23 sources by van Breugel, Miley and Heckman (1984, hereafter vBMH) and the European VLBI/MERLIN survey at λ 18 cm of 15 3CR sources by Fanti *et al.* (1984, hereafter FFPSvB). The principal properties of these sources are as follows:

1. By definition, the radio spectral index is $\alpha \geq 0.5$ in the frequency range around 1-10 GHz. However, the radio flux almost invariably peaks at $\sim 100 - 300$ MHz, and then falls at lower frequencies. This can be interpreted in terms of either synchrotron self-absorption or free-free absorption by ionized gas (the NLR?).

2. The radio size is (by definition) below that of a galaxy (FFPSvB require at least 80% of the flux at 5GHz to come from a radio component less than 13 kpc in size). Typical sizes range from $10^2 - 10^4$ pc for these objects (see also Phillips and Mutel 1981). Note that powerful kpc scale radio cores may be present as the nuclear components in much larger radio sources, even though the larger scale emission is dominant in radio power (e.g., 3C236 - Barthel *et al.* 1984). These objects would not meet the above overall size criterion of FFPSvB, but are probably closely related to the kpc scale sources without strong larger scale radio emission.

3. The radio morphology ranges from double to "core-jet" to complex.* FFPSvB find that there is some tendency for the QSOs to exhibit a "core-jet" or complex radio morphology, while the galaxies tend to be double radio sources. This is based on only 8 QSOs and 7 radio galaxies, and should be followed up by analysis of a larger sample. Examples of radio maps of SSCs are shown in Figures 14 and 15; Figure 14 shows the prototypical SSC radio galaxy 3C305 and Figure 15 a SSC QSO 1153+317 (4C31.38) with z = 1.557 and log P_{20} = 28.30 (W Hz^{-1}).

4. The percentage radio polarization is generally small for SSCs (e.g., vBMH find that $\sim 70 - 80\%$ of the SSCs have integrated polarizations <2% at λ 6 cm, compared to only about 25% of larger steep spectrum radio sources). It is not yet clear, in general, whether the SSCs are strongly Faraday depolarized by a magnetoionic medium, or whether the magnetic fields in the sources are unusually disordered. Multi-frequency polarimetric mapping of a large sample is required to test these possibilities.

---

* "Double" here means that the two radio components appear to straddle the optical nucleus. In the cases where the optical position is not known to the requisite accuracy, "double" means that the two components are roughly equal in angular size and have similar radio spectra. "Core-jet" means that one radio component ("core") is much more compact and/or much closer in position to the optical identification.

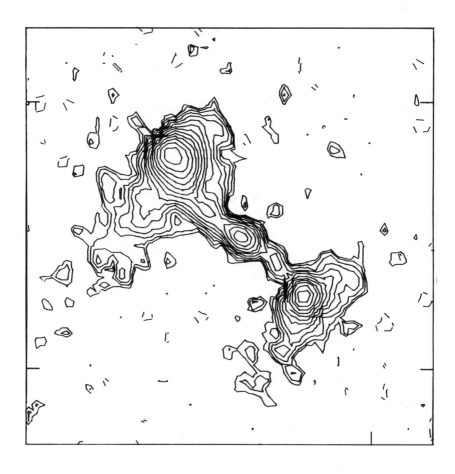

Figure 14: (from Heckman *et al.* 1982) - VLA map of 3C305 (a radio galaxy with a steep spectrum core) at 2 cm. The beam is circular and of FWHM 0.''36. The tick marks are 4'' (∼ 3.3 kpc) apart. See original paper for further details.

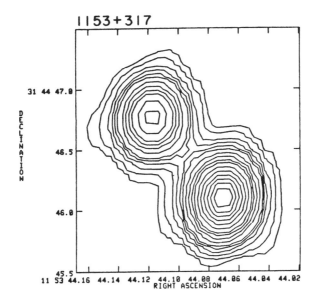

Figure 15: (from van Breugel, Miley and Heckman 1984) - VLA map of 1153+317 = 4C31.38 (a quasar with a steep spectrum core) at 6 cm. The total linear size is 6.8 kpc. See original paper for further details.

5. The radio luminosities ($10^{42} - 10^{46}$ erg s^{-1}) and *minimum* magnetic field plus relativistic particle pressures (10^{-7} to $\geq 10^{-5}$ dyne cm^{-2}) are very high. In fact, the latter significantly exceed pressures in the NLR clouds ($\sim 10^{-8}$ dyne cm^{-2}), let alone any reasonable pressures expected in the interstellar medium of a galaxy. Confinement of these radio sources may then require dynamic effects (i.e., ram pressure).

6. FFPSvB find that of the 166 3CR radio sources examined with the Cambridge 5 km radio telescope by Jenkins, Pooley and Riley (1977), at least 27 ($\sim 16\%$) meet their criteria for inclusion in the SSC class. Thus, at least relative to other powerful radio sources, these objects are not particularly rare.

More detailed investigations of some relatively nearby SSCs provide additional important clues to the nature of this radio class. One such clue is that the ambient gaseous medium in the parent galaxy appears to be unusually cool and/or dense. In several cases (NGC 1167 and NGC 3801, Heckman *et al.* 1983a; 3C293, Baan and Haschick 1981) λ 21 cm HI emission and/or absorption lines are detected. In 3C305 (Heckman *et al.* 1982), 3C293 (Wilson and Ulvestad 1982b; van Breugel *et al.* 1984a), and NGC 3801 (Heckman *et al.* 1985b) the radio source lies within, and interacts with, a rotating system (disk?) of emission line clouds. In fact, Heckman *et al.* (1982) present compelling evidence that the radio source in 3C305 is distorted and Faraday depolarized by the ambient medium. Meanwhile, the jets which power 3C305 also accelerate and ionize the ambient gas. In several other SSCs (M87, e.g., De Young, Condon and Butcher 1980; 4C26.42, van Breugel *et al.* 1984b), the radio source is immersed in the dense X-ray emitting gaseous core of a "cluster dominant" giant elliptical/cD galaxy.

A second tantalizing clue to the nature of SSCs is that many are associated with galaxies having highly peculiar optical morphologies. The optical plumes, shells and "tail-like" structures all suggest a recent interaction and/or merger between two galaxies, at least one of which possessed a stellar disk prior to the encounter (cf. Toomre 1977; Quinn 1984): 3C305 (Heckman *et al.* 1982; 1985a), 3C293 (van Breugel *et al.* 1984a; Heckman *et al.* 1985c), NGC 3801 (Heckman *et al.* 1985b), 3C48 (Heckman *et al.* 1985b), 3C459 (Heckman *et al.* 1985c), 4C12.50 = PKS 1345+125 (Hutchings, talk at this conference), 4C14.82 = PKS 2247+140 (Heckman *et al.* 1985c). The optical spectra of several of these objects show relatively strong stellar Balmer absorption lines, quite unlike the spectra of typical elliptical galaxies (3C48, Boroson and Oke 1982; 3C459, Miller 1981; 3C305, Heckman *et al.* 1982). This may provide additional evidence for an unusual galaxy history (assimilation of a former spiral disk component?).

Together, the available data support the contention of vBMH and FFPSvB that the SSCs are very powerful analogs to the radio sources seen in Seyfert galaxies, and that their properties can be well understood as arising from the interaction of radio jets with an unusually dense, and inhomogeneous ambient medium, which may have been captured through an accretion process. The outflowing jets collide with ambient clouds and presumably entrain (heat and accelerate) the gas. This may account for the bright, high pressure radio knots (shocks in the jets), wide emission lines in the NLR (accelerated clouds), possible strong Faraday depolarization (entrained clumpy gas), low frequency spectral turnovers (free-free absorption by ionized gas), the small radio source size and its frequently complex or "bent" morphology (bending and/or decollimation of the jets by collisions with massive ambient clouds), and (in some well studied cases) the *in situ* ionization of the NLR by the jets, as the data imply (ionization by ultraviolet jet synchrotron radiation, by relativistic particles, or by thermal radiation from hot, shocked gas).

We note that a very similar scheme has been proposed by van Breugel and Heckman (1982), Miley (1983) and (more recently, and in much more detail) by van Breugel *et al.* (1985) to account for the observed properties of optical emission line gas morphologically associated with the *large scale* ($10^4 - 10^5$ pc) radio jets and lobes of radio galaxies and QSOs. In these objects, the radio/optical interaction can be observed in far greater detail (i.e., it can be well resolved spatially), and a generalization of the above picture to somewhat larger scales seems natural. We anticipate that ST observations of SSCs coupled with radio investigations with ≤ 0.1 arc sec resolution will reveal even stronger similarities in radio/optical properties between the SSCs and the large scale radio sources with associated optical line emission.

IV) SUMMARY AND FUTURE DIRECTIONS

In the preceding pages we have attempted to review the individual conclusions which have been gleaned from the now large body of data on the kpc scale properties of emission line gas and radio plasma in AGNs and QSOs. The large number of such conclusions, many of which are so new as to be relatively undigested, probably dooms any attempt to synthesize a full and coherent picture of this region. Nevertheless, we cannot resist the temptation to list what we believe to be the most general and most tantalizing trends to have emerged so far.

First, the importance of gravitational forces in the dynamics of the NLR is increasingly evident, as indicated by, for example, the correlation between stellar velocity dispersion and [O III] $\lambda5007$ emission line width (Fig. 2). The mass of the galaxy bulge may thus be a "prime mover" in determining many kinematic properties on the hundreds of pc to kpc scale. Infall models for the clouds are promising in this sense, but we suspect that gravity is not the whole story in the NLR dynamics. One possibility is a hybrid model in which gravitation dominates in the outer NLR to produce the narrow cores of the emission line profiles (the cores at least statistically lie at V_{sys}). However, the blueshifted broad wings of the emission line profiles may be produced in the inner NLR by outflow (jets or winds) driven in some way by the nuclear activity.

Second the evidence for spatial stratification of physical properties (velocity, density, ionization state) in the NLR is now very strong. The technique of using different emission lines (covering a wide range of ionization potential and critical density) to probe regions having different physical conditions is, in principle, very powerful. It may be used in combination with refined photoionization models to "invert" the data, and gain insight into the spectra of cloud densities, velocities and sizes in the NLR – information of fundamental value in restricting dynamical models. A further important aspect of this work is the evidence link-ing the broad and narrow line regions, suggesting the two may merge smoothly on a scale of a few parsecs. If such continuity does exist, we can then hope that Space Telescope observations of nearby Seyferts (with spatial resolution $\leq$ 10 parsecs) will provide a glimpse of the geometrical and dynamical structure of the "suburbs" of the BLR. At present, our only direct geometrical insight into regions this compact in active nuclei is provided by VLBI observations of radio cores.

Third, the kpc scale radio sources seen in AGNs and QSOs strongly imply that collimated outflow of radio plasma is common in active spiral, and not just elliptical, galaxies. The qualitative similarity of the kpc scale radio sources in Seyferts, nearby E/S0 galaxies, and even powerful radio galaxies and QSOs blurs the distinctions between the radio properties of various optically defined classes of AGNs/QSOs. There is also very clear evidence that the *interaction* between the relativistic (radio emitting) and thermal (optical emitting) material in AGNs and QSOs can be crucial in determining the observed properties of each medium. On the one hand, the NLR may help confine, distort, and even create (through shocks in jet/cloud collisions) regions of bright radio emission. In turn, the jets which power the radio sources seem to influence the NLR kinematics in a complex way, and could be instrumental in the creation of NLR clouds. The effect of the radio source on the kinematics (and possibly the ionization) of the NLR increases with increasing kpc scale radio power, being evident in Seyfert galaxies and very strong (dominant?) in radio galaxies with steep spectrum cores.

Clarification of many of these issues should be possible with a suitable combination of ground based optical and Space Telescope observations. The data base on stellar velocity dispersions and systemic velocities for Seyferts and LINERs needs to be increased to provide further constraints on the gaseous kinematics. The study of the profiles of different ion species is still in its infancy and gives complementary information to that from the Space Telescope. Direct imaging surveys of nearby active galaxies with CCDs, currently underway by a few groups, will provide more estimates of nuclear bulge and disk magnitudes. These are vital basic parameters in the search for the primary variable governing, for example, the radio and infrared powers. These surveys should also search for any galaxy scale differences between carefully chosen samples of broad and narrow line objects (cf. Simkin, Su and Schwarz 1980). If confirmed, such differences would rule out significant evolution between the two classes on timescales $\leq 10^8$ years. The connection between starburst nuclei and active galaxies deserves intensive investigation, primarily from the observational point of view. Again, searches for galaxy scale differences (e.g., in Hubble type) between the classes may prove enlightening.

While the most exciting results may be expected from Space Telescope observations of both stars and gas, information from other wavebands will also give rapid progress in our understanding of the $10 - 10^4$ pc scale phenomena. IRAS data and ground based infrared imaging will probe dust in the NLR, while infrared and mm wave spectroscopy will be used to study Increasingly detailed maps of the synchrotron emitting plasma may be expected from radio interferometers, and AXAF will measure the temperatures, densities and abundances of the hot component of the NLR.

On the theoretical front, more complete investigations of the dynamics of clouds falling under gravity through a hot outflowing wind or jet are needed. The various current models study different facets of this situation, but are all sufficiently incomplete in terms of potentially important physical processes to render comparison with multi-species line profiles unconvincing. Self consistent combined photoionization and dynamical models will eventually be needed. Another process deserving more attention from theorists is the interaction of radio jets with interstellar clouds, both from the point of view of generating the radio "hot spots" and the "in situ" ionization of thermal gas.

ASW thanks the CTIO Telescope Allocation Committee for five cloudy nights, without which this review would have taken much longer to complete. Both authors acknowledge the support of the National Science Foundation under grant AST-82-16553.

REFERENCES

Adams, T.F. 1973, *Ap. J.*, **179**, 417.

Adney, K.J., Wilson, A.S., and Baldwin, J.A. 1984, *A.J.*, **89**, 1514.

Alloin, D., Pelat, D., Boksenberg, A., and Sargent, W.L.W. 1983, *Ap. J.*, **275**, 493.

Anderson, K.S. 1973, *Ap. J.*, **182**, 369.

_____.1974, *Ap. J.*, **187**, 445.

Antonucci, R.R.J. 1982, *Nature*, **299**, 605.

_____. 1983, *Nature*, **303**, 158.

Antonucci, R.R.J., and Miller, J.S. 1985, preprint.

Artyukh, V.A., Kandalian, R.A., Ogannisyan, M.A., and Sanamyan, V.A. 1982, *Astrophysics*, **18**, 130.

Atwood, B., Baldwin, J.A., and Carswell, R.F. 1982, *Ap. J.*, **257**, 559.

Axon, D.J., Briggs, S., Boksenberg, A., and Sargent, W.L.W. 1984, in preparation.

Baan, W.A., and Haschick, A.D. 1981, *Ap. J. (Letters)*, **243**, L143.

Baldwin, J.A., Carswell, R.F., Wampler, E.J., Smith, H.E., Burbidge, E.M., and Boksenberg, A. 1980, *Ap. J.*, **236**, 388.

Baldwin, J.A., Phillips, M.M., and Terlevich, R. 1981, *Pub. A.S.P.*, **93**, 5.

Balick, B., and Heckman, T.M. 1979, *A.J.*, **84**, 302.

Balick, B., and Heckman, T.M. 1985, Preprint.

Balzano, V.A. 1983, *Ap. J.*, **268**, 602.

Barthel, P.D., Schilizzi, R.T., Miley, G.K., Jägers, W.J., and Strom, R.G. 1984 *Astr. Ap.* (submitted).

Becklin, E.E., Scoville, N.Z., and Wynn-Williams, C.G. 1984, Preprint.

Bieging, J.H., Biermann, P., Fricke, K., Pauliny-Toth, I.I.K., and Witzel, A. 1977, *Astr. Ap.*, **60**, 353.

Biermann, P., Clarke, J.N., Fricke, K.J., Pauliny-Toth, I.I.K., Schmidt, J., and Witzel, A. 1980, *Astr. Ap.*, **81**, 235.

Blitz, L., Mathieu, R.D., and Bally, J. 1984, *Ap. J.*, (submitted).

Boksenberg, A. 1977, In IAU Colloquium 40, *Applications Astronomiques des Recepteurs d'Images à Reponse Lineaire* (Paris-Meudon, Paper 13).

Boksenberg, A., Shortridge, K., Allen, D.A., Fosbury, R.A.E., Penston, M.V., and Savage, A. 1975, *M.N.R.A.S.*, **173**, 381.

Booler, R.V., Pedlar, A., and Davies, R.D. 1982, *M.N.R.A.S.*, **199**, 229.

Boroson, T.A., and Oke, J.B. 1982, *Nature*, **296**, 397.

Bridle, A.H., and Fomalont, E.B. 1978, *A.J.*, **83**, 704.

Capriotti, E.R., and Foltz, C.B. 1982, *Ap. J.*, **255**, 48.

Carroll, T.J., and Kwan, J. 1983, *Ap. J.*, **274**, 113 (CK).

Carswell, R.F., Baldwin, J.A., Atwood, B., and Phillips, M.M. 1984, *Ap. J.*, **286**, 464.

Clements, E.D. 1981, *M.N.R.A.S.*, **197**, 829.

Cohen, R.D. 1983, *Ap. J.*, **273**, 489.

Cohen, R.D., and Marcy, G.W. 1983, *Bull. A.A.S.*, **15**, 654.

Condon, J.J., Condon, M.A., Gisler, G., and Puschell, J.J. 1982, *Ap. J.*, **252**, 102.

Contini, M., and Aldrovandi, S.M.V. 1983, *Astr. Ap.*, **127**, 15.

Cutri, R.M., Rudy, R.J., Rieke, G.H., Tokunaga, A.T., and Willner, S.P. 1984, *Ap. J.*, **280**, 521.

Davies, R.L., Efstathiou, G., Fall, S.M., Illingworth, G., and Schechter, P.L. 1983, *Ap. J.*, **266**, 41.

de Bruyn, A.G., and Wilson, A.S. 1976, *Astr. Ap.*, **53**, 93.

_____.1978, *Astr. Ap.*, **64**, 433.

De Robertis, M.M., and Osterbrock, D.E. 1984, *Ap. J.*, **286**, 171.

De Young, D.S., Condon, J.J., and Butcher, H.R. 1980, *Ap. J.*, **242**, 511.

Dressel, L.L., and Condon, J.J. 1978, *Ap. J. Suppl.*, **36**, 53.

Dressler, A., and Sandage, A.R. 1983, *Ap. J.*, **265**, 664.

Duric, N., Seaquist, E.R., Crane, P.C., Bignell, R.C., and Davis, L.E. 1983, *Ap. J.*, **273**, L11.

Ekers, R.D., and Ekers, J.A. 1973, *Astr. Ap.*, **24**, 247.

Faber, S.M., and Jackson, R.E. 1976, *Ap. J.*, **204**, 668.

Fanti, C., Fanti, R., Parma, P., Schilizzi, R.T., and van Breugel, W.J.M. 1984, *Astr. Ap.* (in press) (FFBSvB).

Feldman, F.R., and MacAlpine, G.M. 1978, *Ap. J.*, **221**, 486.

Feldman, F.R., Weedman, D.W., Balzano, V.A., and Ramsey, L.W. 1982, *Ap. J.*, **256**, 427.

Filippenko, A.V., and Halpern, J.P. 1984, *Ap.J.*, **285**, 458 (FH).

Filippenko, A.V., and Sargent, W.L.W. 1985, *Ap.J.*, (in press).

Filippenko, A.V. 1985, *Ap. J.*, **289**, 475.

Ford, H.C., Crane, P.C., Jacoby, G.C., Lawrie, D.G., and van der Hulst, J.M. 1984, Preprint.

Fosbury, R.A.E., Mebold, U., Goss, W.M., and Dopita, M.A. 1978, *M.N.R.A.S.*, **183**, 549.

Fosbury, R.A.E., and Sansom, A.E. 1983, *M.N.R.A.S.*, **204**, 1231.

Fricke, K.J., and Reinhardt, M. 1974, *Astr. Ap.*, **37**, 349.

Glaspey, J.W., Eilek, J.A., Fahlman, G.G., and Auman, J.R. 1976, *Ap. J.*, **203**, 355.

Grandi, S.A. 1977, *Ap. J.*, **215**, 446.

_____.1978, *Ap. J.*, **221**, 501.

Heckman, T.M. 1980, *Astr. Ap.*, **87**, 152.

Heckman, T.M., Balick, B., and Crane, P.C. 1980, *Astr. Ap. Suppl.*, **40**, 295.

Heckman, T.M., Miley, G.K., van Breugel, W.J.M., and Butcher, H.R. 1981, *Ap. J.*, **247**, 403 (HMBB).

Heckman, T.M., Miley, G.K., Balick, B., van Breugel, W.J.M., and Butcher, H.R. 1982, *Ap. J.*, **262**, 529.

Heckman, T.M., and Balick, B. 1983, *Ap. J.*, **268**, 102.

Heckman, T.M., Balick, B., van Breugel, W.J.M., and Miley, G.K. 1983a, *A.J.*, **88**, 583.

Heckman, T.M., van Breugel, W.J.M., Miley, G.K., and Butcher, H.R. 1983b, *A. J.*, **88**, 1077.

Heckman, T.M., Miley, G.K., and Green, R.F. 1984, *Ap. J.*, **281**, 525 (HMG).

Heckman, T.M., Illingworth, G., Miley, G.K., and van Breugel, W.J.M. 1985a, *Ap. J.* submitted.

Heckman, T.M., Illingworth, G., van Breugel, W.J.M., and Miley, G.K. 1985b, in preparation.

Heckman, T.M. *et al.* 1985c, in preparation.

Heeschen, D.S. 1970a, *Ap. Lett*, **6**, 49.

_____.1970b, *A.J.*, **75**, 523.

Huchra, J.P. 1982, "Catalog of Seyfert Galaxies," distributed privately.

Hummel, E. 1980, *Astr. Ap. Suppl.*, **41**, 151.

_____.1981, *Astr. Ap.*, **93**, 93.

Hummel, E., van Gorkom, J.H., and Kotanyi, C.G. 1983, *Ap. J.*, **267**, L5.

Jenkins, C.J., Pooley, G.G., and Riley, J.M. 1977, *Mem. R.A.S.*, **84**, 61.

Johnston, K.J., Elvis, M., Kjer, D., and Shen, B.S.P. 1982, *Ap. J.*, **262**, 61.

Kandalian, R.A. 1982, *Astrophysics*, **18**, 331.

Kapahi, V.K. 1981, *Astr. Ap. Suppl.*, **43**, 381.

Keel, W.C. 1980, *A. J.*, **85**, 198.

_____.1983, *Ap. J.*, **269**, 466.

Keel, W.C., and Miller, J.S. 1983, *Ap. J. (Letters)*, **266**, L89.

Kellermann, K.I., and Pauliny-Toth, I.I.K. 1981, *Ann. Rev. Astr. Ap.*, **19**, 373.

Kojoian, G., Sramek, R.A., Dickinson, D.F., Tovmassian, H., and Purton, C.R. 1976, *Ap. J.*, **203**, 323.

Kormendy, J., and Illingworth, G. 1983, *Ap. J.*, **265**, 632.

Koski, A.T. 1978, *Ap. J.*, **223**, 56.

Krolik, J.H., and Vrtilek, J.M. 1984, *Ap. J.*, **279**, 521.

Kwan, J., and Carroll, T.J. 1982, *Ap. J.*, **261**, 25.

McCutcheon, W.H., and Gregory, P.C. 1978, *A. J.*, **83**, 566.

Meurs, E.J.A. 1982, Ph. D. Thesis, University of Leiden, The Netherlands.

_____. 1984, in preparation.

Meurs, E.J.A., and Wilson, A.S. 1981, *Astr. Ap. Suppl. Ser.*, **45**, 99.

_____.1984, *Astr. Ap.*, **136**, 206 (MW).

Miley, G.K. 1980, *Ann. Rev. Astr. Ap.*, **18**, 165.

_____. 1983, In *Astrophysical Jets,* eds. G.K. Ed. A. Ferrari and A.G. Pacholczyk, p.99 (D. Reidel).

Miley, G.K., and Heckman, T.M. 1982, *Astr. Ap.*, **106**, 163 (MH).

Miller, J.S. 1981, *P.A.S.P.*, **93**, 681.

Mirabel, I.F., and Wilson, A.S. 1984, *Ap. J.*, **277**, 92.

Morris, S.C., Ward, M.J., Whittle, M., Wilson, A.S., and Taylor, K. 1984, *M.N.R.A.S.*, (submitted).

Neff, S.G., and de Bruyn, A.G. 1983, *Astr. Ap.*, **128**, 318.

Netzer, H. 1982, *M.N.R.A.S.*, **198**, 589.

O'Connell, R.W., and Dressel, L.L. 1978, *Nature*, **276**, 374.

Osterbrock, D.E. 1974, *Astrophysics of Gaseous Nebulae* (W.H. Freeman & Co., San Francisco).

Osterbrock, D.E. 1978, *Proc. Nat. Acad. Sci.*, **75**, 540.

_____.1979 *A. J.*, **84**, 901.

_____.1981, *Ap. J.*, **246**, 696.

Osterbrock, D.E. 1983, In IAU Symposium 103, *Planetary Nebulae,* ed. D.R. Flower (Dordrecht: Reidel), p.473.

_____. 1984, *Q.J.R.A.S.*, **25**, 1.

Peacock, J.A., and Wall, J.V. 1982, *M.N.R.A.S.*, **198**, 843.

Pedlar, A., Booler, R.V., Spencer, R.E., and Stewart, O.J. 1983, *M.N.R.A.S.*, **202**, 647.

Pedlar, A., Unger, S.W., and Booler, R.V. 1984, Preprint.

Pedlar, A., Dyson, J., and Unger, S.W. 1985, *M.N.R.A.S.* (submitted).

Pelat, D., and Alloin, D. 1980, *Astr. Ap.*, **81**, 172.

Pelat, D., Alloin, D., and Fosbury, R.A.E. 1981, *M.N.R.A.S.*, **195**, 787.

Penston, M.V., Fosbury, R.A.E., Boksenberg, A., Ward, M.J., and Wilson, A.S. 1984, *M.N.R.A.S.*, **208**, 347.

Penston, M.V., and Perez, E. 1984, *M.N.R.A.S.*, **211**, 33P.

Péquignot, D. 1984, *Astr. Ap.*, **131**, 159.

Peterson, B.M., Foltz, C.B., and Byard, P.L. 1981, *Ap. J. (Lett.*, **243**, L61.

Phillips, M.M. 1976, *Ap. J.*, **208**, 37.

_____. 1977, *Ap. J.*, **215**, 746.

_____. 1978, *Ap. J. Suppl.*, **38**, 187.

Phillips, M.M., Charles, P.A., and Baldwin, J.A. 1983, *Ap. J.*, **266**, 485.

Phillips, M.M., Turtle, A.J., Edmunds, M.G., and Pagel, B.E.J. 1983a, *M.N.R.A.S.*, **203**, 759.

Phillips, M.M., Baldwin, J.A., Atwood, B., and Carswell, R.F. 1983b, *Ap. J.*, **274**, 558.

Phillips, R.B., and Mutel, R.L. 1981, *Ap. J.*, **244**, 19.

Preuss, E., and Fosbury, R.A.E. 1983, *M.N.R.A.S.*, **204**, 783.

Quinn, P.J. 1984, *Ap. J.*, **279**, 596.

Rose, J.A., and Tripicco, M.J. 1984, *Ap. J.*, **285**, 55.

Rubin, V.C., and Ford, Jr., W.K. 1968, *Ap. J.*, **154**, 431.

Rudnick, L., Sitko, M.L., and Stein, W.A. 1984, *A. J.*, **89**, 753.

Sanamyan, V.A., and Kandalian, R.A. 1978, *Astrophysics*, **14**, 352.

_____. 1979, *Astrophysics*, **15**, 459.

_____. 1980, *Astrophysics*, **16**, 252.

Sanamyan, V.A., Kandalian, R.A., and Oganyan, G.A. 1983, *Astrophysics*, **19**, 239.

Sanders, R.H. 1984, Preprint.

Sandqvist, A., Jorsäter, S., and Lindblad, P.O. 1982, *Astr. Ap.*, **110**, 336.

Schechter, P.L. 1983, *Ap. J. Suppl.*, **52**, 425.

Schmidt, G.D., and Miller, J.S. 1980, *Ap. J.*, **240**, 759.

Scoville, N.Z., Young, J.S., and Lucy, L.B. 1983, *Ap. J.*, **270**, 443.

Shuder, J.M. 1981, *Ap. J.*, **244**, 12.

Shuder, J.M., and Osterbrock, D.E. 1981, *Ap. J.*, **250**, 55.

Simkin, S.M. 1979, *Ap. J.*, **234**, 56.

Simkin, S.M., Su, H.J., and Schwarz, M.P. 1980, *Ap. J.*, **237**, 404.

Smith, M.D. 1984, *M.N.R.A.S.*, **209**, 913.

Snijders, M.A.J., Briggs, S.A., and Boksenberg, A. 1982, Proceedings of Third European IUE Conference, Madrid (ESA SP-176).

Sramek, R.A., and Tovmassian, H.M. 1975, *Ap. J.*, **196**, 339.

Stauffer, J.R. 1982, *Ap., J.*, **262**, 66.

Stocke, J.T. 1978, *A. J.*, **83**, 348.

Stockman, H.S., Angel, J.R.P., and Miley, G.K., 1979, *Ap. J. (Letters)*, **227**, L55.

Su, H.J., and Simkin, S.M. 1980, *Ap. J. (Letters)*, **238**, L1.

Sulentic, J.W. 1976, *A. J.*, **81**, 582.

Telesco, C.M., Becklin, E.E., Wynn-Williams, C.G., and Harper, D.A. 1984, *Ap. J.*, **282**, 427.

Tohline, J.E., and Osterbrock, D.E. 1982, *Ap. J. (Letters)*, **252**, L49.

Tonry, J.L., and Davis, M. 1981, *Ap. J.*, **246**, 666.

Toomre, A. 1977, In *The Evolution of Galaxies and Stellar Populations*, eds. B.M. Tinsley and R.B. Larson, p. 401 (New Haven: Yale University Press).

Ulrich, M.-H. 1972, *Ap. J.*, **171**, L37.

_____.1973, *Ap. J.*, **181**, 51.

Ulrich, M.-H. and Péquignot, D. 1980, *Ap. J.*, **238**, 45.

Ulvestad, J.S. 1982, *Ap. J.*, **259**, 96.

Ulvestad, J.S., Wilson, A.S., and Sramek, R.A. 1981, *Ap. J.*, **247**, 419.

Ulvestad, J.S., and Wilson, A.S. 1984a, *Ap. J.*, **278**, 544.

_____. 1984b, *Ap. J.*, **285**, 439.

Unger, S.W., Pedlar, A., Neff, S.G., and de Bruyn, A.G. 1984, *M.N.R.A.S.*, **209**, 15P.

van Breugel, W.J.M., and Heckman, T.M. 1982, In *Extragalactic Radio Sources,* IAU Symposium Nr.97, Ed. D.S. Heeschen and C.M. Wade, p.61 (D. Reidel).

van Breugel, W.J.M., Miley, G.K., and Heckman, T.M. 1984, *A. J.*, **89**, 5 (vBMH).

van Breugel, W.J.M., Heckman, T.M., Butcher, H.R., and Miley, G.K. 1984a, *Ap. J.*, **277**, 82.

van Breugel, W.J.M., Heckman, T.M., and Miley, G.K. 1984b, *Ap. J.*, **276**, 79.

van Breugel, W.J.M., Miley, G.K., Heckman, T.M., Butcher, H.R., and Bridle, A.H. 1985, *Ap. J.* (in press).

van der Hulst, J.M., Crane, P.C., and Keel, W.C. 1981, *A. J.*, **86**, 1175.

van der Hulst, J.M., Hummel, E., and Dickey, J.M. 1982, *Ap. J. (Letters)*, **261**, L59.

van der Kruit, P.C. 1971, *Astr. Ap.*, **15**, 110.

Véron, M.P. 1981, *Astr. Ap.*, **100**, 12.

Vrtilek, J.M. 1983, Ph. D. Thesis, Harvard University.

Wade, C.M. 1968, *A. J.*, **73**, 876.

Walker, M.F. 1968, *Ap. J.*, **151**, 71.

Ward, M.J., and Morris, S. 1984, *M.N.R.A.S.*, **207**, 867.

Weedman, D.W. 1973, *Ap. J.*, **183**, 129.

_____. 1976, *Q.J.R.A.S.*, **17**, 227.

_____. 1977, *Ann. Rev. Astr. Ap.*, **15**, 69.

_____. 1983, *Ap. J.*, **266**, 479.

Whittle, M. 1984a *M.N.R.A.S.*, (in press) (W1).

_____. 1984b *M.N.R.A.S.*, (in press) (W2).

Whitmore, B.C., Kirshner, R.P., and Schechter, P.L. 1979, *Ap. J.*, **234**, 68.

Whitmore, B.C., and Kirshner, R.P. 1981, *Ap. J.*, **250**, 43.

Wilson, A.S. 1979, *Proc. Roy. Soc. London, A.*, **366**, 461.

Wilson, A.S. 1981, In Proc. 2nd ESO/ESA Workshop, *Optical Jets in Galaxies* (ESA SP-162), p.125.

Wilson, A.S. 1982, In *Extragalactic Radio Sources,* IAU Symp. 97, p.179 (Reidel, Dordrecht).

Wilson, A.S. 1983, In *Highlights of Astronomy,* **6**, 467 (Reidel, Dordrecht).

Wilson, A.S., and Willis, A.G. 1980, *Ap. J.*, **240**, 429.

Wilson, A.S., and Meurs, E.J.A. 1982, *Astr. Ap. Suppl. Ser.*, **50**, 217.

Wilson, A.S., and Ulvestad, J.S. 1982a, *Ap. J.*, **260**, 56.

_____. 1982b, *Ap. J.*, **263**, 576.

_____. 1983, *Ap. J.*, **275**, 8.

Wilson, A.S., Baldwin, J.A., and Ulvestad, J.S. 1985, *Ap. J.*, (in press for April 15 issue).

Woltjer, L. 1959, *Ap. J.*, **130**, 38.

Wrobel, J.M., and Heeschen, D.S. 1984, *Ap. J.*, **287**, 41.

Wrobel, J.M. 1984, *Ap. J.*, **284**, 531.

OBSERVATIONS OF BROAD EMISSION-LINE REGIONS

Donald E. Osterbrock

Lick Observatory
Board of Studies, Astronomy and Astrophysics
University of California, Santa Cruz

ABSTRACT

Recent observational results bearing on the structure and velocity field of the broad-line region are discussed. Variations in the strength and form of the broad H I profiles give estimates of the size, and hence density in this region. In some cases densities as high as $N_e \approx 10^{11}$ cm^{-3} are indicated. High quality spectral data show that the profiles of different broad lines in a given AGN are not identical, indicating ionization differences with velocity and thus with position in the nucleus. Many lines of evidence show that a simple dichotomy between the broad and narrow emission-line regions is too simple, and that in many ways they merge continuously into one another. A physical picture that fits most of the observational measurements is that the structure is cylindrically symmetric, with slow inward flow in a rotating plane, and fast radial winds in cones or cylindrical regions perpendicular to the disk or at least outside it. There is a wide range of densities, and the denser regions on the average have higher velocities than the less dense regions.

I. INTRODUCTION

Observations are never meaningful in themselves except for classification purposes. Any physical interpretation or analysis is linked to a theoretical picture, either to test an existing one or to develop a new one. Hence this chapter, though labelled "observational," necessarily deals with theoretical ideas, results and calculations, just as the "theoretical" chapters must necessarily include measured numerical results and line profiles that are based on observational data.

Furthermore, one chapter cannot describe all observations of active galactic nuclei. There are too many of them. Many of the results of past observations are already incorporated in existing theories, or in the crude physical pictures we have of active galactic nuclei. Hence, more than most of the other chapters, the present one necessarily deals mostly with *recent* observational results, and how they have changed our thinking. Most, but not all of the material in this chapter is based on material presented at the Workshop. Wherever possible, references have been added to papers or preprints in which these results appeared, or will appear, in published form.

II. VARIATIONS

Within the past several years, it has become clear that the broad emission lines vary in profile and flux as the optical continuum changes. Fairly extensive observations have been made of the continuum and broad-line variations in 3C 120 (Oke, Readhead, and Sargent 1980; French and Miller 1980), NGC 4151 (Antonucci and Cohen 1983; Ulrich *et al.* 1984), and Akn 120 (Peterson *et al.* 1983, 1985). The response of the broad emission lines to changes in the continuum is of interest because under certain conditions it is possible to determine the velocity field of the broad-line region (BLR) on account of light travel time effects within it: as the continuum changes, different parts of the BLR, with different characteristic line-of-sight velocities if the motion is in any sense ordered, are affected by the continuum change at different times. By examining the continuum light curve and line profile variations it is in principle possible to determine the velocity field (Blandford and McKee 1982; Capriotti, Foltz, and Peterson 1982).

Whether or not line profile changes resulting from continuum changes are observable depends on various time scales. The response of any volume element of the BLR is set by the time scale for establishing ionization equilibrium. This is the recombination time scale, $\tau_{rec} = (N_e \alpha_B)^{-1} \approx N_9^{-1}$ hr where N_9 is the BLR electron density in units of 10^9 cm^{-3}. Secondly, the light-travel time across the BLR establishes how rapidly a change in the continuum flux will affect the line profile. This light size, estimated from Menzel-Baker case B recombination, is

$$\tau_{LT} = 5 \, \frac{L_{42}(H\beta)^{1/3}}{N_9^2 \varepsilon_B} \quad \text{days,}$$

where $L_{42}(H\beta)$ is the Hβ luminosity in units of 10^{42} erg s^{-1} and ε_B is the BLR filling factor. It is important that $\tau_{LT} \gg \tau_{rec}$; if this were not the case, the response of the BLR would be damped and the entire region would respond on the recombination time scale, making it impossible to determine the velocity field. Thirdly, τ_{var}, the time scale for a significant continuum change to occur, must be comparable to τ_{LT} for the emission lines to have detectable time-dependent structure. If $\tau_{LT} \ll \tau_{var}$, changes in the continuum would be so gradual that the line flux would always be proportional to the continuum flux, and there would be no detectable structure in the lines. On the other hand, if $\tau_{var} \ll \tau_{LT}$, the continuum would vary so rapidly that only a thin shell of BLR gas would reflect the continuum level at any given time — in other words, the BLR would be filled with so many continuum pulses that they would effectively be averaged out. In this case, the total line flux would appear to change little as the continuum varied, and changes in the profile structure would be difficult to detect.

Peterson *et al.* (1984) have observed a number of previously studied Seyfert 1 galaxies in order to isolate a few promising candidates to monitor in attempts to map the BLR velocity field. They compared their data with earlier observations made with a different instrument by Osterbrock and his collaborators. To normalize the spectra they assumed that the narrow-line fluxes are constant over several years (τ_{LT} is typically $\sim 30\varepsilon_N^{-1/3}$ years for the NLR, where ε_N is the narrow-line filling factor, and $\tau_{rec} \approx 100N_3^{-1}$ years, where N_3 is the NLR electron density in units of 10^3 cm^{-3}). For most of the sources the change in Hβ flux was found to be proportional to the change in optical continuum flux, so that the Hβ equivalent width remained nearly constant. This is consistent with, but does not prove that, $\tau_{LT} \ll \tau_{var}$ for many of these galaxies. Few, if any, galaxies were found to have constant broad-line flux. The potentially most interesting sources are those few which were not consistent with either $\tau_{LT} \ll \tau_{var}$ or $\tau_{LT} \gg \tau_{var}$.

One of the better candidates that emerged from this study is Akn 120. Its Hβ line profile is known to change with time (Foltz *et al.* 1981), and it has been suggested that these changes are attributable to continuum changes coupled with light travel-time effects (Capriotti, Foltz, and Peterson 1982). The spectrum of Akn 120 has been monitored extensively for several years (Peterson *et al.* 1983, 1985) and the observed variations in the optical continuum and the broad Hβ line are plotted in Figures 1 and 2. They show that the BLR responds to continuum changes on a time scale shorter than about 30 days, which thus sets an upper limfit on τ_{LT}. This upper limit is significantly smaller than the usual estimates which are based on the ionization parameter

$$\Gamma = \int \frac{L_\nu d\nu}{4\pi r^2 h\nu N_e} \approx 10^{-2}.$$

For Akn 120, Γ can be estimated by interpolating L_ν between the far UV IUE measurements and X-ray measurements. This gives $\Gamma \approx 1900\, N_9^{-1} r_d^{-2}$, where r_d is the BLR radius in light days ($H_o = 75$ km s^{-1} Mpc^{-1} is assumed). If $r_d \leq 30$, then $\Gamma \geq 2N_9^{-1} \gg 10^{-2}$ unless $N_9 \geq 10^2$. The usual estimate of the BLR electron density ($N_9 \approx 1$) is based on $N_e \approx N_c \approx 10^{9.6}$ cm^{-3}, the critical density for C III] $\lambda1909$, which is observed in IUE spectra. If $N_9 \approx 10^2$, CIII] $\lambda1909$ and Hβ must arise in physically distinct regions of the BLR; this is consistent with the IUE results for NGC 4151, which reveal that C IV $\lambda1550$, Mg II 2798, and C III] $\lambda1909$ all respond to continuum changes, but with different time delays (Ulrich *et al.* 1984). This is only one of the

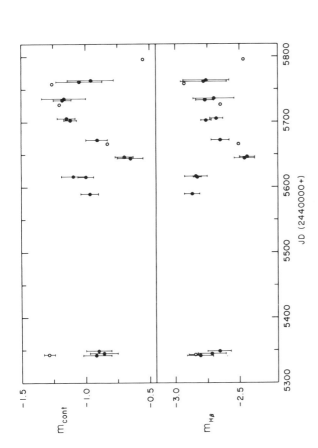

Figure 1: Optical continuum and Hβ magnitudes (on an arbitrary scale) for AKN 120, including observations since 1983 January. The closed-circles represent data obtained with the Ohio State IDS at Lowell Observatory, and the open circles represent data from the Steward Observatory Reticon. (Peterson *et al.* 1985).

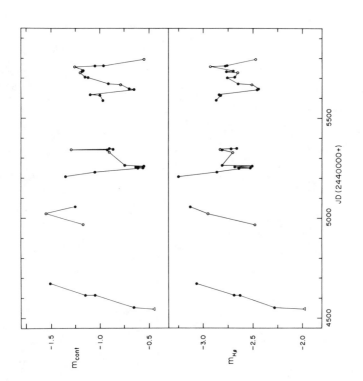

Figure 2: Same as Figure 1, but for data obtained since late 1980 (Peterson *et al.* 1985).

many recently discovered indications of the very great range in densities within many AGN.

The small size of the BLR leads to a possible explanation of why the broad lines in some active galaxies, including Akn 120, are redshifted relative to the systemic velocity by up to several hundred km s^{-1}. If the BLR is small and surrounds a massive collapsed object, radiation from the BLR should be gravitationally redshifted (see Netzer 1977). The mass required to produce the $c\Delta z \approx 400$ km s^{-1} redward displacement of the Balmer lines in Akn 120 is

$$M \approx \frac{c^2 \Delta z r}{G} \approx 2.3 \times 10^7 r_d M_\odot \; ,$$

which is greater than the minimum mass of $\sim 10^6 M_\odot$ imposed by the Eddington limit. However, NGC 3516 and Mrk 876 (see Shuder and Osterbrock 1982) are counter examples in which the broad components seem to be blue shifted with respect to the narrow lines. Another object with very peculiar and asymmetric broad line profiles is OQ 208 = Mrk 668 (Osterbrock and Cohen 1979). The existence of such spectra makes velocity structure appear more plausible than gravitational redshifting in Akn 120 also.

The existing line profile data on Akn 120 are probably inadequate for determining the kinematics of the BLR because the sampling grid is apparently of order τ_{LT}. Nevertheless, the data obtained thus far impose some constraints on models of BLR kinematics:

(1) The large line widths might indicate that equipartition applies in the BLR. The width of an emission line would be approximately given by $v^2 \approx GM/r$, and from above, $M/r \approx c^2 \Delta z / G$, so

$$v \approx c (\Delta z)^{1/2} \; ,$$

where Δz is the gravitational redshift for Akn 120, $c\Delta z \approx 400$ km s^{-1}, so $v \approx 10^4$ km s^{-1}, which compares reasonably well with the measured width of 6200 km s^{-1}. Thus, one can test whether virialized models are appropriate for comparing the redward displacement of the broad lines with their widths.

(2) An additional constraint on virialized models is given by the mean time between cloud collisions,

$$\tau_{coll} \approx \frac{0.05 r_d}{f} \text{ yr},$$

which, for Akn 120, is less than 15 years unless the covering factor f is considerably smaller than the commonly accepted value of 0.1.

(3) Models incorporating radial motion are also constrained by the small size of the BLR. The crossing time for the highest velocity gas in Akn 120 (at 5000 km s^{-1}) is

$$\tau_c \approx 0.16 r_d \text{ yr},$$

which is less than 5 years even if r_d is as large as 30 light days.

Pronik (1983) studied in detail the variation of the emission-line spectrum of NGC 3227 over the years 1971-81. In this study she combined photographic image-tube spectra obtained with the 2.6-m Shajn telescope of the Crimean Astrophysical Observatory with published data measured from spectral scans taken with other telescopes, mostly with other detectors. Large variations were noted, particularly in the H I Balmer lines. In fact the strength of the broad component has varied greatly, for the spectrum of this galaxy was originally classified as a Seyfert 2 by Khachikian and Weedman (1974), but later spectra clearly show its Seyfert 1.5 character (Osterbrock 1977). From her measurements of the Balmer decrement, Pronik concluded that the optical depth of the broad-line region varied, and that this region is inhomogeneous. She further believed that she had found variations in the [O II]/[S II] and [Ne III]/[O III] narrow-line intensity ratios, particularly around 1975, but the evidence for this is weaker. The purported amplitudes of variation are smaller, and may in fact simply reflect differences in the various data-taking systems from which the measurements were taken.

The most nearly complete monitoring of variations in a Seyfert galaxy taken with a single telescope and detector system is the 15-month study of NGC 4151 by Antonucci and Cohen (1983). They obtained at least one scan nearly every month, and sometimes more. The largest period for which they had no observation was between 1980 August 13 and November 9. Their observations confirmed that for all measurements taken on good photometric nights the flux in a narrow line, specifically [O III] $\lambda5007$, was constant to within the errors of observation.

Significant variations were observed in the continuum and in the broad lines. The Hα broad component followed the secular trend of the continuum, but remained unaffected by rapid, temporary continuum changes. Part of the flux of broad Hβ responded immediately to continuum changes, but part responded only gradually. Most or all of the flux in the higher members of the Balmer series and in He II $\lambda4686$ responded immediately. No gross changes occurred in the profiles of any of these lines. Antonucci and Cohen also measured what they called the "blue-UV bump," actually the excess apparent continuum emission at $\lambda4000$, with respect to $\lambda5500$, after correction for the stellar component. The variation of this "bump" approximately mimicked that of the higher Balmer lines, suggesting that much but not all of it comes from the still higher, unresolved members of that series.

The minimum broad emission line response and decay times were found to be less than one month, and probably less than one week. Therefore, much of the broad-line flux must be emitted within a region of this approximate light diameter (when it is bright). Some of the remaining flux in the broad emission lines responded more gradually to changes in the continuum level, with time scales up to the 15-month length of this observational study. Thus gas at distances somewhat greater than one light year makes an appreciable contribution to the broad-line emission. This again demonstrates the wide range in densities and the consequently ill-defined dimensions of "the broad-line region."

The slower changes in the broad Hα flux indicate that the broad-line intensity ratio Hβ/Hα increases and decreases as the continuum (and presumably its extension to the far ultraviolet ionizing continuum) increases and decreases respectively.

Ulrich *et al.* (1984) made an equally thorough study of the variations of the ultraviolet emission lines in NGC 4151 with the IUE. The lines observed were C IV λ1549, C III] λ1909 and Mg II λ2798. All are broad lines, usually having somewhat different widths. Both C IV and Mg II vary as the featureless continuum varies, but the lag time of these variations is approximately 13 days for C IV, and significantly longer for Mg II. They are consistent with a size of approximately 13 light days $\approx 3 \times 10^{16}$ cm for the C IV region, and approximately 25 light days $\approx 6 \times 10^{16}$ cm for the Mg II region. The C III] emission varies considerably less, if at all. Ulrich *et al.* suggest it may come from a larger region, approximately one light year $\approx 10^{21}$ cm in size. It of course has a lower critical density, $N_c \approx 10^{9.5}$ cm^{-3}, than C IV and Mg II, with $N_c \approx 10^{15}$ cm^{-3}. Once again we see evidence that "the broad-line region" actually includes a wide range of densities and velocities.

Penston and Perez (1984) have suggested that the variations in strength of the broad-line components of the Balmer lines in NGC 4151 are great enough that it could be classified as a Seyfert 2 galaxy when they are at minimum (see Figure 3). They therefore proposed that Seyfert 2 galaxies are Seyfert 1s "in which the continuum source is temporarily off." A related idea, which has been put forward by Cohen *et al.* (1984), is that Seyfert 1.9 galaxies, with their weak broad Hα components and nonexistent broad Hβ components, may be Seyfert 1 galaxies at minimum ionizing continuum level. Many Seyfert 1.9s were originally described as Seyfert 2s on the basis of noisy spectral data.

It is impossible to argue that any particular Seyfert 2 may not be a Seyfert 1 with the photoionizing continuum "temporarily" turned off. There are no morphological distinctions between the two types that are always satisfied. However, on the average,

NGC 4151

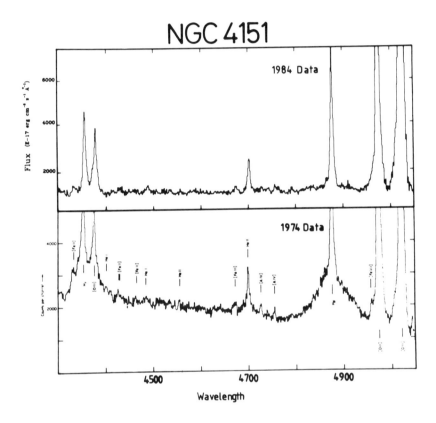

Figure 3: Comparison of 1984 (upper) spectrum of NGC 4151, taken with the Isaac Newton Telelscope (in Spain), and of 1974 (lower) spectrum, taken with the same telescope (in England). Both spectra were obtained with the Boksenberg Image Photo Counting System, and the wavelengths are given in the rest system of the observer. The 1984 data are calibrated in flux units but not the 1974 data. The spectral region from Hγ to the [O III] nebular lines is shown. Note the great change in the broad components of Hγ and Hβ. The broad component of He II λ4686 cannot be seen in the 1984 spectrum (Penston and Perez 1984).

Seyfert 2 galaxies are stronger radio sources than Seyfert 1s, as first discovered by Sramek and Tovmassian and confirmed by several later studies (see e.g., Osterbrock 1984). The radio emitting regions typically have diameters $\sim 10^{2-3}$ pc. Thus *most* of the Seyfert 2 galaxies cannot be Seyfert 1s with the photoionizing continuum turned off with time scales as short as a few years.

Other somewhat similar IUE studies of the broad ultraviolet emission lines in AGN are those of NGC 4593 (Clavel 1984), NGC 5548, (Wamsteker *et al.* 1984), and PG 1351 +64 (Treves *et al.* 1984). In general, the fastest variations are in the shortest wavelength (observed) ultraviolet continuum, down to a size 2.2 light days $\approx 6 \times 10^{15}$ for the high energy *continuum* source in NGC 4593.

Antokhin and Bochkarev (1983) have particularly emphasized the importance of studying carefully rapid variations of emission-line profiles in AGN to gain quantitative information on the structure and velocity fields in these objects. They carried out calculations on the response of three specific types of models (spherical, disk-like, and conical, all three composed of small-scale "clouds") and with various velocity fields (expansion with constant velocity, with acceleration, with deceleration, solid-body rotation, differential rotation, free fall, etc.) to an assumed step function variation of the X-ray ionizing continuum. Immediately after the flash, the strongest effects of course occur in the parts of the profile produced by the clouds that are closest to the photoionizing source.

Detection of such variations require a long series of homogeneous, high signal-to-noise ratio spectral scans, taken at close intervals of time. Bochkarev (1984) has made a start in this direction with a series of five scans in the spectrum of NGC 4151, taken over an interval of six nights with the 6-meter telescope, and another of four scans taken over a five-night interval. There are some apparent small changes in the wings of the broad components of He II λ4686 and of Hβ, but they appear to be close to the level of the noise in these scans. Such programs are important, and clearly many accurately determined profiles will be necessary to begin to discriminate between the various possible models.

Veron, Veron-Cetty and Tarenghi (1985) studied the variations in the ultraviolet absorption-line spectrum of NGC 4151. They analyzed all available, low-dispersion, short-wavelength, large-aperture IUE spectra of NGC 4151 taken prior to March 1982. These spectra show a linear correlation between the depth of the absorption lines and the strength of the underlying emission; the absorption lines vanish while the continuum is still measurable. All the available data are compatible with the following conclusions: The observed absorption lines in the UV spectrum of NGC 4151 are produced in one (or several, as suggested by the splitting of the He I λ 3889 absorption line into three components) cloud(s) associated with NGC 4151, with the probable exception of OI λ1302 which may be mainly of galactic origin. These clouds have high density ($N_e > 10^{8.5}$ cm^{-3}) as shown by the presence of several absorption lines from metastable levels (C III, Si III, He I). The continuum source is double, with one constant component and the other variable. The absorbing clouds cover the variable continuum source and the broad emission-line region, but not the constant continuum source. Possibly the latter is a jet. Taking into account the fact that the non-variable continuum source is not covered by the absorbing cloud, the equivalent width of all the absorption lines is constant in time.

III. LINE WIDTHS AND PROFILES

One of the most interesting questions that must be solved before AGN can be said to be understood is the nature (or natures) of the velocity fields in these objects. Observational data on line profiles are crucial in solving this problem. The ordinary optical region includes broad permitted lines of H I (Balmer series), He I and He II (both involving only transitions between highly excited levels), and narrow forbidden lines. The ultraviolet spectral region, inaccessible with ground-based telescopes, also includes broad permitted resonance lines, such as H I Lα and C IV λ1549, as well as semipermitted broad lines such as C III] λ1909. In high-redshift QSOs the ultraviolet (emitted) spectrum is shifted into the ground-based (observed) optical region, but of course the optical (emitted) spectrum is shifted into the infrared, which has been considerably less well observed to date. No doubt CCD spectrographs will improve this latter situation in the near future.

Low-resolution optical spectra of QSOs and quasars are often stated to have shown that the ultraviolet line profiles have practically the same shapes and velocity widths (e.g., Baldwin and Netzer 1978; Davidson and Netzer 1979). However, the data on which this conclusion was based are mostly relatively noisy, and furthermore the important question actually is quantitatively how similar (or different) the profiles are. Recent high-resolution spectra of nine high-redshift QSOs have given good factual information on these questions (Wilkes 1984). Further work along these lines will be very important. Determining the continuum level, and making proper allowance for weak absorption lines and blended emission features are the major sources of observational error.

In general, the broad line profiles in these QSOs are *roughly* logarithmic in shape, as predicted by the radiation-pressure driven wind model (Blumenthal and Mathews 1975). In each QSO profiles of different ionization species are generally similar, but when studied in detail, differ systematically from one another. In particular, H I Lα is more strongly peaked to the center, and also has more extended wings than C IV λ1549, though their full widths at half maximum, (FWHMs) in velocity units are quite closely the same (in most but not all the objects studied). C III] λ1909 has significantly wider FWHM than Lα and C IV λ1549 in three of the four objects with redshift small enough for it to be observed, and appears narrower than Lα and λ1549 in the fourth. Thus evidently different ions, which occur in emitting as having different (but overlapping) ranges of ionizing photon fluxes and densities, also occur in different (but overlapping) ranges in velocity space. However, weak Al II, Si III] or Fe II in the blue wings may explain the larger widths of C III]. In the spectrum of 2219-299, the one object with narrower C III] studied by Wilkes (1984), its FWHM is subject to unusually large errors in continuum placement, because of the redshift and instrumental parameters.

In these QSOs the Lα profile is not noticeably asymmetric in comparison with C IV λ1549 and other high-ionization lines (Wilkes and Carswell 1982). The individual gas clouds are supposed to be optically thick in Lα, so only the ionized face of a cloud, pointed toward the source of ionizing photons, is expected to be observable. Thus a radial wind would be expected to produce Lα profiles asymmetric to the red, as the approaching clouds would be mostly invisible in this line. The fact that the Lα profiles are observed to be mostly symmetric is thus an argument against the simple radiation-pressure driven wind model.

On the other hand the peaks of Lα and of the high-ionization lines are blueshifted with respect to the peaks of the low-ionization lines O I λ1304 and C II λ1335, on the average by $\Delta v \sim 800$ km sec^{-1} (Gaskell 1982; Wilkes 1984). In low-redshift QSOs, on the other hand, Mg II λ2798 has approximately the same redshift as the narrow-line region (Wilkes 1984). Furthermore in Seyfert 1 galaxies the narrow emission lines have approximately the same redshift as the underlying galaxy. Thus if all these comparisons are taken as depending on ionization, and are assumed valid in all types of AGN, the conclusion is that the peaks of Lα in the high-redshift QSOs are blueshifted with respect to the velocity of the stars which presumably represent the center-of-mass velocity of the system (called the "true" redshift by several authors). This conclusion however is contrary to the radial-wind model with clouds that are optically thick in Lα. It is consistent with radial infall of optically thick clouds, or of a radial wind with optically thin clouds plus dust, that absorbs preferentially Lα emitted from clouds on the far side of the AGN. As Wilkes and Carswell (1982) conclude from a preliminary discussion of these profiles, no simple model can explain these quantitatively measured profiles. Perhaps a wide range of cloud sizes, a complex velocity field, and the combined effects of Lα scattering and dust absorption can be combined in a picture that will explain them all, but this has not been done as yet.

That the chain of reasoning is complicated and does not necessarily lead to a unique conclusion, is illustrated by the fact that Gaskell (1982) from his data on a different group of high-redshift QSOs concluded that Lα may be redshifted with respect to C IV λ1549, the best observed of the high-ionization lines, by 400 ± 100 km/sec, but that "it is, however, difficult to say whether this 1.6 Å shift is real." Wilkes (1984), and Wilkes and Carswell (1982), found from their data that Lα and C IV λ1549 have on the average the same redshift. As so often is the case, "more observational data are needed."

Measurements of these same ultraviolet lines can be made in nearby Seyfert 1 galaxies only from above the Earth's atmosphere. Some early results obtained with the IUE on the C IV λ1549 profile in four fairly bright Seyfert 1 galaxies were published by Wu, Boggess and Gull (1981), but a much more complete body of data is being discussed by Wu, Grady and Boggess (1984). Their preliminary measurements of the full widths at half maximum of Lα, C IV λ1549, C III] λ1909 and Mg II λ2798 in sixteen Seyfert 1 galaxies are listed in Table 1. From these they concluded that C IV λ1549 is certainly broader than the lines from species of lower ionization potential. This is supported by Table 2, where the full widths at 10 percent of maximum intensity they measured from their IUE data are compared with full widths at 10 percent of maximum intensity or at zero intensity of the H I Balmer lines in the same galaxies, taken from published papers. Note however that although their conclusion is true for H I Lα and Mg II λ2798 (in comparison with C IV λ1549) it is not true for C III] λ1909.

TABLE 1

Preliminary Measurements of
Full Widths at Half Maximum Intensity (km s^{-1})

(Wu, Grady and Boggess 1984)

Galaxy	H I Lα	C IV λ 1549	C III] λ 1909	Mg II λ 2798
III Zw 2	4200	4200		
Mrk 352	2960	3200		
Fairall 9	2200	3700		3600
Mrk 817	3830	4570		5940:
Akn 120	5280	5340		6010:
NGC 3783[a]		3140		2780:
NGC 3783[b]		3350	2500	2890:
NGC 4151		6100	2500	4630
Mrk 279	5140	5980		
NGC 5548		4690	4710	5680
NGC 5940	3460	3870		
Mrk 290	2720	3680		
ESO 141-G55[a]	3300	3800	4740:	3700
ESO 141-G55[b]		4780	6470:	3010
Mrk 509	5930	6200	6190	3860
NGC 7213		5620	3320	3320
NGC 7469	3330	3870		3210
MCG-2-58-22	5930	9880		8040

[a] 1979 measurement

[b] 1981 measurement

TABLE 2

Preliminary Measurements of Full Width
at 10 Percent of Maximum Intensity (km s^{-1})

(Wu, Grady and Boggess 1984)

Galaxy	FW 10% I C IV	FW 0% I Hα or (Hβ)	FW 10% I Hα
III Zw 2	12400	17400	
Mrk 352	12780	14300	
Fairall 9	14200	(10650)	
Mrk 817	15470	19400	9440
Akn 120	16500		
NGC 3783[a]	12300		
NGC 3783[b]	11000		
NGC 4151	≥20000	≥12000	
Mrk 279	17470	19400	13160
NGC 5548	17500	14900	
Mrk 290	14300	11800	7540
ESO 141-G55[a]	14500	(9400)	
ESO 141-G55[b]	12900	(9400)	
Mrk 509	16300	12900	
NGC 7213	≥11800		
MCG-2-58-22	(27700)	(22700)	

[a] 1979 measurement

[b] 1981 measurement

In some Seyfert 1 galaxies $\lambda 1549$ is broader (in velocity space) than $\lambda 1909$, in other cases it has essentially the same width, and in still other cases it is narrower. Thus the IUE measurements of Seyfert 1 galaxy line profiles, though necessarily based on noisier, lower-resolution spectra, agree with the ground-based measurements of QSO profiles, that no single, simple model will fit all the data.

Wu, Grady, and Boggess (1984) believed that their profile measurements of Seyfert 1 galaxies showed more pronounced differences than occur in the profiles in high-luminosity QSOs. As stated above, this statement is at best only marginally confirmed by Wilkes' (1984) measurements. To the extent it is true, it may bear out the interpretation suggested earlier by Wu, Boggess and Gull (1983). They measured equivalent widths of Lα, C IV $\lambda 1549$, C III] $\lambda 1909$ and Mg II $\lambda 2798$ in Seyfert 1 galaxies, and compared them with published equivalent widths of the same lines in high-redshift QSOs. These comparisons cover a factor of about 10^5 in continuum luminosity (in the ultraviolet at $\lambda 1450$). Their main result was additional confirmation that photoionization is the main energy input mechanism to the broad line gas. They also found that the covering factor increases systematically with decreasing luminosity, typical high-luminosity QSOs having smaller covering factors than typical lower-luminosity Seyfert 1s. This conclusion is more model dependent, and less firmly based than the photoionization result. However, Wu, Grady and Boggess (1984) accept the higher covering factor for Seyfert 1 galaxies, which according to them leads to more pronounced optical depth effects on the ionizing radiation, hence more pronounced stratification of the broad-line emitting region by ionization potential, and hence more pronounced differences in the line profiles. This would be correct if the individual broad-line region clouds were optically thin to ionizing radiation, but not if they are optically thick.

These complications throw into doubt the simplest methods of estimating "the ionization parameter," for if the observed C III] and C IV line emissions come in part from different regions (as indicated by their different profiles in many objects), their ratio of strengths depends on many structure-dependent parameters.

IV. HIGH IONIZATION

It is now clear that the "two-region" model for the emission lines in AGN, i.e., a low-density extended region and a high-density, high-velocity compact region, is an oversimplification. There is mounting evidence that the emission lines of the highly ionized species [Fe VII], [Fe X] and [Fe XI] are formed chiefly in regions intermediate between the classic BLR and the extended and sometimes resolved NLR emitting for example [O III] (Penston *et al.* 1984; De Robertis and Osterbrock 1984). These highly ionized iron lines are often considerably broader than other forbidden lines, e.g., [Fe XI] 7892 in NGC 3783 has been stated to have FW0I $\sim$ 2500 km s^{-1} (Ward and Morris 1984).

The [Fe X] line at $\lambda6375$ is also broad, although it is less 'clean' due to blending with [O I] $\lambda6364$. This is an extreme case; careful study of the line profiles shows that in many Seyfert 1 galaxies there is a progression of line width with ionization potential, the lowest ionization lines like [S II] and [O I] being relatively narrow, and [Fe X] and [Fe XI] the broadest. Superimposed on this, in many objects, is a correlation of line width with critical density, so that [S II] $\lambda\lambda6716, 6731$, which have $N_c \approx 2 \times 10^3$ cm^{-3} are typically narrower than [O I] $\lambda6300$, which has $N_c \approx 2 \times 10^6$ cm^{-3}, and [O III] $\lambda4363$, which has $N_c \approx 3 \times 10^7$ cm^{-3}, is often wider than [O III] $\lambda\lambda4959, 5007$, which have $N_c \approx 7 \times 10^5$ cm^{-3} (Pelat, Alloin and Fosbury 1981, Atwood, Baldwin and Carswell 1983, Filippenko and Halpern 1984, De Robertis and Osterbrock 1984). These observations strongly suggest that the flux of ionizing photons, the energy of the highest-energy ionizing photons, the mean density, and the internal velocity all decrease more or less continuously from the central ionizing source (which is presumably also the central mass) outward. What we call the broad-line region is some average densest zone with the highest internal velocities;

what we call the narrow-line region is some average outermost, least dense, zone with the smallest internal motions.

In III Zw 77 (Osterbrock 1981), Tololo 0109-1236 (Fosbury and Sanson 1983), and NGC 3783 (Ward and Morris 1984; Penston *et al.* 1984), temperature estimates have been made for [Fe VII] from observed line ratios, and generally range from 15,000 to 40,000 K. These temperatures rule out collisional ionization for [Fe VII] and strongly favor photoionization. The good correlations of [Fe X] and [Fe XI] with [Fe VII] suggest photoionization as the origin of these stages of ionization also, but do not prove it.

The possible variation of [Fe X] $\lambda 6375$ in NGC 4151 and the apparent absence of collisional deexcitation limit the radius of the [Fe X] emitting zone to between 1×10^{-4} and 0.5 pc, and its density to between 4×10^4 and 1.2×10^{11} cm^{-3}. The [Fe X] and [Fe XI] lines are blueshifted with respect to the systemic velocity of the galaxy, typically by ~ 120 km s^{-1}. These effects are probably the result of a combination of higher outflow (or inflow) velocities closer to the central source and obscuration (Penston *et al.* 1984).

The emission line O I $\lambda 8446$ is believed to be formed by a fluorescence mechanism in Seyfert 1 galaxies. Comparisons of the O I and Hα profiles for NGC 4151 (Grandi 1980) and NGC 3783 (Ward and Morris 1984) show that O I lacks any narrow component, implying that it is formed exclusively in the high-density BLR. This line would therefore be expected to be absent in the spectra of Seyfert 2s. Indeed it is not seen in high signal/noise spectra of NGC 1068 (Grandi 1978) or in NGC 4507 and NGC 3081 (Ward and Morris 1985).

However, O I 8446 has been seen by these latter authors in NGC 5506, a galaxy with narrow lines commonly considered to be a Seyfert 2 type galaxy. A narrow feature at the correct wavelength for redshifted O I $\lambda 8446$ was detected in two independent observations of this galaxy. This result is of great interest, as it seems an unambiguous indicator of the existence of a high-density region (Seyfert 1 type) in an object which, from the remainder of its optical spectrum, would be classed as a Seyfert 2 galaxy. One should immediately note some of the peculiarities of this object: (i) it has been classed as an NLXG (narrow line X-ray galaxy), an acronym taken to cover X-ray luminous objects with narrow emission lines; (ii) very weak broad wings have been detected in the Hα profile (Shuder 1980); (iii) the AGN of NGC 5506 lies in a very low inclination, dusty parent galaxy. The line ratios Hα/[O I] λ6300, Hα/[N II], and Hα/[S II], all relatively insensitive to reddening, lie in the fairly narrow range characteristic of Seyfert 2s. Also, Ulvestad and Wilson (1984) have stated that NGC 5506 has radio properties more in common with Seyfert 2 galaxies (i.e., stronger and more extended radio emission) than with Seyfert 1s. Although under the standard definition NGC 5506 cannot really be classified as a Seyfert 1.9, because of the very weak broad Hα, we may nevertheless still be seeing a weak obscured BLR via the O I λ8446.

It should be noted that the narrowness of the "broad" line emission implied by the profile of O I 8446 is not unique. For example Mrk 42 (FWHM $\sim$ 550 km s^{-1}) and Akn 564 (FWHM $\sim$ 620 km s^{-1}) are classified as Seyfert 1 galaxies, and are both known to emit O I 8446. This suggests that in some AGN, the high- and low-density gas (historically termed the broad- and narrow-line regions) need not have greatly differing velocities.

Thus, for galaxies which appear highly active, for example in terms of X-ray luminosity, but which otherwise are like Seyfert 2s, the detection of O I 8446 may prove a useful signature for the presence of a high-density region (Ward and Morris 1985).

V. BROAD FORBIDDEN LINES

The detection of forbidden-line emission from the broad-line region of active galactic nuclei would allow a more definite determination of gas densities in this region. It has been suggested at various times by different authors that the [O III] $\lambda\lambda$4959, 5007 emission lines may contain a small contribution from the broad-line region. This idea has been investigated in a detailed way by van Groningen and de Bruyn (1985) and by Meyers and Peterson (1985).

Van Groningen and de Bruyn (1985) looked particularly for a broad wing on the long wavelength side of [O III] λ5007. This spectral region is fairly clear of emission lines except for Fe II λ5018. They took high signal-to-noise ratio scans of six Seyfert 1s or BLRGs selected to have weak Fe II, to reduce contamination by λ5018. According to their results, all these galaxies, NGC 7469, Mrk 335, 509 and 618, 3C 120 and Fairall 9, have weak broad [O III] wings, with peak intensities of the order of 3 to 10% of the narrow-line peaks. They measured the intensities in these red [O III] λ5007 wings as high as 20% of the continuum in this spectral region.

This observational result is not certain. Broad sensitivity variations, waves in an underlying galaxy continuous spectrum, or the integrated effect of several other unresolved weak, narrow, forbidden lines, or few weak, broad, permitted lines, all might explain the intensities measured in the spectra. A good test of the reality of these reported red wings would be to obtain even higher signal-to-noise, carefully calibrated spectra of one or two of the best cases reported by van Groningen and de Bruyn (1985), and to see if blue wings to λ4959 could also be detected in these objects. It should be possible to understand the entire blend to a high level of accuracy as the sum of two similar profiles (including "broad" plus "narrow" components), with relative strengths fixed by the known relative transition probabilities of λλ4959, 5007.

Meyers and Peterson (1985) on the other hand regarded the best possibility of detecting faint, broad [O III] emission as being in the region of what they call the "shelf" of "excess emission" on the red side of Hβ, under the narrow λλ4959, 5007 lines and blended with broad Hβ emission. Neither Hα nor Hγ show asymmetry to the extent seen in the red wing of Hβ, in their view, so they conclude that this shelf is probably not due to intrinsic asymmetry in the Hβ line. To eliminate the possible effect of contributions from broad Fe II $\lambda\lambda$4924, 5018 emission, which coincide with the position of the purported shelf, they also measured the relative fluxes in the Fe II $\lambda\lambda$4570, 5250 blends. A strong correlation between the "shelf" flux and the $\lambda\lambda$4570, 5250 flux would be expected if the "shelf" is composed entirely of blended Fe II $\lambda\lambda$4924, 5018. Meyers and Peterson (1985) removed the narrow [O III] $\lambda\lambda$4959, 5007 lines, and tried to remove the red Hβ wing by assuming this line has a symmetric profile, and reflecting the blue wing. Their result, shown in Figure 4, is that the flux in the "shelf" is not well correlated with the flux in the strong Fe II emission blends. The correlation coefficient of the least-squares fit shown by the straight line is only 0.36. From the same data, the Fe II $\lambda\lambda$4570, 5250 blends were found to be very well correlated with one another; their correlation coefficient was 0.90. The conclusion of Meyers and Peterson is that shelf is not primarily due to Fe II emission, and as they had eliminated all other possibilities, that it must be weak broad [O III] $\lambda\lambda$4959, 5007.

They further tested this result in Akn 120, for which they had the most complete data, by forming a symmetric Hβ profile, as described above, and modelling various assumed combinations of broad line with this profile. In this way they showed that broad Fe II $\lambda\lambda$4924, 5018 alone do not fit the "shelf" region well; that broad [O III] $\lambda\lambda$4959, 5007 fit it considerably better, and that broad Fe II and [O III] together fit it best of all. Earlier, essentially the same procedure, applied to scans of the same Seyfert 1 galaxy, Akn 120, taken with a different telescope and spectrograph, had given nearly identical results (Foltz, Wilkes and Peterson 1983).

The broad [O III] lines, if actually present, probably come mostly from regions with densities $N_e \approx 10^7$ cm^{-3}. If their width is taken as an additional free parameter, they seem to be somewhat narrower than the broad H I lines, but broader than the forbidden lines (Meyers and Peterson 1985). This fits in well with the idea that there is a continuous range in density, higher density being correlated with higher internal velocity, lower density with lower internal velocity. The names "broad-line region" and "narrower-line region" are convenient shorthand notations for the two extremes into which it can be somewhat artificially divided. Of course, the critical density for collisional deexcitation of the [O III] ^{1}S level (which emits $\lambda4363$) is $N_c \approx 3\times10^7$ cm^{-3}, so this

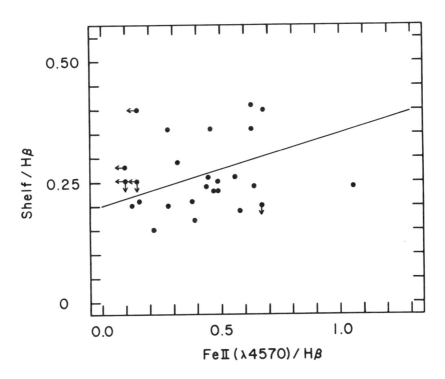

Figure 4: The relative flux in the shelf on the red wing of Hβ, remaining after a symmetrized broad Hβ profile has been subtracted, plotted against the Fe II $\lambda4570$ relative flux (Meyers and Peterson 1985).

line should be relatively much stronger with respect to λλ4959, 5007 than in the narrow-line components. Applying the same careful model deconvolution procedures to determining λ4363 profiles from similar high signal-to-noise ratio spectra of the same Seyfert 1 galaxies, (to Akn 120 in particular) would be an acid test of this idea.

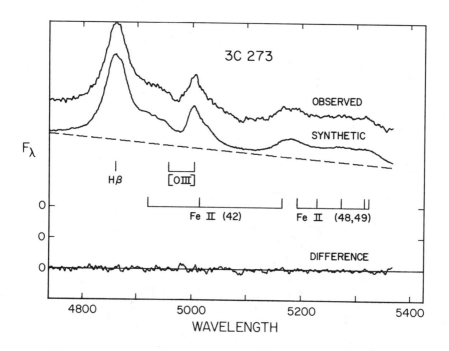

Figure 5: The spectrum of 3C 273 λλ4750-5420 at a resolution ~5 Å. The upper curve is the observed spectrum, the middle curve is the synthetic spectrum along with its continuum, and the lower near straight line is the difference. The Fe II lines were assumed to have the same profiles as Hβ; the [O III] widths were adjusted to give the best fit and were found to have FWHMs ≈ 1700 km S^{-1}. (Shuder 1982).

Broad [O III] emission lines have been directly observed in a few objects. One is 3C 273, long known to have weak [O III] $\lambda\lambda4959$, 5007, badly blended with Fe II $\lambda\lambda4924$, 5018 (Phillips 1978). Using a very high signal-to-noise ratio scan, Shuder (1984) found that the measured spectrum can best be fitted with a synthetic spectrum in which the [O III] lines have FWHM = 1700 km s^{-1}, a little over half that of Hβ and the Fe II lines (which were assumed to have the same profiles as Hβ). This comparison is illustrated in Figure 5. Peterson, Meyers and Capriotti (1984) confirmed this result in 3C 273 by basically similar analysis of independent data. They also measured the widths of weak broad [O III] $\lambda\lambda4959$, 5007 in two Seyfert 1s by similar techniques, FWHM = 1500 km s^{-1} in I Zw 1, and FWHM = 940 km s^{-1} in Mrk 478. All three of these objects are highly luminous AGN. Evidently there is some correlation of line width with luminosity for the "narrow" lines, as well as for the "broad" lines.

VI. Fe II EMISSION LINES

Strong permitted Fe II emission lines are characteristic features of the broad-line spectra of Seyfert 1 galaxies. They are observed in the optical spectral region in nearly all Seyfert 1s, but with a wide range of apparent strengths. More recently, IUE observations have shown the Fe II ultraviolet multiplets in essentially every Seyfert 1 for which reasonably good signal-to-noise ratio data have been obtained. Fe II blends are a major part of the ultraviolet emission from these objects. The composite ultraviolet spectrum formed by Veron, Veron and Tarenghi (1983) by summing the IUE spectra of 27 Seyfert 1 galaxies, representing altogether a total of about 150 hours observing time in the short-wavelength region, and about 100 hours in the long-wavelength region, shows these Fe II features very well.

With the long wavelength baseline thus made available, it is clear that neither the earlier resonance-fluorescence nor collisional excitation mechanisms can satisfactorily explain the observed Fe II emission-line spectrum. There is no doubt that large optical depths must occur in the Fe II resonance lines in Seyfert 1 galaxies, as shown by comparisons with calculations assuming either of these mechanisms. Empirically, however, larger populations in relatively highly excited terms, such as would be expected at temperatures $T \gtrsim 10^4$, are needed to match the measured Fe II relative intensities (Grandi 1981). He also determined that more levels, and in particular many more highly excited levels, must be included in the theoretical calculations to have any hope of fitting the observational data.

Recently such calculations have been made, taking into account many more terms and multiplets, and including the effects not only of collisional excitation and continuum fluorescence, but also of line fluorescence (Netzer and Wills 1983). They are described more fully in the chapter by Shields and Ferland. They still do not include individual lines and levels, the ideal. The results of these calculations show much better agreement with the observational data over the entire available wavelength range (Wills, Netzer, and Wills 1985). Synthetic spectra calculated including all these terms and effects seem to offer the best hope of subtracting the strong Fe II emission contribution, thus making it possible to study the purported "broad bump" and "narrow bump" in the continuum in the near ultraviolet, as described in the chapter by Stein and O'Dell. Also, matching these synthetic spectra with observational data provides a good method of measuring the total strength of the Fe II features, which is otherwise difficult because of continuum placement.

One of the most interesting differences between the optical spectra of radio-loud and radio-quiet AGNs is that the former tend to have considerably stronger Fe II emission than the latter, as first reported in the context of Seyfert 1s and BLRGs by Osterbrock (1977). This observational result has been confirmed by several later studies of other groups of objects, most recently by Bergeron and Kunth (1984) for a large number of QSOs and quasars. Various attempts have been made at theoretical interpretations of this difference, mostly having to do with geometry, covering factors, and the presence or absence of gas outside the source of relativistic radio-emitting plasma, that may "muffle" it and convert some of its energy to heat in partly ionized regions, and thus increase the strength of Fe II emission in radio-quiet objects (see *e.g.* Osterbrock 1984). Other well established differences are that BLRGs tend, on the average, to have larger $H\alpha/H\beta$ ratios and relatively stronger narrow forbidden lines and H I components than the Seyfert 1s.

The ultraviolet Fe II emission features are much stronger than the optical ones. These ultraviolet features have even been detected in AGNs with very weak optical Fe II emission, including the Seyfert 1 Mrk 290 and the BLRG 3C 390.3, by fitting theoretically derived synthetic spectra, previously confirmed and refined observationally in objects with stronger Fe II emission (Netzer *et al.* 1985). Wills (1985) has emphasized that because many of the radio-loud AGNs have broader H I and Fe II emission lines than the radio-quiet ones (Bergeron and Kunth 1984), there can be a tendency for the optical Fe II features to be lost. They become so broad that it is difficult to find clear regions between them that define the continuum against which they must be measured. Wills, adopting a mechanical method of determining the continuum, found that with it she could explain statistically the differences in apparent strengths of UV and optical Fe II features between the objects with narrow and broad lines.

There is no doubt that there is a tendency in this direction. Even the earliest papers emphasized that the main problems in measuring faint, broad emission lines in the optical spectra of Seyfert 1 galaxies and BLRGs is the highly subjective operation of defining the continuum (see e.g. Osterbrock 1977). However, it does not seem likely that the entire difference in optical Fe II emission-feature strengths between typical Seyfert 1s and typical BLRGs can be traced to this observational uncertainty. There are real differences in Fe II strengths among AGNs with comparable broad-line widths. This is illustrated in Figure 6, where the scans of two Seyfert 1 galaxies are shown in the $\lambda\lambda4000$-5500 spectral region, which includes the main Fe II optical blends. It can be seen that although the broad-line widths are similar, the Fe II features are approximately three times as strong (with respect to Hβ) in Mrk 376 as in Mrk 279.

Spectral scans of two other Seyfert 1 galaxies, with somewhat narrower but comparable broad lines, are plotted in Figure 7. Here it can be seen that the Fe II features in Mrk 771 are about twice as strong as those in Mrk 506. Finally, the spectral scans of the BLRG 3C 120 and the Seyfert 1 galaxy Mrk 734, which have comparable broad-line widths, are shown in Figure 8. It can be seen that the Fe II features are definitely present in 3C 120, but considerably weaker than those in Mrk 734. The previously published measured strengths of these objects, and of 3C 390.3 (in which Fe II was also detected) are listed in Table 3. These results are taken from Osterbrock (1977), except for Mrk 771, which was measured as Akn 374 by Phillips (1978). Note that in 3C 120 and 3C 390.3, although the Fe II $\lambda\lambda$ 5190, 5320 blends were measured as weakly present, Fe II $\lambda4570$ could not be measured because it is blended with strong broad He II $\lambda4686$, exactly the problem mentioned by Wills, Netzer and Wills (1985). Though optical Fe II was detected in 3C 120, 3C 390.3, and 3C 445, it was too weak to be seen in 3C 227 and 3C 382 with the then available spectra and reduction techniques (Osterbrock 1977). Very probably it is faintly present in these latter objects also and measurements of these (and other BLRG) by the synthesis technique will be of great interest.

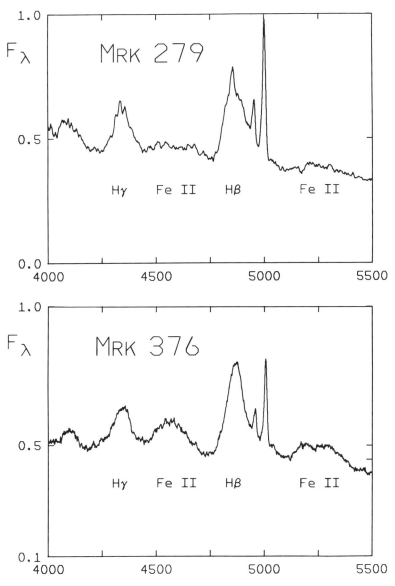

Figure 6: Lick Observatory spectral scans of the Seyfert 1 galaxies Mrk 279 and Mrk 376, with similar broad-line widths but different relative Fe II/Hβ ratios. The scans are plotted as relative flux per unit wavelength interval vs. wavelength in the rest system of the emitting object.

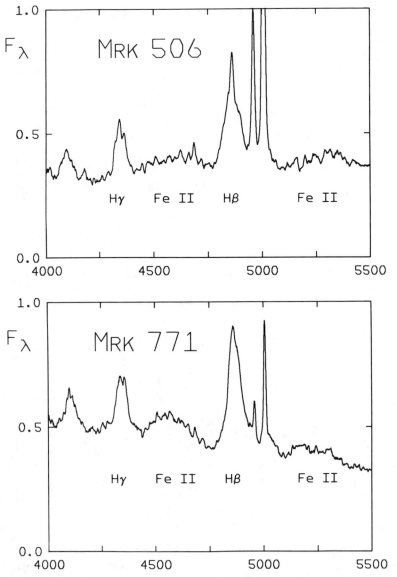

Figure 7: Lick Observatory spectral scans of the Seyfert 1 galaxies Mrk 506 and Mrk 771 (=Akn 375), with similar broad-line widths but different relative Fe II/Hβ ratios. The scales are as in Figure 6.

TABLE 3

Measured Relative Strengths of Optical Fe II Blends

	Fe II λ4570 Hβ	Fe II (λ5190+ λ5320) Hβ
Mrk 279	0.15	0.16
Mrk 376	0.58	0.40
Mrk 506	0.22	0.24
Mrk 734	–	–
Mrk 771	0.53	0.38
3C 120	–	0.12
3C 390.3	–	0.11

Gaskell reported on a study of the correlation of broad and narrow emission line properties with radio properties. Dividing quasars into radio-compact (flatter than $F_\nu \propto \nu^{-0.5}$, radio-extended) steeper spectra than $F_\nu \propto \nu^{-0.5}$ and radio-quiet, he confirmed the earlier results of Setti and Woltjer (1977) that radio compact or radio quiet quasars are much stronger Fe II emitters. He found that 64% of the "compact" quasars have strong optical Fe II emission (Fe II λ 4570/Hβ > 0.5), 18% of radio quiet quasars, and none of the radio extended ones. Gaskell also found that the broad emission line properties are correlated with the narrow emission line properties. In the strong Fe II emitting quasars the median equivalent width of the strong [O III] λ5007 line is three times greater than in the Fe II-weak quasars. The interrelationships between the broad-line, narrow-line and radio properties clearly exclude some simple unified theories which seek to explain different types of active galactic nucleus as similar objects seen from different angles. Gaskell felt instead that the evidence favored the galactic environment (e.g., pressure and density of the

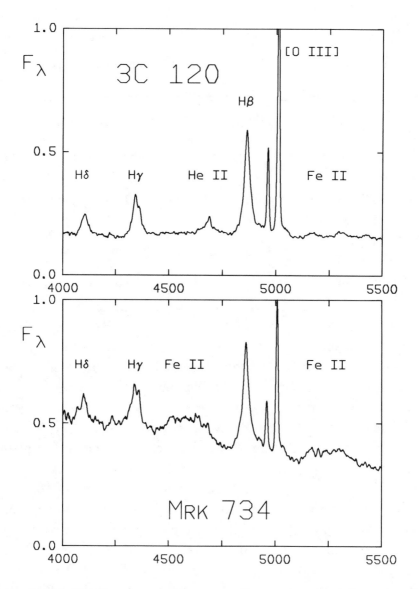

Figure 8: Lick Observatory spectral scans of the BLRG 3C 120 and the Seyfert 1 galaxy Mrk 771, with similar broad-line widths but different relative Fe II/Hβ ratios. The scales are as in Figure 6.

interstellar medium) being the key factor governing the radio and emission line properties of an active galactic nucleus.

VII. FORMS OF BROAD-LINE PROFILES

The forms of the line profiles contain information on the velocity field in the region or regions in which they are emitted. Any complete model of an AGN must include a prediction of the velocity field and hence of the detailed forms of all the profiles; disagreement between such predictions and observed profiles would eliminate from consideration the model used to make the predictions. As stated in Section III, in general the broad-line profiles of QSOs are roughly logarithmic in shape, as predicted by the radiation-pressure wind model (Blumenthal and Mathews 1975). However, a detailed study of good signal-to-noise ratio spectra of a group of QSOs shows that Lα is generally symmetric, which cannot be the case for radial flow in an object optically thick in this line (Wilkes and Carswell 1982). Hence either there must be little radial motion in the gas, contrary to the radiation-pressure driven wind picture, or most of the Lα is formed in clouds that are optically thin in that line, contrary to all the theoretical models for the H I lines. Some support for this optically thin picture is provded by the possible occurrence of Lβ emission in the spectra of two of these objects, Q0000-398 with Lβ/L$\alpha \sim$ 0.06, and 2212-299 with Lβ/L$\alpha \sim$ 0.08 (Wilkes 1984).

There is also evidence for a blueshift of the peak of Lα and the peaks of the higher ionization lines with respect to the lower-ionization lines. This is consistent with radial flow and some form of obscuration near the nucleus (Gaskell 1982). The other broad lines in these QSOs are relatively symmetric, with roughly logarithmic forms (Wilkes 1984).

A large number of high signal-to-noise broad Hα, Hβ, and Hγ profiles, together with a few H I λ5867 and He II λ4686 profiles of Seyfert 1 galaxies have been published in graphical form by Osterbrock and Shuder (1982). They attempted to correct for the overlying Fe II and [O III] features as objectively as possible. After these corrections, 10 of the 19 Seyfert 1 galaxies they studied had approximately symmetric H I line profiles, 6 had significant redward asymmetries, and 3 had sufficient blueward asymmetries. Though no detailed fitting analysis was carried out, the profiles appear very roughly logarithmic in form. Van Groningen (1983) applied detailed fitting techniques to the Hα and Hβ profiles of twelve of the best measured galaxies in this sample. He found that assumed power-law forms fitted more of the observed profiles than either logarithmic forms or Gaussian forms. In many of these AGN Hβ is significantly wider than the Hα (the average ratio is Hβ FWHM/Hα FWHM = 1.16 $\pm$ 0.05), indicating that the Balmer decrements, as well as the ratios of He I λ5876 to the Balmer lines, are functions of velocity, through the dependence of average physical conditions on velocity (Osterbrock and Shuder 1982).

Shuder (1982) analyzed the observed mean Hβ/Hα and He I λ5876/Hβ ratios as functions of velocity. On the average, both these ratios increase from the center to the far wing of a typical Seyfert 1 broad-line profile. Shuder found that, under all presently known models of the line emitting regions, either the electron density or the ionization parameter

$$\Gamma = \frac{4\pi}{N_e c} \int_{\nu_o}^{\infty} \frac{J_\nu d\nu}{h\nu} = \frac{4\pi}{N_e c} \int_{\nu_o}^{\infty} Q_\nu \, d\nu$$

$$= \frac{density \ of \ ionizing \ photons}{density \ of \ electrons}$$

must increase with increasing velocity. This comparison thus suggests that, on the average, the high-velocity clouds that emit preferentially the wings of the H I Balmer lines are closer to the central ionizing source and central mass than are the low-velocity clouds that emit preferentiallly the centers of these lines.

Shuder (1984) further extended this work by obtaining similarly high-accuracy Hα, Hβ, Hγ and He I λ5876 profiles in six low-redshift QSOs, with higher average luminosities (in the featureless continuum) than the Seyfert 1s. In the QSOs the differences between the Hβ, Hα, and He I λ5876 profiles are less pronounced compared with the latter objects. This had been suggested, but not proved observationally, in his earlier paper. This result indicates that in a typical low-redshift QSO, the conditions are more nearly similar from cloud to cloud than in a typical Seyfert 1. Shuder (1984) also found that, on the average, the FWHMs of the broad H I lines in Seyfert 1 galaxies and QSOs increase with increasing luminosity of the central source in the featureless continuum. There is a large scatter about the mean relationship, which increases from FWHM $\approx 10^3$ km s^{-1} at L$_{\lambda 4800}$ = 10^{28} erg s^{-1} Hz^{-1} to FWHM $\approx 4 \times 10^3$ km s^{-1} at L$_{\lambda 4800}$ = 10^{30} erg s^{-1} Hz^{-1}, and then apparently levels off, though this latter point is less certain as it is based on C IV λ1549 profiles rather than H I Balmer lines.

Van Groningen (1983) fitted the profiles published by Osterbrock and Shuder (1982), and found that in many cases they have power-law forms which can be fitted by calculated profiles based on a rotating-disk picture. The main assumed broadening mechanism is rotation, with local turbulence or electron scattering as a secondary mechanism. Profiles calculated on this picture fit the observed profiles relatively well in the wings, but predict a double-peak structure with a central minimum at the center of the line. This is a general problem of models based on rotating disks with internal Keplerian velocities. Whether magnetic forces, decelerating the gas near the center of such a disk into a velocity field closer to solid-body rotation, could actually slow down the material nearest the central mass sufficiently to fill in this central minimum in the line profile has not been investigated.

The observed asymmetries in the line profiles cannot occur under purely rotational velocity fields. To fit them van Groningen (1983) assumed, in addition to the rotating disks, anisotropically radiating filaments in two oppositely directed jets emanating from the center of the disk, and by radial motions of material in or about the disk.

Furthermore, van Groningen (1984) has applied such a combined rotating disk plus radial wind "model" to fit the observed line profiles of the Seyfert 1 galaxy Mrk 335 he obtained at Mount Wilson and Las Campanas Observatories. It has relatively narrow but fairly asymmetric (to the blue) H I lines. On this picture, the disk has a relatively high density, and produces about 80% of the Balmer-line emission with symmetric profiles. The wind has considerably lower density ($N_e \ll 10^9$ cm^{-3}), and emits the blue wings of the Balmer lines, but *most* of the Lα and higher-ionization lines such as C IV λ1549. Though not a true physical model, this picture has a considerable number of physical ideas contained within it. It fits this Seyfert 1 galaxy's line profiles fairly well. Van Groningen (1984) further speculates that the relative contributions of the disk and the wind to the emission-line profiles are dependent on luminosity. The observed dependences, summarized above, then require that in Seyfert 1s, the disk is the dominant source of emission, as in the Mrk 335 interpretation, but that in QSOs, the wind is the dominant source.

De Robertis (1985a) also obtained high-resolution (instrumental FWHM <5 Å) observations of the Hβ region in 27 QSOs and Seyfert 1s. He removed Fe II $\lambda\lambda$4924, 5018 from the observed profiles using the Fe II blends at $\lambda\lambda$4590, 5190, 5320, the strength of Fe II λ5169, the third line of multiplet (42), and the requirement that the red wings of [O III] $\lambda\lambda$4959, 5007 have identical forms, to estimate the optical Fe II strength. He also attempted to remove the narrow Hβ emission component using the empirical result that there is often a discontinuity in the Hβ profile between narrow and broad components at this resolution. (This is not true for some of the objects with strong optical Fe II emission, however.) Line widths and asymmetries were then measured for these "decontaminanted" Hβ profiles.

De Robertis (1985a) found that in the majority of these objects, the Hβ profiles are symmetric to within the estimated errors. However, there are also some redward asymmetric profiles and some blueward ones in agreement with the findings of Osterbrock and Shuder (1982). The widths of the profiles at various fractions of peak intensity normalized by the FWHM, were found to be rather similar in nearly all the objects included in this study. This was also found to be true for the profiles measured by Osterbrock and Shuder (1982). There is some indication that the profiles might even better be subdivided into two categories: (optical) "Fe II strong" and "Fe II weak." The normalized widths at various fractions of peak intensity are also similar to those in the narrow-line profiles in Seyfert 1 galaxies reported by De Robertis and Osterbrock (1984). This lends some credence to the idea of similar velocity fields in the broad-line and narrow-line regions, though the differing behavior of the asymmetries of the two types of lines does not seem to agree with this picture.

De Robertis (1985b) attempted to match these observed profiles with synthetic profiles calculated from a cylindrically symmetric picture of the broad-line region, consisting of a gravitationally dominated, rotating accretion-disk like structure, plus two conical regions (along the axis of the disk) from which the line emission occurs. The disk is assumed to be small, dense and thick, and thus to make essentially no contribution to the observed line profile. In the conical regions the broad-line clouds are supposed to be accelerated by radiation pressure, an assumption that determines their kinematics. Synthetic line profiles calculated from this picture depend most sensitively on only two parameters, the inclination angle of the axes of the conical emitting regions to the line of sight, and the opening angle of this cone (from 0° for an essentially linear jet to 180° for an essentially spherically symmetric situation).

The result found was that the symmetric "decontaminated" broad Hβ profiles can be reproduced rather well over a limited range of these parameters. Moderate opening angles fit most of the individual profiles better than either small opening angles or spherically symmetric models. These structures are thus quite similar in concept to those found by van Groningen (1983) to fit the observed profiles, in the limit of zero emission from the disk.

This description, though crude, seems to provide a fairly realistic picture of the broad-line region. Simultaneous outward acceleration of emission-line clouds near the axis, and inward dissipational accretion flow, providing fuel for the central supermassive compact object are naturally included in it. The asymmetry and the variability observed in many AGNs can then be understood as resulting from differences in the mass-injection rates (inhomogeneities) within the two emission-line cones. Geometrical effects (inclination) may explain why there is not a good correlation between line width and continuum luminosity.

Gaskell (1983) has proposed that the unusual line profiles discovered in a number of quasar-like objects are the result of *two* centers of broad line clouds, each one associated with a massive black hole. He argued that such supermassive binaries are a natural result of galactic mergers and so should be relatively common (3C 75 = 0255 + 058 with its double nuclei and double radio jets he believes probably to be an example of an early stage of such a merger). The observed velocities are in the range expected for massive binary black holes. (The velocities have to be greater than the stellar velocity dispersions, but low enough to avoid catastrophic gravitational radiation losses.) An alternative exploration of objects with displaced or double peaked broad emission lines is that they represent two jets going in opposite directions. This is inconsistent with the unusual line profiles preferentially being found in radio-extended objects. Since compact sources (especially superluminal ones) are believed to have the jets along our line of sight one would expect *them* to be the ones showing the widest separations of double peaks. This is definitely not the case.

Gaskell (1985) has argued that the Balmer lines are suppressed in AGN with very narrow broad lines. He attributes this to collisional destruction of the Balmer lines. These narrow broad-line objects (perhaps narrow line Seyfert 1s is a better description), such as Mrk 42 and 5C 3.100, are in no way like typical Seyfert 2 galaxies.

V. CONCLUSION

The broad-line region of AGN is complex. We do not have a complete physical model of it. Several independent lines of analysis suggest the structure is cylindrically symmetric, with slow inward flow in a plane, probably rotating, and fast radial winds in cones or cylindrical regions perpendicular to or at least outside the disk. Several lines of evidence show that there is a wide range of densities within the broad-line region, and that practically all densities occur. The denser regions on the average have higher velocities than the less dense regions. Variations occur on many time scales, evidently as new clouds form, or are introduced into the broad-line region.

The main observational questions to be answered are the form and symmetry, density, ionization and velocity field throughout the ionized gas, from the densest parts of the "broad-line region" to the least dense parts of the "narrow-line region." No doubt the structure is complicated and involves many parameters. Once the structure is unambiguously described, we may hope for success in understanding the physical principles that govern and maintain it. After they are understood, studies of the origin, evolution and final state of active galactic nuclei will become much more meaningful than at present.

I am very grateful to Drs. N G. Bochkarev, M. M. De Robertis, C. M. Gaskell, K. A. Meyers, B. M. Peterson, E. Perez, E. van Groningen, P. Veron, M. Wamsteker, M. Ward, B. J. Wilkes, B. J. Wills, and C.-C. Wu, all of whom helped me by providing reprints, preprints, or other material describing their recent contributions in this field. As always, I am grateful to the National Science Foundation for partial support of my own research in this field, most recently under grant AST 83-11585.

REFERENCES

Antokhin, I.I., and Bochkarev, N.G. 1983, *Astron. Zh.*, **60**, 448.

Antonucci, R.R.J., and Cohen, R.D. 1983 *Ap. J.*, **271**, 564.

Baldwin, J. A., and Netzer, H. 1978, *Ap. J.*, **226**, 1.

Bergeron, J., and Kunth, D. 1984 *M.N.R.A.S.*, **207**, 263.

Blandford, R.D., and McKee, C.F. 1982, *Ap. J.*, **255**, 419.

Blumenthal, G.R., and Mathews, W.G. 1975, *Ap. J.*, **198**, 517.

Bochkarev, N.G. 1984, *Soviet Astron. Lett.* in press.

Capriotti, E.R., Foltz, C.B., and Peterson, B.M. 1982, *Ap. J.*, **261**, 35.

Clavel, J. 1984, *Proc. 4th European IUE Conf., NASA CP-2349*, p.83.

Cohen, R.D., Puetter, R.C., Rudy, R.J., Foltz, C.B., and Ake, T.B. 1984, *Bull. A.A.S.*, **16**, 441.

Davidson, K., and Netzer, H. 1979, *Rev. Mod. Phys.*, **51**, 715.

De Robertis, M.M., and Osterbrock, D.E. 1984, *Ap. J.*, **286**, 171.

De Robertis, M.M. 1985a, *Ap. J.*, **288**, in press.

_____. 1985b, *Ap. J.*, in preparation.

Filippenko, A.V., and Halpern, J.P. 1984, *Ap. J.*, **285**, 458.

Foltz, C.B., Peterson, B.M., Capriotti, E.R., Byard, P.L., Bertram, R., and Lawrie, D.G. 1981, *Ap. J.*, **250**, 508.

Foltz, C.B., Wilkes, B.J., and Peterson, B.M. 1983, *A.J.*, **88**, 1702.

Fosbury, R.A.E., and Sansom, A.E. 1983, *M.N.R.A.S.*, **204**, 1231.

French, H.B., and Miller, J.S. 1980, *Pub. A.S.P.*, **92**, 753.

Gaskell, C.M. 1982, *Ap. J.*, **263**, 79.

_____. 1983, Liege Colloquium, p. 473.

_____. 1985, *Ap. J.*, in press.

Grandi, S.A. 1980, *Ap. J.*, **238**, 10.

_____. 1981, *Ap. J.*, **251**, 451.

Khachikian, E.Y., and Weedman, D.W. 1974, *Ap. J.*, **192**, 581.

Meyers, K. A., and Peterson, B.M. 1985, *Ap. J.*, submitted.

Netzer, H. 1977, *M.N.R.A.S.*, **181**, 89P.

Netzer, H., and Wills, B.J. 1983, *Ap. J.*, **275**, 445.

Netzer, H., Wamsteker, W., Wills, B.J., and Wills, D., 1985 *Ap. J.*, in press.

Oke, J.B., Readhead, A.C.S., and Sargent, W.L.W. 1980, *Pub. A.S.P.*, **92**, 758.

Osterbrock, D.E. 1977, *Ap. J.*, **215**, 733.

_____. 1981, *Ap. J.*, **246**, 696.

_____. 1984, *Q.J.R.A.S.*, **25**, 1.

Osterbrock, D.E., and Cohen, R. 1979, *M.N.R.A.S*, **187**, 61P.

Osterbrock, D.E., and Phillips, M.M. 1977, *Pub. A.S.P.*, **89**, 251.

Osterbrock, D.E., and Shuder, J.M. 1982, *Ap. J. Suppl.*, **49**, 149.

Penston, M.V., Fosbury, R.A.E., Boksenberg, A., Ward, M.J. and Wilson, A.S. 1984, *M.N.R.A.S.*, **208**, 347.

Penston, M.V., and Perez, E. 1984, *M.N.R.A.S.*, **211**, 33P.

Peterson, B.M., Foltz, C.B., Crenshaw, D.M., Meyers, K.A., and Byard, P.L. 1984, *Ap. J.*, **279**, 529.

Peterson, B.M., Foltz, C.B., Miller, H.R., Wagner, R.M., Crenshaw, D.M., Meyers, K.A., and Byard, P.L. 1983, *A. J.*, **88**, 926.

Peterson, B.M., Meyers, K.A., and Capriotti, E.R. 1984, *Ap. J.*,, **283**, 529.

Peterson, B.M., Meyers, K.A., Capriotti, E.R., Foltz, C.B., Wilkes, B.J., and Miller H.R. 1985, *Ap. J.*, **292**, in press.

Phillips, M.M. 1978, *Ap. J. Suppl.*, **38**, 187.

Pronik, I.I. 1983, *Pub. Crimean Obs.*, **68**, 81.

Setti, G., and Woltjer, L. 1977, *Ap. J. (Letters)*, **218**, L33.

Shuder, J.M. 1980 *Ap. J.*, **240**, 32.

_____. 1982 *Ap. J.*, **259**. 48.

_____. 1984 *Ap. J.*, **280**, 491.

Treves, A., Drew, J., Falomo, R., Maraschi, L., Tanzi, E.G., and Wilson, R. 1984, *Proc. 4th European IUE Conf., NASA CP-2349*, p. 000.

Ulrich, M.H., *et al.*, 1984, *M.N.R.A.S.*, **206**, 221.

Ulvestad, J.S., and Wilson, A.S. 1984, *Ap. J.*, **285**, 439.

van Groningen, E. 1984, Ph.D. Thesis, Leiden University.

_____. 1983, *Astron. Ap.*, **126**, 363.

van Groningen, E., and de Bruyn, A. G. 1985, *Astron. Ap.*, in preparation.

Veron, P., Veron, M.-P., and Tarenghi, M. 1983, *Astron. Ap.*, **119**, 69.

_____. 1985, *Astron. Ap.*, submitted.

Wamsteker, W., *et al.*, 1984 *Proc. 4th European IUE Conf., NASA CP-2349*, p. 148.

Ward, M., and Morris, S. 1984, *M.N.R.A.S.*, **207**, 867.

Ward, M., and Morris, S. 1985, *M.N.R.A.S.*, submitted.

Wilkes, B.J. 1984, *M.N.R.A.S.*, **207**, 73.

Wilkes, B.J., and Carswell, R.F. 1982, *M.N.R.A.S.*, **201**, 645.

Wills, B.J. 1985, in preparation.

Wills, B.J., Netzer, H., and Wills, D. 1985, *Ap. J.,* **288**, 94.

Wu, C.-C., Boggess, A., and Gull, T.R. 1981, *Ap. J.,* **247**, 449.

_____. 1983, *Ap. J.,* **226**, 28.

Wu, C.-C., Grady, C.A., and Boggess, A. 1984, *Bull. A.A.S.,* **16**, 1984.

THE THEORY OF EMISSION-LINE REGIONS
IN ACTIVE GALACTIC NUCLEI

G. J. Ferland

Department of Physics and Astronomy
University of Kentucky

and

G. A. Shields

Department of Astronomy
University of Texas at Austin

ABSTRACT

The theory of the broad emission lines in recent years has
seen photoionization models emphasizing X-ray heating at increasingly large depths in dense clouds. Calculations including detailed
solutions of a many-level hydrogen atom can account fairly well for
the strength of the Balmer lines relative to Lyman alpha; but they
have not succeeded in explaining all the relative intensities of the
Paschen, Balmer, and Lyman lines. Calculations of the Fe II emission spectrum have included huge numbers of lines and line-line
fluorescence, and the relative intensites of lines and multiplets are
fairly well explained. However, photoionization models generally
predict less than the observed amount of energy in the Fe II lines
and the Balmer continuum; and this, along with problems of the
Balmer decrement, has caused some investigators to postulate an
additional, nonphotoionized region to supplement the intensities
of the low ionizations lines. The nagging question of reddening
remains a serious uncertainty affecting the interpretation of the
lines and continuum. Narrow line emission from AGN, ranging in
ionization level from Seyfert galaxies to LINERs, can be accounted
for by photoionization by a nonthermal continuum for appropriate values of the ionization parameter. X-rays can raise the gas
temperature enough for collisional excitation to affect the Balmer

decrement.

I. INTRODUCTION

The 1984 Santa Cruz Workshop on Active Galactic Nuclei did not witness a great deal of attention to the modeling of the emission-line regions of these objects. A casual observer might interpret this as indicating that the theory is well understood and is in good agreement with observations. After the 1978 Santa Cruz workshop focussed attention on the low ratio of $L\alpha$ to $H\beta$ in AGN, modeling of photoionized emission-line regions did indeed make substantial progress. Does this mean that the "standard" photoionization model is free of major difficulties? Or have recent successes created an uncritical atmosphere of relief? In this chapter we have two goals in mind. The first is to survey some highlights of the progress in photoionization modeling since the comprehensive review by Davidson and Netzer (1979), and the second is to examine the question of how well current models really succeed in explaining the observations.

Photoionization modeling of AGN emission-line regions can be traced at least as far back as the work of Bahcall and Kozlovski (1969). Their fixed temperature calculations were superceded by thermal balance models by Davidson (1972) and MacAlpine (1972), who used computational methods similar to those of Williams (1967). These studies indicated that photoionization could roughly account for the relative intensities of the strong lines, and by implication the temperature and degree of ionization of the gas. Details of the calculations improved throughout the 1970's, and included such processes as Auger ionization and density suppression of dielectronic recombination (MacAlpine 1974; Davidson 1975). Photoionization models of AGN during this period relied for the most part on the same physics as that used in models of Galactic nebulae and the Crab nebula. This period ended with the calculations by Davidson (1977), the last paper written before the full realization that AGN hydrogen-line ratios are far from simple recombination values. This realization ushered in the modern era, in which models must take detailed account of many complicated processes related to the high densities, large optical depths, and strong X-ray fluxes in AGN emission-line regions.

The operating assumption has generally been that one should first try to explain the observations in terms of gas of roughly solar composition photoionized by the "observed nonthermal continuum" of the nucleus. This conservative attitude may be rooted partly in Seyfert's (1943) comparison of AGN spectra with those of planetary nebulae, and Searle and Sargent's (1968) observation that the equivalent widths of the broad hydrogen lines are consistent with photoionization. Recent ultraviolet and X-ray observations from space support the sufficiency of the ionizing continuum as an energy source for the emission lines.

Inspection of the spectra of AGN usually reveals two distinct types of emission-line profile: (1) very broad lines, with full widths at zero intensity (FWZI) $\sim 10^4$ km s^{-1} seen only in the permitted and intercombination lines, and (2) narrower lines (FWZI $\sim 10^3$ km s^{-1}) seen both in the permitted and forbidden lines. This led to a model with two distinct regions, a "broad line region" (BLR) with fast-moving gas at a density high enough ($N_e > 10^8$ cm^{-3}) to suppress the forbidden-line emission, and a "narrow line region" (NLR) with lower velocities and densities (e.g., Shields 1974). A combination of observational and theoretical arguments led to a standard picture in which the BLR has gas with a density $N \approx 10^9$ to 10^{10} cm^{-3} at a distance $R \approx 10^{18}$ cm from the nucleus, and the NLR has a range of densities $N \approx 10^3$ to 10^6 cm^{-3} at $R \approx 10^{20}$ to 10^{21} cm. For both regions, the line-emitting gas occupies only a small fraction of the volume $4\pi R^3/3$; and in most models, it is assumed to take the form of small clouds that are optically thick to the Lyman continuum ($\tau > 1$).

II. THE BROAD LINE REGION

The BLR has received the most attention from theorists, because it lies closer to the continuum source than does the NLR and involves more complicated physics. In 1978, the general view was that photoionization models could account for the strengths of the strong ultraviolet lines of the heavy elements relative to each other and to Lyα. Models were characterized by an ionizing continuum shape, often a power law such as $L_\nu \propto \nu^{-1}$, by the atomic number density N in a plane-parallel slab of gas, and an ionization parameter $U = \Phi_H/Nc$, where Φ_H is the flux of ionizing photons per cm^2 per second incident on the cloud. (Some models specify a constant gas pressure through the cloud, rather than a constant density.) The substantial strength of Mg II $\lambda2800$ implied that the clouds were optically thick to the Lyman continuum, $\tau_L \gg 1$, so that the ionization varied greatly from the front face to the H$^\circ$ zone deep in the cloud. The strength of C III] $\lambda1909$ was taken to imply that the BLR had an electron density $N_e \lesssim 10^{9.5}$ cm^{-3}, the critical density for collisional deactivation of this line. The ratios of C III] and C IV $\lambda1549$ relative to Lyα were used to deduce a value $U \approx 10^{-2}$; and when it was noticed that this gives O VI $\lambda1034$ and N V $\lambda1240$ intensities weaker than observed, one surmised that some gas with higher U was also present (Davidson 1977; Netzer 1976; MacAlpine 1972). The hydrogen lines were assumed to arise mostly from recombination, with some collisional excitation of Lyα and Hα. There was some awareness of the importance of Balmer line self-absorption and collisional excitation from excited states (e.g., Shields 1974; Netzer 1975) and of collisional excitation of He I $\lambda5876$ (MacAlpine 1976; Netzer 1978), but these effects were viewed as perturbations on the concept of the BLR as just a dense photoionized nebula.

Full appreciation of the problems of the hydrogen line ratios was delayed by the difficulty of making simultaneous measurements of the Lyman, Balmer, and Paschen lines. Baldwin (1977a) combined optical spectra of 26 QSOs covering a wide range of redshifts to find $L\alpha/H\beta \approx 3$. Davidson, Hartig, and Fastie (1977) obtained the first rocket spectrum of a low-Z QSO (3C273) and found a low value of $Ly\alpha/H\beta$. Soon afterwards came the first infrared measurements of $H\alpha$ in high-redshift QSOs and more space measurements of the ultraviolet spectra of low redshift objects. All these measurements gave $L\alpha/H\beta \approx 3$ to 10, in contrast to the value ~ 50 predicted by the photoionization models of the day (including collisional excitation).

The "$Ly\alpha/H\alpha$ problem" raised serious concerns about the validity of photoionization in the BLR. Could photoionization models be modified to explain the observed low values of $Ly\alpha/H\alpha$, or was a completely new approach required? Zirin (1978) noted that the $Ly\alpha/H\alpha$ ratio in solar flares was similarly low. Calculations for uniform slabs of photoionized hydrogen, including collisional transitions and line transfer, showed that low values of $L\alpha/H\alpha$ could indeed be achieved (e.g., Krolik and McKee 1978; Mathews, Blumenthal, and Grandi 1980; Drake and Ulrich 1980; Canfield and Peutter 1980; Collin-Souffrin *et al.* 1981). The models involved large column densities and moderate degrees of ionization, so that $Ly\alpha$ photons were destroyed by multiple scatterings ending in collisional deexcitation, and the Balmer lines were enhanced by collisional excitation from excited states. However, the $L\alpha/H\alpha$ ratio in these calculations varied widely with assumed parameters, and they did not represent a model of the complete ionization structure of a cloud.

The modern era is characterized by photoionization models that solve, as a function of depth, the ionization, temperature, and line transfer in clouds with large column densities and heating of the deeper regions by X-rays (Kwan and Krolik 1979, 1981; Canfield and Puetter 1980; Weisheit, Shields, and Tarter 1981; Collin-Souffrin, Dumont, and Tully 1982; Kwan 1984). Ionizing ultraviolet photons produce a highly ionized zone on the front face of the cloud, resembling the earlier photoionization models; this zone produces most of the $Ly\alpha$ flux as well as the lines of C IV,

C III], etc. Deeper in the cloud, penetrating X-rays heat the gas and maintain an extended "partially ionized zone" with $H^+/H^\circ \approx 10^{-1}$ and $T \approx 8,000$ K. This zone emits strongly in the Balmer lines, the Fe II lines, and the Balmer continuum; but $Ly\alpha$ is unable to escape. The partially ionized zone dominates the emission in the Balmer lines and leads to $Ly\alpha/H\alpha$ ratios lower than the recombination values.

X-ray heating at large depths is the key element in these new models, and this has necessitated the inclusion of additional physical processes and a detailed treatment of line transfer. To be considered correct today, a calculation of the BLR spectrum must include all physical processes affecting a 5 to 10 level hydrogen atom. One of the most important effects is line trapping, particularly of $Ly\alpha$, since this effectively overpopulates excited states of hydrogen. At present two techniques for treating radiative transfer are in the literature. The first, and most commonly used, is the mean escape probability method, applied and discussed by Netzer (1975) and Kwan and Krolik (1981). Here one assumes that all photons scatter locally, without diffusing in space. This approximation is justified, at least qualitatively, by studies of resonance line transfer, which show that photons scatter in frequency at their point of creation, until receiving a large frequency shift into the line wings, where the gas is optically thin and the photon immediately escapes. The wide acceptance of this approximation was largely due to the fact that it could be easily incorporated into the framework of the standard photoionization modeling techniques. This is to divide an optically thick slab into a large number of small zones, and then to solve for the physical conditions within each zone, independently of preceding or following zones (aside from attenuation of the ionizing continuum from the central source). In some cases, a second iteration is used to treat diffuse fields more correctly (cf. Williams 1967; Osterbrock 1974). The power of this technique lies in its simplicity; a single pass solution is generally within a few tens of percent of the final, fully converged solution.

Certainly the most serious simplification in the mean escape probability formalism is its pivotal assumption that all scatterings occur locally. In a series of papers, Puetter and co-workers (cf. Hubbard and Puetter 1985) have tried to make the calculations more realistic by loosening the assumption that all transfer is local. They employ a "flux divergence coefficient" in place of the mean escape probability, but otherwise use similar assumptions in solving for the level populations of the hydrogen atom. The mechanics of solving the problem are more cumbersome because this coefficient is a non-local quantity. The technique obviously represents an advance over the mean escape formalism, since all layers of the cloud are coupled, but it also represents a great increase in the computational complexity. The most recent application has been to a pure hydrogen cloud, with temperature and ionization solutions (Hubbard and Puetter 1985). Although the flux divergence technique is on a firmer theoretical footing, the differences between emergent line ratios in the two formalisms are not great if the same assumptions concerning the heavy element abundances are made (see Ferland and Mushotzky 1984). For conditions appropriate to BLR clouds, the line ratios are typically in roughly 20% agreement; and this is less than the differences caused by neglecting the heavier elements, which affects the temperature and ionization structure and thereby the hydrogen lines.

Other processes affecting excited states of hydrogen, along with a development of the formalism to treat them, are discussed by Elitzur (1984). Of particular importance are collisional ionization (see Drake and Ulrich 1980 for rate coefficients) and three-body recombination. Photoionization from all states must, of course, be included; an important factor in the smaller $L\alpha/H\beta$ ratio now achieved by models is the enhancement of Balmer lines by photoionization from the n=2 and higher states, followed by recombination (Kwan and Krolik 1979). For parameters of interest to models of BLRs, induced recombination is significant only for high n states, where both the very strong continuum and the larger phase space factor make induced processes important. Corrections for stimulated emission must also be made to the optical depth scale for n > 5 (cf. Krolik and McKee 1978). Collisional processes are very important even for NLR models, where they result in Balmer decrements steeper than case B (see Netzer 1982; Halpern 1982; Gaskell and Ferland 1984; and Ferland and Osterbrock 1985). Recent rates are given by Aggarwall (1984).

Besides hydrogen, at least another half dozen elements should be included in the heating, cooling, and ionization solutions. Their influence upon the cooling of the gas is obvious; these elements produce strong emission lines. Less obvious are their effects upon the ionization structure and heating. Both are affected by the large opacities of heavy elements at high energies; helium is the dominant contributor to the opacity for energies of 50-100 eV, while K-shell electrons of the second row elements (particularly the abundant C and O) dominate at energies of a few keV. As a result, they increase both the heating rates and the attenuation of more energetic radiation by large factors. A less obvious but equally important effect is that of the "knock-on" secondary electrons produced following inner shell ionization; these electrons typically have energies of ~500 eV and produce many secondary ionizations before sharing portions of their energy with the free electrons. All of these high energy effects are important and have been discussed by, for instance, Halpern and Steiner (1983), Kallman and McCray (1982), and Kallman (1984).

Line transfer effects are also important for some lines of heavy elements. Some of the cooling lines, particularly the Li-sequence (see Shuder and MacAlpine 1979), can be optically thick and, as a result, can be less efficient coolants. Particular attention has recently been paid to lines with possible utility as reddening indicators, including the O I $\lambda 1304/\lambda 8446$ and He II $\lambda 1640/\lambda 4686$ ratios. MacAlpine (1981) reviews the problems and possibilities (see also Grandi 1983a; Netzer 1985). Basically, these ions have lines that overlap with strong hydrogen lines and can be radiatively excited under certain conditions.

Fortunately, one historical frontier, the atomic data base,

has seen substantial advances. The recent compendium by Mendoza (1983) documents the work done up to 1983. Important developments that have occurred since the Davidson and Netzer review include the work by Dalgarno and co-workers on charge transfer (see Butler, Heil, and Dalgarno 1982), and dielectronic recombination at nebular temperatures (cf. Storey 1981; Nussbaumer and Storey 1985). Both have strong influences on the ionization equilibria of elements. Further work in atomic physics along these lines, particularly on the third row of elements and iron, will have important consequences for photoionization models.

In addition to the Lyα/Hβ ratio, good progress has been made over the last few years in understanding the Fe II emission. Prominent emission bands of Fe II are seen in the ultraviolet and optical spectra, including features at $\lambda\lambda$2240-2650 and $\lambda\lambda$4450-4750. These features are emitted by terms lying $\sim$ 4 to 6 eV above the ground state. Phillips (1977, 1978) showed that optical depths in UV multiplet 3 (λ2350) needed to be $\gtrsim 5 \times 10^3$ to give the observed intensity ratios of lines within the multiplet. Netzer (1980) showed that the excitation mechanism had to be collisional, a conclusion supported observationally by the identification of emission in the main UV multiplets from the low lying terms. Current models include a huge number of lines. Grandi (1983b), using 8400 lines, found that, for traditional BLR densities, the predicted $\lambda\lambda$2240-2650 feature was dominated by peaks at a few strong lines much more than the observations show. Netzer and Wills (1983) showed that fluorescence among various overlapping ultraviolet lines largely cures this problem by enhancing the intensities of many weak lines and in particular by pumping levels at $\sim$ 8 eV. All calculations agree that the optical to ultraviolet ratio increases with increasing optical depth, and that observed values correspond to cloud optical depths $\gtrsim 10^5$ in the Lyman continuum.

The physical processes incorporated in recent models certainly make them more realistic and improve agreement with observation. But is the agreement really good? The old problem with N V and O VI remains. Kwan (1984) illustrates the variation of a number of line intensities as a function of model parameters, including ionization parameter. C IV, N V, and O VI all increase relative to Lyα with increasing U. The observed values of C IV/Lyα and C III]/C IV favor U $\lesssim$ 0.01, whereas O VI/Lα and N V/Lα favor U $\gtrsim$ 0.03.

The new models are largely aimed at explaining the hydrogen line ratios. How well do they succeed? For models with large Lyman continuum optical depths Kwan (1984) finds Lα/Hβ $\approx$ 6 to 14. This is much less than the recombination value of ~35, and it is close to the mean observed value Lα/Hβ = 7 adopted by Netzer (1985). Thus, the models do succeed in solving the "Lα/Hβ" problem. (If broad line regions turn out to be heavily reddened, the models may have gone too far!)

What about the other hydrogen line ratios? Collin-Souffrin *et al.* (1982) compute models of photoionized hydrogen slabs and compare various escape probability formulations. The use of an escape probability formula due to Ivanov (1973), together with allowance for escape of line photons from both sides of a finite slab, gives good agreement with an "exact numerical method." For optically thick clouds with standard parameters, Collin-Souffrin *et al.* (1982) find Hα/Hβ $\gtrsim$ 10, whereas values of ~ 3 to 4 are typically observed. These authors find that densities N $\approx 10^{11}$ cm^{-3} give small enough Hα/Hβ ratios. They propose a two component model in which the Balmer lines, Balmer continuum, and Fe II lines come from a dense region (not heated by photoionization in their model), and the higher ionization lines and Lyα come from a photoionized zone with conventional parameters. Other modern calculations tend to support the idea that photoionization models with conventional parameters predict steep Balmer decrements. For example, models with $N_e \approx 10^9$ cm^3 by Netzer and Ferland (1984) and Wills, Netzer, and Wills (1985, hereinafter referred to as WNW) give Hα/Hβ $\approx$ 6 to 8, whereas the latter reference gives higher density models with Hα/Hβ $\approx$ 3 to 4.

The models of Kwan and Krolik (1981) for high column densities and N $\gtrsim 10^{9.6}$ cm^{-3} give Hα/Hβ $\lesssim 4$. However, Collin-Souffrin *et al.* (1982) and Hubbard and Puetter (1985) have criticized the escape probabilities used by Kwan and Krolik; and Netzer (1985) claims that Kwan and Krolik's continuum gives an X-ray to ultraviolet flux ratio 10 times larger than is typically observed. Kwan's (1984) results (which use the same continuum) indicate that Hα/Hβ is dependent mainly on Φ_H, with Hα/Hβ $<$ 4 corresponding to $\Phi_H > 10^{18.4}$ cm^{-2} s^{-1}, somewhat larger than the "standard" value.

Measurements have been presented by Lacy *et al.* (1982) of the Pα/Hα/Hβ/Lα ratios for a number of AGN, mostly broad line objects. For the well measured objects, the Pα/Hα ratio varies from 0.04 to 0.3, and Hα/Hβ from 2.7 to 6. A majority of objects fall near Pα/Hα = 0.10, Hα/Hβ = 2.8 (the case B recombination value) or along the reddening vector from this point. However, the observed Lyα intensities are too weak for a simple recombination plus reddening picture. There appears to be another group of objects falling near the line Pα/Hβ = 0.28 (again near the case B value). This could be explained if Pα and Hβ are optically thin, or more generally if they have equal escape probabilities; but what causes the range in Hα/Hβ among these objects? The photoionization models by WNW and Kwan (1984) give Pα/Hα close to 0.10, with extreme parameters giving a range $\sim$ 0.05 to 0.13. The observed range is wider, especially in the direction of large Pα/Hα. Kwan's results show Pα/Hα and Hα/Hβ increasing together as Φ_H decreases, with a slope similar to reddening; but the high optical depth models fall well to the high Hα/Hβ side of the reddening line where most observed objects are found. WNW's results indicate that Pα/Hα decreases from 0.12 as N increases above 10^{10} cm^{-3}. Thus, the models have difficulty accounting for the larger Pα/Hα values observed as well as the combined Pα/Hα/Hβ values of most objects.

The nature of the $\lambda3000$ "bump" has been an intriguing question. The Workshop saw the emergence of the terms "little bump" and "big bump" to distinguish between the excess in the $\lambda\lambda 2000$-4000 region and the much broader excess continuum discussed by Malkan at the Workshop as possibly being thermal continuum from an accretion disk. The suspicion that the little bump is a combination of Balmer continuum and Fe II emission has gradually been reinforced. Gaskell (1981) illustrated the way in which a power law, Balmer continuum, and Fe II might account for the $\lambda\lambda 2000$ to 4000 region of a composite QSO spectrum. Puetter and Levan (1982) showed that large Balmer continuum optical depths, a plausible possibility, would modify the shape of the Bac in a way that might improve agreement with observation. The current state-of-the-art is the work by WNW, discussed at the Workshop. These authors computed photoionization models to give the intensities of the lines, and the Balmer continuum. Detailed calculations of the Fe II spectrum from a slab representing the partially ionized zone, were calculated including 3400 lines and line-line fluorescence. A power-law continuum was subtracted from the observed spectrum of several QSOs, and the remaining emission, consisting of lines and the "little bump," was compared to the theoretical spectrum artificially Doppler broadened to agree with the observed line widths. Figure 1 indicates the success of this approach for quasar 0742+318. Although not perfect, the model accounts quite well for the overall shape of the little bump, and some of its details. This supports the idea that the little bump is primarily a blend of Fe II and Bac. However, the total energy observed in the Balmer continuum and Fe II is larger than the models predict. WNW find values of Fe II(total)/Lyα in the range ~ 1 to 2 and Bac/H$\beta \approx 5$ to 10. WNW's standard models predict Fe II/Ly$\alpha = 0.2$ and Bac/H$\beta \approx 2$ to 3 for a solar iron abundance. Kwan's (1984) results indicate that Bac/Hβ is as strong as observed for $N \gtrsim 10^{9.5}$ cm^{-3} (the "standard" density), but this may be due to the large X-ray luminosity assumed. Kwan's results underpredict the Fe II/Mg II by a factor $\gtrsim 5$ even for high Φ_H. Collin-Souffrin *et al.* (1980) and Joly (1981) have argued that the Fe II emission requires a dense ($N_e \approx 10^{11}$ cm^{-3}) region heated by something other than photoionization. Although the work of WNW improves the success of photoionization in explaining the relative Fe II line ratios, it leaves room for an additional dense region of emission in Fe II and H I. The possiblity of two distinct broad line emitting regions is supported by the discovery that the low ionization lines are systemically redshifted with respect to the high ionization lines and Lyα, by about 800 km s^{-1} (Gaskell 1982; Wilkes and Carswell 1982; Wilkes 1984). If there is a separate region emitting strong Fe II and Balmer lines with a flat decrement, the relative weakness of this zone in broad line radio galaxies could explain the observation that these objects have weaker Fe II and steeper Balmer decrements than Seyfert 1 galaxies (Osterbrock 1977).

Higher densities than the standard $10^{9.5}$ cm^{-3} would improve the agreement of photoionization models with theory in several ways, including the Balmer decrement, the Bac/Hβ ratio and possibly the Fe II emission. The argument against high densities has been that C III] would be too weak. Hubbard and Peutter (1983) suggested that if C III] is optically thick and thermalized, then its intensity will be fairly constant relative to the intensities of other thermalized permitted lines. Kwan (1984) has examined this argument and found that in photoionization models with reasonable values of U, the optical depth in C III] is small. He concludes that the observed C III] intensity, relative to C IV, N IV] λ1486, O IV] λ1402 + Si IV λ1397, and O III] λ1663, precludes significant emission from gas with N > $10^{10.5}$ cm $^{-3}$. Gaskell suggested at the Workshop that objects with unusually large values of Si III] λ1892/C III] may reflect collisional suppression of C III] at electron densities N$_e$ > 10^{10} cm^{-3}.

Figure 1: The quasar 0742+318. The upper panel gives observed flux (ergs s^{-1} cm^{-2} $Å^{-1}$) as a function of rest wavelength, after correction for Galactic extinction. The power-law used in the modeling is shown. The second panel shows the same spectrum with the power law subtracted and a synthetic broad line spectrum superposed. The hydrogen Balmer lines, C III] $\lambda1909$ and Mg II $\lambda2798$ lines are indicated as are the regions of the spectrum that have been corrected for the atmospheric A and B bands. Narrow lines of [Ne V] $\lambda\lambda$ 3346, 3426, [O II] $\lambda3727$, [Ne III] $\lambda\lambda3869$, 3968, [S II] $\lambda\lambda4069$, 4076, [O III] $\lambda4363$, $\lambda\lambda4959$, 5007 and narrow Balmer lines are often present but not included in the models. The third and fourth panels show, on the same scale as the second panel, the components of the synthetic broad line spectra for Fe II, and for all other broad lines plus the Balmer continuum, respectively. Figure courtesy of B. J. Wills.

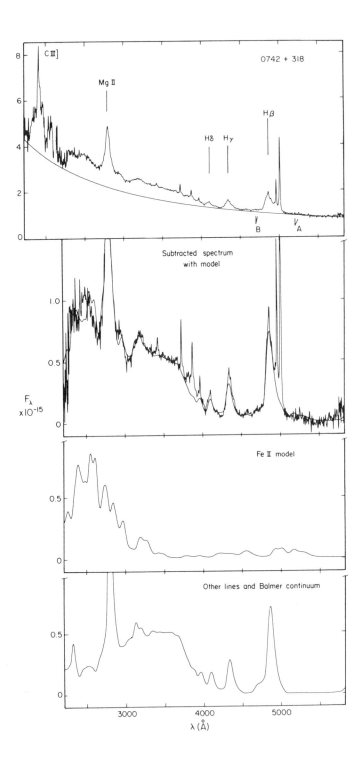

Yet another indication of nonstandard BLR parameters was discussed at the Workshop. Monitoring of Akn 120 by Peterson *et al.* (1985) shows rapid changes in the broad line fluxes, and any timelag behind the continuum variations appears to be less than 1 month. (The chapter by Osterbrock discusses this and other recent observations.) If much of the BLR lies within 1 light month of the continuum source, then $\Phi_H \gtrsim 10^{20}$ cm^{-2} s^{-1}, much larger than the "standard" value $\sim 10^{18}$ cm^{-2} s^{-1}. If the ionization parameter has the "standard" value, U $\approx$ 0.01 to 0.03, then the density is N $\gtrsim 10^{11.5}$ cm^{-3}.

In contrast to the indications of high densities in BLR gas, there was extensive discussion of broad forbidden lines in the spectra of AGN. Typically, forbidden lines have widths of $\lesssim$ 500 km s^{-1}, and are dominated by the [O III] λ5007, 4959 lines. It is difficult to search for broad forbidden lines because of the superimposed strong narrow components, as well as the pervasive Fe II emission which occurs in the 5000 A region. Two studies were discussed at the Workshop, by K. Meyers and E. Van Gröningen, each arriving at the same conclusion; careful subtraction of the sharp component, and removal of the Fe II blends, suggests that strong, broad [O III] emission is present. In some cases, the intensity of the claimed broad [O III] lines can amount to as much as 30% of the broad Hβ. These observations present serious challenges to models. The gas producing the [O III] emission presumably has a density not greatly above the critical density for the upper state, N $\lesssim 10^7$ cm^{-3}. The width of the broad [O III] component (poorly defined, but 50 to 100% of the Balmer line widths) suggests that this emission is related to the BLR. How can gas with such a low density have a significant amount of doubly ionized oxygen if it is located as near to the continuum source as is usually assumed for the BLR? If the broad line widths reflect outflow, perhaps the simplest explanation is that the broad [O III] comes from BLR gas that has coasted relatively far from the nucleus, where the ambient pressure is less.

If there are substantial variations, among or within objects, in the conditions of the BLR, this should be reflected in the line intensities and profiles. Kwan (1984) illustrates a number of line ratios that depend on the ionizing flux incident on a photoionized cloud. The ratios Hβ/Hα, O I/Lyα, He I/Hβ, C IV/Mg II, and Fe II/Mg II all increase with Φ_H. Kwan cites several observations in which line ratios vary with continuum changes in the predicted manner, including the Hα/Hβ/He I intensities in NGC 4151 (Antonucci and Cohen 1983). If Akn 120 really has $\Phi_H \gtrsim 10^{20}$ cm^{-2} s^{-1} (see above), then Kwan's results predict He I $\lambda5876$/Hβ $\gtrsim 0.8$. Unpublished spectra by B. J. Wills (personal communication) indicate that He I/H$\beta \approx 0.2$, which is indeed larger than the typical value ~0.1 but not as extreme as the foregoing prediction. Do the several AGN with He I/H$\beta \sim 0.2$ show other evidence of high values of Φ_H?

The dependence of line ratios on Φ_H may be a useful tool to investigate the broad line region's velocity field. In a given object, Φ_H varies as R^{-2}. If the cloud motions are Keplerian, then the high velocity material, which emits the line wings, should have line ratios characteristic of high Φ_H. This implies, for example, that He I should be broader than Hβ, as is often observed (Netzer 1978; Shuder 1982). Shuder finds that Hβ is broader than Hα in Seyfert galaxies, implying that the ratio of Hβ to Hα increases with increasing velocity in the line profile. Also, Wilkes (1984) has found that O I $\lambda1304$ is narrower than Lyα, although the meaning of this is clouded by the redshift of O I relative to Lyα. These line-width differences are consistent with Keplerian velocities but cannot be taken as proof.

The subject of profile differences among lines in a given object illustrates an important future direction for theoretical studies of AGN emission lines. The Workshop saw many examples of sensitive, high resolution observational studies that focus attention on the profile differences rather than on their rough similarity. Although problems remain in explaining the integrated line intensities, future models will have to confront the problem of explaining both the intensities and profiles in the context of a

dynamical theory of what determines the velocities and densities
of clouds as a function of radius in an active galactic nucleus.

Netzer raised serious questions at the Workshop concerning the overall energy budget of the emission-line region (Netzer
1985; see also MacAlpine *et al.* 1985 and references therein). In
his mean observed spectrum, the total line emission and Balmer
continuum is 8 times the Lyα flux. General considerations imply that this requires an ultraviolet spectral index $\alpha < 0.4$, where
$F_\nu \propto \nu^{-\alpha}$. In contrast, values $\alpha \geq 0.5$ are consistent with many
observations (e.g. WNW; Oke, Shields, and Korycansky 1984).
Reddening of the BLR alone improves this situation by reducing the total line energy relative to Lyα, while reddening of the
continuum also helps by allowing the intrinsic ultraviolet slope to
be flatter. The energy budget problem might be helped by γ-
ray heating at column depths $\sim 10^{24}$ cm^{-2}, which produces strong
Bac and presumably Fe II (Oke *et al.* 1984). However, the large
Bac optical depth in this model leads to a Paschen continuum to
Balmer continuum ratio larger than may be allowed by the observations. Moreover, Netzer (personal communication) argues that
γ-ray to ultraviolet ratios of AGN must in general be smaller than
assumed in Oke *et al.*'s calculation be consistent with the cosmic
background.

The presence of dust within the BLR clouds themselves
is questionable. Gaskell, Shields, and Wampler (1981) noted that
the intensities of Mg, Si, and Fe emission preclude the order-
of-magnitude depletions of refractory elements typically observed
where dust is present in the interstellar medium. They also argue
that if grains do not evaporate quickly, radiation pressure would
expel grains from BLR clouds; and grains could not survive in a
10^8 K confining medium. Rudy and Puetter (1982) have considered the temperature of grains in BLR clouds, including heating
by trapped line radiation.

Related to the energy budget problem is the issue of the
covering factor. The small number of QSOs with an observed

cutoff at the Lyman limit suggests that the BLR intercepts only a small fraction of the solid angle around the continuum source, $\Omega/4\pi \approx 10^{-1}$ (Davidson and Netzer 1979). If slopes as flat as $\alpha \approx 0.5$ (e.g. Oke *et al.* 1984; WNW) continue into the ionizing ultraviolet, then the equivalent widths of the hydrogen lines indicate small covering factors. On the other hand, the incidence of X-ray absorption by "cold" gas with BLR column densities in Seyfert 1 galaxies has led to the suggestion that the covering factor increases with decreasing luminosity (Lawrence and Elvis 1982), and may be close to unity in NGC 4151 (Holt *et al.* 1980). WNW argue that the ratio of the Bac to the underlying power-law continuum is a good measure of the covering factor; and values $\Omega/4\pi \approx 0.25$ are typical, including for NGC 4151.

The covering factor has been considered as a possible factor in the so-called "Baldwin effect," which describes the tendency for the equivalent width of C IV to decrease with increasing continuum luminosity (Baldwin 1977b; Wampler *et al.* 1984). Mushotzky and Ferland (1984) have interpreted this in terms of a decrease in the ionization parameter, $U \propto L^{-0.25}$. This is derived on the basis of the observed locations of AGN on a plot of C IV/Lα versus C III]/C IV, but it leads to an explanation of why the Baldwin effect is seen in the equivalent width of C IV but not in the equivalent widths of the hydrogen lines (Yee 1980; Shuder 1982). For lower luminosity Seyferts, a variation of covering factor, $\Omega/4\pi \propto L^{-0.2}$, is still required. Variations of N, U, and $\Omega/4\pi$ with luminosity would provide important clues to the origin of the broad line gas. Regarding the possible role of dust in the Baldwin effect, see Shuder and MacAlpine (1979).

Concerning the chemical abundances, little can be said beyond Davidson and Netzer's (1979) assessment that the CNO ratios are roughly solar and that C/H is neither depleted by an order of magnitude nor strongly enhanced. Kwan (1984) predicts N V/O VI = 0.3 for U = 0.06, whereas Netzer's (1984) mean observed value is 0.8. If N and U can indeed be determined from the C IV/Lα - C III]/C IV plane, this will facilitate the use of the N III], N IV], O III] and O IV] intensities to determine the CNO abundance ratios (Shields 1976). Uomoto (1984) finds roughly solar C:N:O ratios in 6 quasars except for indications of C/N enhancements of ~0.6 dex in some objects. The N/O and N/C ratios appear to be larger in NGC 1068 than in NGC 4151 (Shields and Mushotzky 1979). The lack of refractory element depletions has been noted above. WNW note that the underprediction of Fe II/Lyα could be ameliorated by increasing the iron abundance above solar; however, there is no support for this in the [Fe VII]/[Ne V] ratio observed in narrow line regions (Nussbaumer and Osterbrock 1970).

III. THE NARROW LINE REGION

Most broad line objects (QSOs, broad line radio galaxies, and Seyfert 1 galaxies) have a narrow emission-line component in their spectra. Seyfert 2 galaxies, by definition, have only the narrow lines. The classical narrow line spectrum has permitted and forbidden lines representing a wide range of ionization potentials (Seyfert 1943). The fact that the NLR typically shows an even wider range of ionization than planetary nebulae, from the presence of [Fe X] to strong [O I], can be accounted for in terms of photoionization by a power-law continuum together with the placement of some gas relatively close to the continuum source. Nevertheless, the theory of the NLR has witnessed a long-running debate over the importance of photoionization relative to heating by shock waves. This debate was fueled by the fact that the [O III] line ratio, $R = I(\lambda\lambda5007,4959)/I(\lambda4363)$ often is much lower than the value predicted for low density gas ($N_e \lesssim 10^5$ cm^{-3}) at the temperatures ~12,000 K given by photoionization models. If interpreted in terms of a high temperature, low values of R suggest shock heating. Recent observations have undermined this argument for shock heating. The fact that a range of densities is present in the NLR has long been known. Recent, high resolution spectrophotometry of the narrow line profiles indicates that, in some objects, the width of the forbidden lines is larger for lines with higher critical densities for collisional deexcitation (e.g., Filippenko and Halpern 1984). This implies an increase in gas velocity with increasing density, and it shows that collisional deexcitation can be responsible for low values of R in the NLR. However, some studies, such as by De Robertis and Osterbrock (1984) and Pelat, Alloin, and Fosbury (1981), relate the narrow line widths to ionization potential rather than critical density. Pequignot (1984) has made a detailed photoionization model analysis of the narrow emission-line spectrum of NGC 1052, and concluded that it can be explained by photoionization if a range of densities from $< 10^3$ to $\geq 10^7$ cm^{-3} is present.

Photoionization models are fairly successful in explaining the strong lines of the NLR in terms of photoionization by a nonthermal continuum and gas with characteristic densities $\sim 10^3$-10^4 cm^{-3} distances up to ~ 100 pc from the nucleus, consistent with observed angular sizes in nearby cases. Ferland and Netzer (1983) and Halpern and Steiner (1983) find that NLRs of Seyfert galaxies and low ionization nuclear emission regions (LINERs) can be explained by photoionization with an ionization parameter that decreases from Seyferts to LINERs (see also Rose and Searle 1981). Ferland and Netzer find that an underabundance of heavy elements, [O/H] ≈ -0.5, is required to fit the strong line ratios; but Pequignot (1984) finds that a range of densities in the NLR can mimic the effect of a deficiency of oxygen. Pequignot does find a strong depletion of gas phase magnesium, in NGC 1052, in contrast to the nondepletion of iron previously found in NLRs (Nussbaumer and Osterbrock 1970; Shields and Oke 1975).

The last several years have seen a flurry of activity on the reddening of the NLR, in which theory has played a significant role. X-rays in the ionizing continuum can lead to an equilibrium temperature around the H$^+$ to H$^\circ$ transition zone high enough that collisional excitation from the ground state increases

Lyα and Hα significantly with respect to Hβ (Halpern 1982; Netzer 1982; Halpern and Steiner 1983). The effect is enhanced if
the temperature is raised by a high density or a low abundance
of heavy elements. Gaskell and Ferland (1984) emphasize that
collisional excitation and reddening give nearly orthogonal trajectories on the Lyα/Hβ, Hα/Hβ plane. Analysis of a number
of Seyferts suggests that most NLRs have a reddening corrected
values Hα/Hβ $\approx$ 3.1 (Gaskell 1982, 1983; Malkan 1983), slightly
steeper than the Case B recombination value Hα/Hβ = 2.8. The
Balmer lines are optically thin in the NLR, and the Pα/Hβ ratio
is close to the case B value. Gaskell and Ferland (1984) suggest
that the narrow hydrogen lines are well understood, but their own
models give Hα/Hβ = 3.1 only for low metal abundances or high
densities.

The physics of line emission in the NLR may be less complicated than for the BLR, but the observations point to a complex
nature of this region with a range of densities, velocities and radii
contributing. This is underscored by the tendency of the higher
ionization lines to be blueshifted relative to the lower ionization
forbidden lines (e.g., Koski 1977; Pelat, Alloin, and Fosbury 1981).

IV. THE FUTURE OF PHOTOIONIZATION MODELS

Just as photoionization calculations themselves have ma-
tured over the past decades, the observational demands placed on
them have expanded also. It seems possible that the main physical processes have been identified, and that future progress in the
calculation of a specific model will occur because of advances in
atomic physics, as well as studies of formation of particular lines.
Netzer and Ferland (1984) conclude that the different photoionization codes now running are reasonably consistent and that the
predicted intensities of the strong lines (i.e., Lα and C IV) in single
component models have changed modestly over the past 15 years.

Modelling in the past decade has considered mainly the
integrated intensities of individual lines. This was inspired by

practical considerations (simplicity) as well as by the fact that observations suggested that emission lines all had similar profiles. Clearly, the era of the single component model is over; observations now show that a wide range of densities and ionization parameters contribute to the net spectrum, and that contributions from gas at various radii must produce the various line profiles.

The direction that future modelling must take is to try to describe the full global picture, including line profiles, line polarization, etc. Physical theories are needed to help restrict the continuous range of model parameters. In the near future, efforts are likely to follow along the lines of McCray (1979) and Krolik, McKee, and Tarter (1981), in whose view BLR clouds are in pressure equilibrium with a Compton heated intercloud medium. Ferland discussed work that suggests an understanding of the properties of BLR clouds in terms of the two-phase models with the additional consideration of stability against disruption by radiation pressure (Ferland and Elitzur 1984). By determining the run of intercloud medium pressure with radius, it is possible to specify the BLR cloud pressure, and constrain the possible ensembles of BLR clouds available to compare with observations. An attempt to understand the narrow line profiles in such a manner has been made by Krolik and Vrtilek (1984). Broad line region models along these lines were described by Kwan in the Workshop, involving clouds falling on parabolic orbits around the continuum source. This work makes predictions of emission-line profiles in addition to total intensities.

The authors express their gratitude to Lick Observatory and the University of California, Santa Cruz for their hospitality during the summer of 1984. We have benefited from helpful discussions with many colleagues. Special thanks are due to M. Gaskell, H. Netzer, B. Wills, and D. Wills for discussions and comments on the manuscript. This material is based in part on work supported by NSF grants AST 83-05094 and AST 83-14962 and NASA grant NSG 7232. This chapter is intended to outline some of the theoretical highlights of the Workshop and to illustrate the developments in the field in recent years. We have not attempted an exhaustive review of the published literature, and we apologize to the authors of the many excellent papers that we have neglected to mention.

REFERENCES

Aggarwall, K. M. 1984, *M.N.R.A.S.*, **202**, 15P.

Antonucci, R. R. J., and Cohen, R. D. 1983, *Ap. J.*, **271**, 564.

Bahcall, J. N. and Kozlovsky, B. 1969, *Ap. J.*, **155**, 1077.

Baldwin, J. A. 1977a, *M.N.R.A.S.*, **178**, 67P.

Baldwin, J. A. 1977b, *Ap. J.*, **214**, 679.

Butler, S., Heil, T. G., and Dalgarno, A. 1980, *Ap. J.*, **241**, 442.

Canfield, R. C. and Peutter, R. C. 1980, *Ap. J. (Letters)*, **236**, L7.

Collin-Souffrin, S., Dumont, S., Heidmann, N., and Joly, M. 1980, *Astr. Ap.*, **83**, 190.

Collin-Souffrin, S., Delache, Ph., Dumont, S., Frisch, H. 1981, *Astr. Ap.*, **104**, 264.

Collin-Souffrin, S., Dumont, S., and Tully, J. 1982, *Astr. Ap.*, **106**, 362.

Davidson, A. F., Hartig, G. F., and Fastie, W. G. 1977, *Nature*, **269**, 203.

Davidson, K. 1972, *Ap. J.*, **171**, 213.

_____ . 1975, *Ap. J.*, **195**, 285.

_____ . 1977, *Ap. J.*, **218**, 20.

Davidson, K., and Netzer, H. 1979, *Rev. Mod. Phys.*, **51**, 715.

De Robertis, M. M., and Osterbrock, D. E. 1984, *Ap. J.*, **286**, 171.

Drake, S. A., and Ulrich, R. K. 1980, *Ap. J. Suppl.*, **42**, 177.

Elitzur, M. 1984, *Ap. J.*, **280**, 653.

Ferland, G. J., and Elitzur, M. 1984, *Ap. J.*, **285**, L11.

Ferland, G. J., and Mushotzky, R. F. 1984, *Ap. J.*, **286**, 42.

Ferland, G. J., and Netzer, H. 1983, *Ap. J.*, **264**, 105.

Ferland, G. J., and Osterbrock, D. E. 1985, *Ap. J.*, **290**, in press.

Filippenko, A. V., and Halpern, J. P. 1984, *Ap. J.*, **285**, 485.

Gaskell, C. M. 1981, Ph.D. Thesis, University of California, Santa Cruz.

_____. 1982, *Ap. J.*, **263**, 79.

_____. 1982, *Pub. A. S. P.* **94**, 891.

_____. 1983, *Ap. Letters*, **24**, 43.

Gaskell, C. M., and Ferland, G. J. 1984, *Pub. A. S. P.* **96**, 393.

Gaskell, C. M., Shields, G. A., and Wampler, E. J. 1981, *Ap. J.*, **249**, 443.

Grandi, S. A. 1983a, *Ap. J.*, **268**, 591.

_____. 1983b, *Liege Ap. Colloq.* **24**, p. 453.

Halpern, J. P. 1982, Ph.D. Thesis, Harvard University.

Halpern, J. P., and Steiner, J. E. 1983, Ap. J. (Letters), **269**, L37.

Holt, S. S., Mushotzky, R. F., Becker, R. H., Boldt, E. A., Serlemitsos, P. J., Szymkowiak, A. E., and White, N.E. 1980, *Ap. J.*, **241**, L13.

Hubbard, E. N., and Puetter, R. F. 1983, *Ap. J.*, **265**, 35.

Hubbard, E. N., and Puetter, R. C. 1985, *Ap. J.*, **290**, in press.

Ivanov, V. V. 1973, "Transfer of Radiation in Spectral Lines," NBS SP-285, U. S. Dept. of Commerce, Washington, D. C., translated by D. G. Hummer and E. Woppner.

Joly, M. 1981, *Astr. Ap.*, **102**, 321.

Kallman, T. R. 1984, *Ap. J.*, **280**, 269.

Kallman, T. R., and McCray, R. 1982, *Ap. J. Suppl.*, **50**, 263.

Koski, A. T. 1977, *Ap. J.*, **223**, 56.

Krolik, J. H., and McKee, C. F. 1978, *Ap. J. Suppl.*, **37**, 459.

Krolik, J. H., and Vrtilek, J. M. 1984, *Ap. J.*, **279**, 521.

Krolik, J. H. McKee, C. F., and Tarter, C. B. 1981, *Ap. J.*, **249**, 422.

Kwan, J. 1984, *Ap. J.*, **283**, 70.

Kwan, J., and Krolik, J. H. 1979, *Ap. J. (Letters)*, **233**, L91.

_____. 1981, *Ap. J.*, **250**, 478.

Lacy, J. H. *et al.* 1982, *Ap. J.*, **256**, 75.

Lawrence, L., and Elvis, M. 1982, *Ap. J.*, **256**, 410.

MacAlpine, G. M. 1972, *Ap. J.*, **175**, 11.

_____. 1974, *Ap. J.*, **193**, 37.

_____. 1976, *Ap. J.*, **204**, 694.

_____. 1981, *Ap. J.*, **251**, 465.

MacCray, R. A. 1979, in *Active Galactic Nuclei,* ed. C. R. Hazard, and S. Mitton (Cambridge: Cambridge University Press).

Malkan, M. A. 1983, *Ap. J. (Letters)*, **264**, L1.

Mathews, W. G., Blumenthal, G. R., and Grandi, S. A. 1980, *Ap. J.*, **235**, 977.

Mendoza, C. 1983, in *Planetary Nebulae, I.A.U. Symposium No. 103,* D. R. Flower, ed. (Dordrecht: Reidel), p. 143.

Mushotzky, R. and Ferland, G. J. 1984, *Ap. J.*, **278**, 558.

Netzer, H. 1975, *M.N.R.A.S.*, **171**, 395.

_____. 1976, *M.N.R.A.S.*, **177**, 473.

_____. 1978, *Ap. J.*, **19**, 822.

_____. 1980, *Ap. J.*, **236**, 406.

_____. 1982, *M.N.R.A.S.*, **198**, 589.

_____. 1985, preprint.

Netzer, H., and Ferland, G. J. 1984, Pub. A.S.P. **96**, 593.

Netzer, H., and Wills, B. J. 1983, *Ap. J.*, **275**, 445.

Nussbaumer, H., and Osterbrock, D. E. 1970, *Ap. J.*, **161**, 811.

Nussbaumer, H., and Storey, P. J. 1985, *Astr. Ap. Suppl.*, in press.

Oke, J. B., Shields, G. A., and Korycansky, D. G. 1984, *Ap. J.*, **277**, 64.

Osterbrock, D. E. 1974, *Astrophysics of Gaseous Nebulae*, (San Francisco: W. H. Freeman and Co.).

Osterbrock, D. E. 1977, *Ap. J.*, **215**, 733.

Pelat, D., Alloin, D., and Fosbury, R. A. E. 1981, *M.N.R.A.S.*, **195**, 787.

Pequignot, D. 1984, *Astr. Ap.*, **131**, 159.

Peterson, B. M., Meyers, K. A., Capriotti, E. R., Foltz, C. B., Wilkes, B. J., and Killer, H. R. 1985, preprint.

Phillips, M. M. 1977, *Ap. J.*, **215**, 746.

_____. 1978, *Ap. J.*, **226**, 736.

Puetter, R. C., and Levan, P. D. 1982, *Ap. J.*, **260**, 44.

Rose, J. A., and Searle, L. 1981, *Ap. J.*, **253**, 556.

Rudy, R. J., and Puetter, R. C. 1982, *Ap. J.*, **263**, 43.

Searle, L., and Sargent, W. L. W. 1968, *Ap. J.*, **153**, 1003.

Seyfert, C. 1943, *Ap. J.*, **97**, 28.

Shields, G. A. 1974, *Ap. J.*, **191**, 309.

_____. 1976, *Ap. J.*, **204**, 330.

Shields, G. A., and Mushotzky, R. F. 1979, *Astr. Ap.*, **79**, 56.

Shields, G. A. and Oke, J. B. 1975, *Ap. J.*, **197**, 5.

Shuder, J. M. 1982, *Ap. J.*, **259**, 48.

Shuder, J. M., and MacAlpine, G. M. 1979, *Ap. J.*, **230**, 348.

Storey, P. J. 1981, *M.N.R.A.S.*, **195**, 27P.

Uomoto, A. 1984, *Ap. J.*, **284**, 297.

Wampler, E. J., Gaskell, C. M., Burke, W. L., and Baldwin, J. A. 1984, *Ap. J.*, **276**, 403.

Weisheit, J. C., Shields, G. A., and Tarter, C. B. 1981, *Ap. J.*, **245**, 406.

Wilkes, B. J. 1984, *M.N.R.A.S.*, **207**, 73.

Wilkes, B. J. and Carswell, R. F. 1982, *M.N.R.A.S.*, **201**, 645.

Williams, R. E. 1967, *Ap. J.*, **147**, 556.

Wills, B. J., Netzer, H., and Wills, D. 1985, *Ap. J.*, **288**, ????

Yee, H. K. C. 1980, *Ap. J.*, **241**, 894.

Zirin, H. 1978, *Ap. J. (Letters)*, **222**, L105.

STRUCTURE AND DYNAMICS OF THE
BROAD LINE REGION

William G. Mathews

Lick Observatory, University of California, Santa Cruz

and

Eugene R. Capriotti

Perkins Observatory,

The Ohio State and Ohio Wesleyan Universities

Department of Astronomy, Ohio State University

ABSTRACT

Observational constraints on the density, temperature, and geometrical disposition of the broad line emitting gas are discussed. X-ray absorption and fluorescence observations suggest an approximately spherical arrangement of emitting elements or clouds surrounding a small central source of hard photons. Dynamical theories of the motion of the emitting regions are limited by the quality of observed line profiles, both in the paucity of high signal-to-noise observations and the natural limitations due to line blending and variability.

The dynamics and stability of radial cloud motion in the broad line region are discussed, with an emphasis on the importance of drag and radiation forces. The acceleration of optically thin and optically thick clouds depends on different physical parameters so their line profiles might be expected to differ. This effect may be responsible for some of the variety observed among line profiles in individual Seyferts and some quasars.

Clouds orbiting in a gravitational potential require enormous masses to account for the broad line widths in quasars, larger than those indicated by an galactic stellar velocity dispersion observed so far. In addition, differential Poynting-Robertson shear on orbiting clouds rapidly reduces their optical depths. Central depressions in emission line profiles expected from line-emitting gaseous disks or disks of clouds are not generally observed. However, logarithmic emission line profiles similar to those observed can be produced by radially-moving clouds in a variety of circumstances.

Time variability of emission lines may ultimately reveal the spatial and velocity structure of the broad line region, but Seyferts with rapid, high amplitude variability – such as NGC 4151 – may never obtain a dynamical steady state typical of the vast majority of objects.

Finally, we present a brief review of several models of the broad line region presented at the workshop.

I. INTRODUCTION

While our primary goal in this review is to report on new theoretical and observational results presented at the workshop that bear directly on the geometrical and dynamical nature of the broad line region, it seemed that a more general review of broad line dynamics would provide a useful frame of reference and background for consideration of the workshop results. In this review we emphasize the cloud model for the broad line region, first providing the standard rationale for cloud geometry, then reviewing the issues of cloud confinement and the various forces which may act on the clouds due to drag, gravity, and radiation. The physical attributes and consequences of radial and orbital motion of these clouds are discussed as well as that of line emitting accretion disks. Although this provides a useful framework for discussing the workshop results, it does also quite frankly reflect the authors' current inclinations and preferences. Our review is therefore not comprehensive and many interesting areas of discussion – acceleration of clouds with cosmic rays, production of clouds with instabilities or radiation-driven shocks, gas dynamics of the intercloud medium and its relation to the accretion disk, etc. – are not considered. We hope that a more fervent observational and theoretical effort will be made in the near future to discriminate between these many quite different models of the broad line region.

II. GEOMETRY OF THE BROAD LINE REGION

The remarkable breadths of emission lines observed in quasars and Seyfert galaxies are usually regarded as arising from the collective motions of an ensemble of individual clouds which fill only a small fraction of the emitting volume surrounding the source of ionizing radiation. Some support for the cloud model has come from detailed photoionization models (Kwan and Krolik 1979, 1981; Clavel and Joly 1984) in which the emission line spectrum is calculated from finite slabs of gas irradiated by nonstellar radiation typical of quasars and active galaxies. The basic parameters of the photoionization calculation, the density n, the column density N, and the ionization parameter Γ, are varied until the best agreement with the mean emission line flux ratios is obtained. These calculations also require knowledge of the continuous spectrum which is still somewhat uncertain in the ultraviolet and at the highest X-ray energies. Reasonably good agreement is usually obtained with cosmic or nearly cosmic abundances. Radiation from lines of Lα, C III], and C IV arises from fully ionized gas at column densities less than the Stromgren column, $N_s = \Gamma c/\alpha$ where α is the effective recombination coefficient and $\Gamma = L_{ph}/4\pi R^2 nc$ is the ratio of the density of ionizing photons to the electron density in the clouds at a distance R from the source of ionizing radiation. Typically, $\Gamma \sim 10^{-2}$ is required to produce commonly observed C III]/C IV ratios, but Γ is also constrained by dynamical considerations. Small values of $\Gamma n^{-1/2}$ can result in plasma pressures which are dominated by resonance line radiation in $Ly\alpha$ and especially Mg II λ 2798 (Ferland and Elitzur 1984), a dynamically unstable condition in many situations. Clouds accelerated by photoionizing radiation having $\Gamma \gtrsim 0.24$ are unstable to radiation driven sound waves (Mathews 1976). At columns greater than N_s, photoionization models establish a partially ionized zone (PIZ) heated and ionized (to $\sim 10\%$) by hard UV and X-radiation.

The PIZ is required to produce emission in the Balmer lines and continuum, Mg II, and Fe II. The small $L\alpha/H\alpha$ ratios observed in QSOs and Seyferts can be understood as amplification of Balmer line emission by collisional excitation of optically thick hydrogen transitions in the PIZ requiring both high densities n $\sim 10^9$ - 10^{10} cm^{-3} and large columns $N_{PIZ} \sim 10N_s$. The general absence of strong broad forbidden line emission also indicates high densities; in order to reduce the flux in [O III]λ 4959,5007 to less than one percent of its low density value, densities must be greater than 10^8 cm^{-3}. An upper limit of $\sim 10^{10}$ cm^{-3} is required by the presence of the C III]λ 1909 line. For fixed density, the plasma temperature is a weakly increasing function of Γ, and $T \sim 10^4$ K is typical.

The finite column N_{PIZ} and physical size of the partially ionized zone in these calculations has been an argument for the existance of small emitting elements or clouds. In the calculation of Kwan and Krolik, for example, the C II]λ 2326 line which arises entirely from the PIZ exceeds its observed value relative to other lines unless the ionized slabs are truncated at $N \sim 10^{22}$. However, the strength of this line is affected by collisional de-excitation when $n \gtrsim 10^9$ cm^{-3} (Kwan 1984) and is also somewhat sensitive to the particular ionizing spectrum chosen by Kwan and Krolik, that of the bright quasar 3C273, which may not be typical of the majority of ionizing continua. Recently, Kwan(1984) has suggested that the ratio OI 1304/8446 and emission from certain multiplets of Fe II are more uniquely sensitive to the column depth. However, few of these lines or line ratios can be easily or unambiguously observed in many objects. Altogether, the argument for finite column densities, i.e. clouds, based on photoionization models needs further attention. In any case, the high electron densities $n \sim 10^9 - 10^{10}$, together with column densities $N \sim 10^{22} - 10^{23}$, which adequately account for the observed emission line spectra, suggest physical depths of $r = N/n \sim 10^{12}$ cm which, on the cloud hypothesis, is identified with the cloud radius. This dimension is very much smaller than the implied distance R of the emitting regions from the central source of radiation,

$R = (L_{ph}/\Gamma 4\pi n c)^{1/2} \sim 3 \times 10^{18} f_{sq} L_{46}^{1/2} \Gamma_{-2}^{-1/2} n_{10}^{-1/2}$ cm , based on observed ionizing photon luminosities $L_{ph} = L/\langle h\nu \rangle$ and values of n and Γ that fit the line spectrum best. The luminosity $L_{46} = L/(10^{46} \text{ ergs s}^{-1})$ is typical for quasars while Seyferts are generally ~ 100 times less luminous. The factor

$$f_{sq} = 1.0 \quad for \quad quasars;$$

$$f_{sq} = 0.1 \quad for \quad Seyferts,$$

can be regarded as an approximate scale factor to conveniently adjust numerical coefficients to Seyfert values. Since the size of the emitting elements $r \ll R$, the broad line emission is often regarded as the collective emission from a large number of small clouds that fill only a small fraction of the volume of the broad line region $4\pi R^3/3$. Observations of high redshift objects (e.g. Baldwin and Netzer 1978; Osmer 1979; Smith *et al.* 1981; Oke and Korycansky 1982) have not found absorption at the Lyman edge as might be produced by broad line clouds. These results are consistent with a quasar cloud covering factor of $\Omega \lesssim 0.1$ derived from photoionization models and the efficiency of $L\alpha$ emission.

The smoothness of observed emission line profiles can be used to establish a lower limit on the number of clouds required. Since the thermal width of the CIV line, for example, is ~ 4 km s^{-1}, at least 10^4 clouds are required to account for emission lines having widths $\sim 10^4$ km s^{-1} (Carswell *et al.* 1980; Capriotti *et al.* 1981; Richstone, Ratnatunga, and Schaeffer 1980). However, the number of clouds required to produce observed line fluxes is likely to be much greater than this. The observed mean $H\beta$ luminosities of Seyferts and QSOs, $L_{H\beta}$, are $10^8 L_\odot$ and $10^{10} L_\odot$ respectively. The observed flux in $H\beta$ requires a total illuminated surface of size

$$R_{H\beta} \sim (\alpha L_{H\beta}/4\pi c\Gamma n\epsilon_{H\beta} f_{H\beta})^{1/2}$$
$$\approx 5 \times 10^{17} (L_{H\beta 10}/\Gamma_{-2} n_{10} f_{sq})^{1/2} \ cm.$$

Here $\epsilon_{H\beta} = 1.25 \times 10^{-25}$ ergs cm^3 s^{-1} is the Case B emissivity in $H\beta$, $f_{H\beta} \approx 10$ is a correction for the enhancement of $H\beta$ emission by collisions and optical depth effects not included in the Case B assumptions, and $L_{H\beta 10} = L_{H\beta}/10^{10}L_\odot$. If this emission is shared equally by clouds of dimension $r \sim 10^{12}$, then $(R_{H\beta}/r)^2 \approx 10^{12}$ clouds are required. The remarkably small total mass of line-emitting gas can be estimated from the $H\beta$ flux:

$$M_g \approx \frac{L_{H\beta} M}{\epsilon_{H\beta} f_{H\beta} n} \approx 2.7 L_{H\beta 10} n_{10}^{-1} f_{sq}^{-2} \ M_\odot$$

where M is the proton mass. The ratio of the emitting volume to the total volume implied by the single cloud photoionization model is the filling factor

$$\epsilon \approx \frac{\pi R_{H\beta}^2 r_s}{(4\pi R^3/3)} \approx 10^{-9} (\Gamma_{-2}\langle h\nu \rangle)^{3/2} n_{10}^{-1/2} L_{H\beta 10} L_{46}^{-3/2} f_{sq}^{1/2},$$

where $\langle h\nu \rangle$ is the mean photon energy in Rydbergs, and $r_s = N_s/n$ is the physical Strömgren depth. Only a tiny fraction of the volume of the broad line region is filled with radiating gas, a result consistent with the cloud hypothesis.

Direct observational evidence for the cloud model is provided by intrinsic low energy X-ray absorption observed in active galaxies of low luminosity (Holt *et al.* 1980; Mushotzky 1982; Reichert *et al.* 1984). The range of observed column densities in Seyfert nuclei is $2 - 13 \times 10^{22}$ cm^{-2}, very similar to column densities required to account for the optical and UV line emission in photoionization models. The low energy X-radiation is, however, not entirely quenched in this absorption, indicating that the central source is only partially covered by the absorbing clouds. The lack of absorption in quasars or high luminosity Seyferts is evidently due to the larger size of the central radiation source in these objects while the size of the absorbing clouds may be similar in all objects (Carswell and Ferland 1980; Mushotsky 1984;

Reichert 1984). In a few cases, e.g. Barr *et al.* 1983), the X-ray absorption from Seyferts and broad line radio galaxies has varied on time scales of ~ 1 *yr*, suggesting sizes of the broad line region consistent with the photoionization estimates above.

In two bright active galaxies, Cen-A (Mushotzky *et al.* 1978) and NGC 4151 (Holt *et al.* 1980), the 7.1 keV Fe K-absorption edge and the associated 6.4 keV fluorescent line have been observed in addition to continuum absorption. In both cases, the strength of the observed emission relative to absorption requires an ensemble of clouds which is spherically or nearly spherically disposed around the central source of radiation. A flattened disklike distribution of clouds observed face-on would be seen only in emission while viewed edge-on would be primarily in absorption.

III. QUALITY OF OBSERVED EMISSION LINE PROFILES

Development of a successful dynamical theory for the broad line region depends critically on accurate observations of emission line profiles with high signal to noise ratios. Yet even when observations of high precision are available, the emission profiles are often polluted by other extraneous lines. For example, $H\beta$ is contaminated by broad Fe II emission (Osterbrock and Shuder 1982; De Robertis 1984), as well as $H\beta$ and [O III] from the narrow line region. Meyers and Peterson (1984) presented evidence at the workshop for further contamination of $H\beta$ by broad [O III]. Stellar absorption features may also produce irregularities in emission line profiles, particularly in nearby rather low luminosity Seyferts (Crenshaw and Peterson 1984). Contamination of CIII]λ1909 by Si III]λ1892, Al III λ1858, and Fe IIλ1860 has been widely discussed (Wills *et al.* 1980; Gaskell 1981).

In spite of some nearby Fe II emission, C IVλ1549 is relatively uncontaminated, but unresolved self-absorption features could conceivably produce asymmetries and irregularities in this line (Smith 1980) similar to those found in $H\beta$ in NGC 4151 (Anderson and Kraft 1969) which are known to vary in timescales

consistent with the size of the broad line region (Cromwell and
Weymann 1970). The IUE broad line profile data obtained by Wu
and his collaborators have been examined for self-absorption features by Capriotti and Peterson. Of roughly ten Seyferts, only one
(NGC 7469) shows an indication of (blueward) self absorption in
Mg IIλ2798. The visibility of such self-absorption features depends
on the geometrical size of the absorbing region compared to that
of the underlying continuum emitting region. If the absorbing regions along the line of sight are large compared to the background
illumination, then only a small fraction of emission lines would be
self absorbed, consistent with the small covering factor suggested
by Lyman edge observations of quasars. In the opposite limit,
when the projected solid angle of the absorbing regions is small
compared to the continuum source, self absorption should occur
at some level in all objects.

Finally, we note that line profile irregularities can also
be expected from excitation inhomogenieties arising from light
travel time effects in objects having variable continuum fluxes.
Provided the continuum variation timescales are comparable to
the light crossing time and greater than the recombination time in
the emitting plasma, detailed high precision observations of such
profile changes could in principle map out both the spatial and
velocity geometry of the broad line region (Blandford and McKee
1982; Capriotti *et al.* 1982).

IV. THE CLOUD MODEL

a) Cloud Confinement and Drag

Emission line clouds having dimensions comparable to the
physical depths of slabs required to produce a good approximation
to the observed line flux ratios, i. e., $r_{12} = r/10^{12}$ cm, cannot be
confined by self-gravity since the ratio of thermal to gravitational

energies greatly exceeds unity:

$$\frac{e_{th}}{e_{grav}} \approx \frac{3kT}{M}\frac{3r}{4\pi r^3 nGM} = 5.4 \times 10^8 T_4 r_{12}^{-2} n_{10}^{-1}.$$

In addition, the time required for sound to cross the cloud

$$t_{sc} = r/c_s = 0.025 r_{12} T_4^{-1/2} \quad yr$$

is much less than the time for the cloud to flow through the broad line region:

$$t_{fl} = R/u = 32 R_{18} f_{sq}/u_9 \quad yr.$$

Therefore, unless clouds are being produced at prodigious rates, for which the extremely large mass flux through the broad line system would be difficult to understand (see below), it is necessary to assume that the clouds are confined by a hot intercloud medium of relativly low density (Mathews 1974). In comparison with these dynamical times, the small recombination time

$$t_{rec} = (n\alpha)^{-1} = 1.22 \times 10^{-5} n_{10}^{-1} T_4^{0.8} \quad yr$$

indicates that the clouds are in radiative and thermal equlibrium to high accuracy. Here $\alpha_B = 2.60 \times 10^{-13} T_4^{0.8}$ cm^3 s^{-1} is the Case B recombination coefficient which should be accurate except perhaps at densities $n \geq 10^{10}$ cm^{-3} where many recombinations are collisionally returned to the continuum (Mathews, Blumenthal, and Grandi 1980).

The nature of the hot cloud-confining medium is of central importance in understanding cloud dynamics and the environment of the central energy source. Compton interactions in the strong continuum radiation fields of quasars and Seyfert nuclei can very efficiently heat low density gas in the broad line region to high temperatures, $\hat{T} = \langle h\nu \rangle/(4k) \approx 10^8$K, (Levich and Sunyaev 1970, 1971) , where $\langle h\nu \rangle$ is the mean photon energy in the ionizing spectrum and quantities with hats, such as $\hat{T}$, refer to the intercloud medium. McCray (1979) and Krolik, McKee, and Tarter (1981) have noted that plasma at high densities, as in the emission line clouds, can be heated (by photoionization) and cooled (by line and thermal continuum radiation) to $\approx 10^4$ K by the same radiation field that maintains the low density intercloud medium at $\approx 10^8$ K by Compton processes. Provided Compton heating is the dominant heating mechanism in the intercloud medium, the high and low density phases can be in pressure equilibrium only in a relatively small range of pressures in the vicinity of $(\hat{n}\hat{T}) \approx 10^{13} - 10^{14}$ K cm^{-3} similar to pressures required in detailed photoionization studies. If additional heating sources are available, the range of $(\hat{n}\hat{T})$ is extended toward larger values. For $\hat{T} \approx 10^8$ K the mass in the intercloud medium

$$\hat{M}_g \approx \frac{4}{3}\pi R^3 M \frac{(nT)}{\hat{T}} \approx 3.5 \times 10^3 (nT)_{14}\hat{T}_8^{-1}R_{18}^3 f sq^3 M_\odot$$

is considerably larger than that in the system of line-emitting clouds estimated above.

The drag force exerted on a radially-moving cloud with crossectional area $\approx \pi r^2$ and velocity u by an intercloud medium moving with a radial wind or accretion flow velocity $\hat{u}$ is

$$f_d = \pi r^2 \hat{n} M(\hat{u} - u)|\hat{u} - u|.$$

The drag force will strongly affect a cloud's motion through the intercloud medium in a stopping distance

$$\delta R_{stop} \approx \frac{\hat{T}N}{(nT)} \sim 10^{17}\hat{T}_8 N_{23}(nT)_{14}^{-1} \ cm,$$

where N_{23} is the column density in the cloud. Since the stopping distance can be less than the dimensions of the broad line region for $\hat{T} \sim 10^8$, a cloud can be expected to approach a terminal velocity relative to the intercloud medium such that the sum of gravitational and radiative forces on the cloud is $\approx f_d$. For many cloud models of interest, however, the drag-limited velocity $u_t \sim (g\delta R)^{1/2}$ is too small to account for the full widths of the observed line profiles. For example, for radiative acceleration by UV radiation, $u_t \sim 400(\Gamma_{-2}n_{10}\hat{T}_8)^{1/2}(nT)_{14}^{-1/2}$ km s^{-1}. In addition, a strong Rayleigh-Taylor instability is expected at the edge of a cloud which is accelerated or deaccelerated by a strong drag force. Finally, when the drag force is large, the sense of motion in the intercloud medium must be known in order to determine cloud trajectories. The virial temperature T_v which charactizes motion in the gravitational field of a black hole of mass $M_{H9} = M_H/10^9 M_\odot$ is given by the condition

$$\frac{3kT_v}{M} = \frac{GM_H}{2R}$$

i. e.

$$T_v = 2.7 \times 10^8 M_{H9} R_{18}^{-1}.$$

Whenever $T_v < \hat{T}$, the intercloud medium probably flows out as a wind. However, for sufficiently small R, $T_v > \hat{T}$ must occur and intercloud gas within this radius will be Compton cooled in a time

$$t_{cc} \approx \frac{3k\hat{T}}{2} \frac{4kT\sigma_T L}{mc^2 4\pi R^2} \approx 6R_{18}^2 L_{46}^{-1} \ yr,$$

which, if less than the free fall time, results in an accretion flow at small R. Such a divided flow, in which $\hat{u}$ takes both signs, necessarily requires a volume source for the intercloud gas and complicates the calculation of emission line profiles of emission line clouds whenever drag forces are important in the cloud dynamics. The relative simplicity and uniformity of line profiles among observed quasars and Seyferts suggests, however, that cloud motions are not highly complex or sensitive to the location of the stagnation radius in the confining flow.

Such complications can be avoided if the intercloud temperature $\hat{T}$ is significantly higher than that predicted by Compton heating alone. Heating of the intercloud medium by either the motion of clouds or by cosmic rays can exceed Compton heating by an order of magnitude (Mathews 1974; Krolik, McKee, and Tarter 1981). The power generated by the motion of one cloud moving at velocity u_r relative to the intercloud medium is $f_d u_r$. An entire ensemble of moving clouds of size r generates a power $N_{cl} = M_g/m_c$ times greater. If this power generation is balanced by Compton cooling,

$$M_g \frac{3 T u_r^3}{4 \hat{T} r} = \hat{n} \sigma_T \frac{4 k \hat{T}}{m c^2} \frac{L}{4 \pi R^2} \frac{4}{3} \pi R^3,$$

the resulting equlibrium temperature

$$\hat{T} = 3 \times 10^8 \frac{L_{H\beta}/L}{4 \times 10^{-3}} \frac{T_4 u_9^3}{(f_{H\beta}/10) r_{12} (nT)_{14} R_{18} n_{10} f_{sq}} \; K$$

is comparable to that of Compton heating in quasars but is about ten times larger in Seyferts.

In view of the fundamental similarity and overlapping observed properties among quasars and Seyferts in continuous emission, line flux ratios, and emission line profiles, it is likely that the same physical processes and environment dominate in both types of objects. We therefore adopt the point of view that a physical process (such as heating of the intercloud medium in excess of the Compton rate) which is required to interpret Seyferts or quasars alone must hold for objects of all luminosities. Without this fundamental assumption, dissimilar processes would have to conspire to produce similar observed features. However, certain scalings – such as the approximate constancy of L/R^2 – are required to preserve the emission line spectrum among objects of different luminosity.

Weymann *et al.* (1982) have considered cloud motions and emission line profiles in a hot thermal wind that receives momentum and energy from radially streaming relativistic electrons.

The equipartition nonthermal pressures in quasars having compact radio sources are comparable to those expected in broad line clouds (Blumenthal and Mathews 1975), and such relativistic particles could be a property of all broad line regions but only radiate if the magnetic field is sufficiently large. Weymann *et al.* argue that a thermal plasma in the presence of streaming cosmic rays can be heated above the Compton temperature, to $\hat{T} \approx 10^9 K$, by collective plasma processes resulting in an intercloud wind. Clouds placed in the wind are initially accelerated outward by radation pressure to velocities faster than the wind, but eventually the drag interaction increases and the clouds are ultimately accelerated by the momentum of the nonrelativistic component in the wind to velocities comparable to the wind terminal velocity. The emission line profiles produced in this self-consistent model are similar to those observed.

The existence of clouds as a possible model for the broad emission line region is occasionally questioned because of the small apparent thermal evaporation time in the hot intercloud medium, but this difficulty is easily avoided if a small magnetic field is present. Thermal conduction into clouds of size $r \sim 10^{12} - 10^{13} cm$ is saturated and the flux is given by $3\hat{n}M\hat{c}_s^3$ rather than the usual combination of conductivity and temperature gradient (Cowie and McKee 1977). The associated thermal evaporation time (Krolik, McKee, and Tarter 1981)

$$t_{evap} \approx 0.3 N_{22}^{7/6} (\hat{n}\hat{T})_{14}^{-1} T_4^{1/6} \quad yr$$

can be much shorter than the expected dynamical lifetime of the cloud in the broad line region. But even a trivally small magnetic field can reduce thermal conduction to essentially zero perpendicular to the field lines. The ratio of parallel and perpendicular thermal conductivities is (Braginskii 1965)

$$\frac{\kappa_\parallel}{\kappa_\perp} \approx (\omega \tau_{ee})^2 \approx 10^{21} \frac{\hat{\beta}\hat{T}_8^5}{(nT)_{14}^2},$$

where ω is the gyrofrequency, τ_{ee} is the electron relaxation time, and $\hat{\beta}$ is the ratio of gas to magnetic pressure in the intercloud medium. Internal circulation within the moving clouds is likely to produce magnetic fields which are preferentially tangential to the cloud surface, effectively blocking thermal contact with the intercloud medium. In any case, it is easy to show that the magnetic field within the cloud H cannot connect with that in the intercloud medium $\hat{H}$. Suppose for example that saturated thermal conduction is occurring in a region $r_{sat} \gtrsim r$ and that the internal field is being convected out and is reconnecting with the ambient intercloud field on a reconnection timescale $t_{recon} \approx r_{sat}/0.1\hat{u}_A$, where $\hat{u}_A$ is the Alfven speed in the local intercloud medium. Reconnection is expected to be surpressed if the time a moving cloud spends near the ambient field, r_{sat}/u, is less than t_{recon}, *i. e.*

$$u > 0.1\hat{u}_A = 180\hat{\beta}^{1/2}\hat{T}_8^{1/2} \ km \ s^{-1},$$

where $\hat{\beta} < 1$. Therefore, it appears that once the clouds achieve an appreciable velocity relative to the confining medium, they are effectively protected against thermal evaporation by magnetic thermal insulation.

b) Radial Cloud Motion

i) Radial Forces

Radial motion of emission line clouds can be generated by gravitational and radiative forces but may be restricted by the influence of drag forces against the intercloud medium. The gravitational acceleration depends on the poorly known mass M_H of the hypothetical central black hole

$$g = GM_H/R^2.$$

A distributed mass of stars having a combined mass comparable to that of the black hole can also exist within the radius of the broad line region without suffering cataclysmic stellar collisions (Mathews 1983). For simplicity in the following discussions, however, this distributed component is generally ignored.

The mass of the black hole is difficult to estimate. If the luminosity of the central object is derived from gravitational accretion with an energy conversion efficiency $\epsilon_a \approx 0.1$, the total mass accumulated by a quasar black hole is $M_H = c^{-2}\epsilon_a^{-1}L_Q t_Q$, where L_Q is the mean luminosity during the quasar lifetime t_Q. Although neither t_Q nor M_H is known for any object, Soltan(1982) used number counts to establish a limit on the total luminous energy emitted by quasars $L_Q t_Q$ which in turn establishes a lower limit on the central mass in quasars, $M_H > 10^8 M_\odot$. If the black holes have masses in the range $10^8 - 10^9 M_\odot$ (Soltan 1982), the current space density of dead quasars is $10^5 - 10^6$ Gpc^{-3}. The space density of all galaxies, $\sim 10^7$ Gpc^{-3}, suggests that 1-10% of present day galaxies are vestigal quasars. Finally, since the luminosities of Seyferts are ~ 100 times less than that of quasars, it is reasonable to adopt central condensed masses that are proportionally lower.

If gravity were the only radial force, very large central masses would be necessary to produce the observed velocities in the broad line region:

$$u \approx \left(\frac{GM_H}{R}\right)^{1/2} \approx 11000 \; M_{H10}^{1/2} R_{18}^{-1/2} \; km \; s^{-1}.$$

A condensed mass of $M_H = 10^{10} M_\odot$ in a galactic nucleus would produce stellar velocities of 660 km s^{-1} at a distance of 100 pc, which is considerably larger than any nuclear stellar velocity dispersion observed so far. Therefore, black hole masses greater than about $10^9 M_O$ are inconsistent with the hypothesis that any galaxy with measured stellar velocity dispersion is a vestigal quasar. To achieve 10^4 km s^{-1} in a smaller Seyfert broad line region, the central mass required, $M_H \approx 10^9 M_O$, would produce velocities of $\sim$ 200 km s^{-1} at 100 *pc*, which may be consistent with observations.

There is an obvious need for more detailed observations of nuclear velocity dispersions in active galaxies having the broadest lines.

The attraction of gravity toward the center can however be moderated or overwhelmed by outward radiation pressure forces. In the fully ionized regions of the clouds every recombination is followed immediately by the absorption of an ionizing photon of mean momentum $\langle h\nu \rangle / c$. Since the number of recombinations per proton per second is $n\alpha$, the ultraviolet radiative acceleration is

$$g_{r,uv} = \phi \frac{n\alpha}{M} \frac{h\nu_o}{c} \equiv Bn,$$

where $\phi \approx 2$ roughly corrects for the presence of helium and represents the ratio of the Rydberg energy $h\nu_o$ to the mean photon energy. Since $g_{r,uv}$ is recombination-limited, it is proportinal to the plasma density and is independent of the column density to a good approximation. More detailed allowance for the UV radiative transfer results in a modest dependance of $g_{r,uv}$ on the column density (McKee and Tarter 1975).

Most of the photons less energetic than about $h\nu_s \approx 200$ eV are absorbed in the fully ionized part of quasar clouds (Davidson and Netzer 1979), but the remaining higher energy photons apply radiative forces to the partially ionized regions beyond the Strömgren column. The acceleration associated with this X-ray absorption is (Mathews 1982)

$$g_{r,x} = \frac{1}{nM} \int_{h\nu_s}^{\infty} \frac{L_\nu}{4\pi R^2 h\nu} e^{-N\sigma_\nu} \left(\frac{h\nu}{c} \right) n\sigma_\nu d\nu \quad cm \ s^{-2}.$$

Unlike $g_{r,uv}$, $g_{r,x}$ is proportional to the metal abundance which is incorporated into the specific crossection per proton σ_ν. This expression can be approximated reasonably well with

$$g_{r,x} = \frac{\kappa}{R^2 (1 + \frac{N}{N_o})},$$

where $\kappa \approx 10^{36} L_{sx45}$ is proportional to the soft (2-10 keV) X-ray luminosity L_{sx} and $N_o \approx 2 \times 10^{20}$ cm^{-2}. Both κ and N_o depend somewhat on the X-ray continuum spectral index α_x. The total X-ray acceleration on a slab or cloud of column density N is

$$g_{r,xt} = \frac{\kappa}{R^2} \frac{N_o}{N} \ln\left(1 + \frac{N}{N_o}\right),$$

which may be important for both optically thin $(N \leq N_s)$ and thick $(N \geq N_s)$ clouds.

The equation of motion for radially moving clouds of constant mass $m_c = (4/3)\pi r^3 n M$ is therefore

$$\frac{du}{dt} = -g + g_{r,uv} + g_{r,xt} + f_d/m_c.$$

While this equation of motion is reasonably complete, it must be kept in mind that additional poorly understood acceleration mechanisms may exist; such a mechanism has been assumed in the ballistic outflow model hypothesized by Capriotti, Foltz, and Byard (1980) which produces line profiles in excellent agreement with those observed. Clearly, if gravity is the dominant influence on radially moving clouds, larger velocities are expected at small R. This is consistent with the observation that He I λ5876 is often broader than $H\beta$ since He I λ5876 is thought to be enhanced in stronger radiation fields (Netzer 1978; Shuder 1982). Although individual clouds accelerated outward by radiation forces necessarily have greater velocities at large R, an ensemble of such clouds originating in a volume around the central continuum source would also produce larger velocities at small R where the cloud densities and radiative fluxes are expected to be larger. For this reason, the He I λ5876 line width is not a unequivocal test of the sense of cloud motion.

ii) Optically Thin Clouds

The apparent symmetry of the $Ly\alpha$ line observed in many quasars and a few Seyferts imposes an important limit or constraint on the column depths allowed in dynamical models involving radially moving clouds. This constraint arises from the extremely high optical depths ($10^9 - 10^{10}$) presented to $Ly\alpha$ photons by the extensive partially ionized zone on the nonirradiated sides of optically thick clouds such as those calculated by Kwan and Krolik (1981). Since all but a few percent of the $Ly\alpha$ photons escape through the irradiated side of these clouds, if their collective motion were primarily radial, either in or out, the $Ly\alpha$ line profile would be very asymmetric, in sharp contrast to many observed profiles (Wilkes and Carswell 1982). The implicit assumption here is that the source of ionizing photons is incident on the cloud from a relatively small source near the center of the cloud system. At the workshop, Kallman proposed that a significant number of ionizing photons could be scattered from the intercloud medium and diffusely illuminate the clouds from all directions. In such an environment the $Ly\alpha$ profile can be made more symmetric even for radially streaming clouds. However, it may be difficult to fine tune the optical depth of the intercloud medium to provide sufficiently symmetric profiles in all objects, particularly if the electron scattering optical depth depends on the continuum luminosity, as in Kallman's model.

For these reasons it seems necessary for the radially moving cloud model to abandon the widespread notion – adopted in most photoionization models – that a single type of emission line cloud is responsible for the entire line spectrum observed. Instead it is reasonable to assume that most of the $Ly\alpha$ radiation, as well as that of CIV and other lines generated in fully ionized regions, is produced by optically thin clouds moving radially and emitting isotropically. Additional support for assuming the presence of clouds with a wide variety of optical depths is provided by numerous recent observations of quasars and especially Seyfert galaxies (Shuder 1982; Wilkes and Carswell 1982; Ulrich and Boisson 1983; Junkkarinen, Burbidge, and Smith 1983; Wilkes 1984; Wu 1984) which have demonstrated that emission lines of different ions have noticably dissimilar line widths. Occasionally it is claimed that

Lyβ or *Lyγ* is present at levels that may be consistent with optically thin clouds. Therefore the "single cloud photoionization model," which produces the optimally best total flux ratios for all emission lines, although useful for preliminary photoionization studies, must be modified or abandoned.

Optically thin clouds $(N \leq N_s)$ can be efficiently accelerated by ultraviolet radiation and, under a wide variety of ambient conditions, can account naturally for the observed line profiles. Assuming for the moment that $g_{r,xt} \ll g_{r,uv}$, the ratio of the first two terms in the equation of motion

$$\frac{g_{r,uv}}{g} = \frac{n\alpha h\nu_0\phi}{Mc} \frac{R^2}{GM_H} = 17 n_{10} R_{18}^2 M_{H9}^{-1}$$

indicates that radiative forces dominate those of gravity even for very large central masses. The bulk motion of these clouds will therefore be outward. In the absence of strong drag forces, the outward radial velocities can be estimated by setting $du/dt \sim u^2/R \approx g_{r,uv}$, i.e.

$$u \approx (\alpha\phi h\nu_0 nR/Mc)^{1/2} \approx 15000 n_{10}^{1/2} R_{18}^{1/2} f_{sq}^{1/2} \ km \ s^{-1}$$

or, alternatively, using the definition of the ionization parameter,

$$u \approx 26000(L_{46}f_{sq}^2 n_{10}\Gamma_{-2})^{1/4} \ km \ s^{-1}.$$

The desired velocities follow directly from the observed luminosities and values of nR consistent with broad line spectra. The weak dependance of the line width on luminosity is consistent with observations of quasars and Seyfert galaxies.

In addition, clouds accelerated by UV photoionizing radiation can account for the observed line profiles of lines produced in this region in a most natural manner under a wide variety of ambient conditions. The equation of motion for an optically thin

$(N \leq N_s)$ cloud is independent of the cloud mass:

$$\frac{du}{dt} = u\frac{du}{dR} = \frac{n\alpha\phi h\nu_o}{Mc}$$

provided drag forces are not dominant. The acceleration of the cloud is remarkably coherent. The equation of continuity for a spherical ensemble of such clouds requires that the mass flux in the entire cloud system is

$$\dot{m}_c = m_c n_c u 4\pi r^2,$$

where n_c is the space density of clouds. The specific photon luminosity of an emission line L_ν can be determined by integrating the observed contributions from all clouds over radius and angle $\theta = cos^{-1}(\mu)$ between the velocity of the cloud and the line of sight:

$$L_\nu = \int_{R_o}^{\infty} dR \int_0^1 d\mu \delta[\nu - n\nu_l(1 + \frac{u}{c}\mu)]\epsilon_c n_c 2\pi R^2$$

for the blue $(\mu > 1)$ side of the symmetric line. Here $\nu_l(1 + u/c\mu)$ is the Doppler shifted observed frequency and $\epsilon_c = n\alpha_l m_c/M$ is the number of photons produced per second by each cloud of mean mass m assuming an effective recombination rate α_l appropriate to the fully ionized condition of the clouds. The integral of μ over the delta function is $c/\nu_l u$ provided $0 < cx/u < 1$ where $x = (\nu - \nu_l)/\nu_l$. The equation of motion can be used to convert the remaining integral to an integral over velocity:

$$L_\nu = \frac{\dot{m}_c \alpha_l c}{2M\nu_l} \int_{cx}^{\infty} \frac{n}{u^2} |\frac{dr}{du}| du = \left(\frac{\dot{m}_c c^2 \alpha_l}{\nu_l h\nu_o \alpha}\right) \int_{cx}^{\infty} \frac{du}{u} \equiv \Lambda \ln \frac{u_{max}}{cx}.$$

This is the logarithmic line profile expressed in dimensionless frequency displacement from line center (Blumenthal and Mathews

1975,1979). The maximum velocity u_{max} conveniently arises from a terminal velocity if the cloud density varies as R^{-s} with $s > 1$. The log profile for clouds originating at a particular radius is independent of the variation of $n(R)$, but an ensemble of clouds having different initial R produces a combined profile which is the sum of log profiles and the total profile may be somewhat dependent on $n(R)$.

The log profile, an excellent fit to many symmetric emission lines, arises naturally from outward radial motion of optically thin and therefore isotropically emitting clouds. Capriotti, Foltz, and Byard (1980) demonstrated, however, that logarithmic line profiles result in any physical situation for which $\epsilon_c n_c 2\pi R^2 dR \propto u du$. This is consistent with the applicability of the log profile calculation above in the optically thick limit where all the Lyman continuum photons are absorbed by the cloud. They note also that isotropically emitting clouds infalling in a gravitational field can produce log profiles if the cloud radius (and therefore the confining pressure) is assumed to remain constant along the cloud's trajectory.

Observational support for outwardly moving clouds is provided by the P-Cygni line profiles of the PHL 5200 class of quasars and observed blue-shifted absorption features in 3C 390.3 and NGC 4151 (Anderson and Kraft 1969). Miller and Antonucci (1983) have observed redshifted polarized companions to emission lines in NGC 1068 which may arise from outflow, but alternative explanations of these observations may also be possible. Gaskell (1982) and Wilkes (1984) have observed that line profiles of high ionization lines in quasars are preferentially blue-shifted relative to the others and to the quasar rest frame (forbidden line redshift), as could result from outwardly moving clouds partially occulted by an accretion disk or optically thick central core. The enhanced blue wing asymmetry often observed in the C IV line in both quasars (Young *et al.* 1982; Wilkes 1984) and Seyferts (Wu 1984) could also be a consequence of occulted outflow. Broad emission features in [O III] were reported by Meyers at the workshop – such emission is characteristic of outward radial motion but is more difficult to understand if the emitting regions are infalling or orbiting (Shields 1978). Finally, Gaskell (1984a,b) also has observed a decrease in the $H\beta$ equivalent width with decreasing emission line width, a phenomenon not shared by optical Fe II emission. If this can be explained as an effect of increasing density, as Gaskell proposes, it appears to be another attribute of radial cloud motion generated by nongravitational forces that are sensitive to density.

In order that the acceleration of an optically thin cloud be thoroughly independent of its motion relative to the confining medium, the intercloud gas temperature must exceed $\sim 10^8$ K. This results from the requirement that the distance over which the acceleration occurs $\delta R_{acc} = u^2/g_{r,uv}$ not exceed the stopping distance $\delta R_{stop} \approx N/\hat{n}$, i.e., $N > 10^{24}(\hat{n}\hat{T})_{14}R_{18}f_{sq}\hat{T}_8^{-1}$. Therefore, even if $\hat{T} \sim 10^{10}$ K, the confining pressure $(\hat{n}\hat{T})$ may have to be 3-10 times smaller than 10^{14} in order to satisfy this inequality comfortably and permit $N < N_s$. It is possible nevertheless to construct essentially logarithmic profiles for an ensemble of clouds if the drag force is about ten times larger than this inequality would suggest (Blumenthal and Mathews 1979).

Another concern for outward radial cloud motion dominated by $g_{r,uv}$ is the origin of the emitting gas. If the ambient pressure, and therefore the cloud density varies with distance R from the central source as $n \propto R^{-s}$, with $s > 2$ then clouds can move outward from very small distances provided $g_{r,uv} > g$ is satisfied throughout the broad line region. But if s should be < 2 in the broad line region, the outflow model above requires that the emission line gas be produced in some finite volume surrounding the central source. This situation could also result in infalling gas at small radii. A likely volumetric source of the emission line gas in this case could be stars orbiting the central mass, but no fully successful model for this has been produced (Shull 1983, 1984; Mathews 1984; Verbunt, Fabian, and Rees 1984). If the emission line gas originates from any source (i.e., stars, massive clouds, etc.) moving at or near the local virial velocity, however, this velocity must be small compared to the velocity width of the emission line produced so that the central line profile is not dominated by the kinematics of the source objects. For example, in the outflow model described above, the line broadening due to the velocity u_* of the virially moving source objects will exceed ~ 0.1 that of the terminal velocity of radiative acceleration unless $g < 0.1 g_{r,uv}$ which requires that central masses satisfy $M_H \leq 9 \times 10^8 n_{10} R_{18}^2 \ M_\odot$.

Models involving radially inflowing clouds are also stressed to account for the mass flow rate through the broad line region. For example, a Seyfert galaxy must replenish $M_g \approx 0.027 L_{H\beta 8} n_{10}$ solar masses of gas in the broad line region each radial flow time $t_{fl} \approx 0.32 R_{17}/u_9$ yrs. The mass flow rate $M_g/t_{fl} \approx 0.01 M_\odot \ yr^{-1}$ represents the entire mass loss expected from a $10^{10} M_\odot$ galactic bulge of typical old stars. However, heating of this ejected gas by supernovae may prevent some or all of it from reaching the central parsec where it can participate in the broad line emission (Mathews and Baker 1971). If the galactic bulge is rotating, angular momentum must be lost by gas reaching the center. This implies that any infalling clouds entering the broad line region arrive on nearly circular, rather than radial, trajectories. Such a reservoir of gas moving into the emitting region from the outside might be expected to be visible in emission or in absorption against the central nonstellar continuum.

iii) Optically Thick Clouds

Clouds having total column densities N greater than N_s but less than the Compton column $N_c = \sigma_T^{-1} = 1.50 \times 10^{24}$ cm^{-2} experience an outward radiative force due to absorption of X-radiation which exceeds the attraction of the central mass whenever

$$g_{r,xt} = \frac{\kappa N_o}{R^2 N} \ln(1 + \frac{N}{N_o}) > g = \frac{GM_H}{R^2}.$$

Both the critical central mass M_{Hx}, which just balances the outward radiative force, and the expected cloud velocity $u_x \approx (g_{r,xt}R)^{1/2}$ resulting from acceleration by X-radiation (ignoring gravity) depend on the total column density N of the cloud.

Table 1

X-ray Acceleration of Clouds[a]

log n	$g_{r,xt}$ (cm s^{-2})	u_x (km s^{-1})	$M_{HX}/M_\odot$
21	55.6	24000	4×10^9
22	12.6	11200	9×10^8
23	2.0	4500	1.5×10^8
24	0.3	1700	2×10^7

[a]For L (2-10 keV) = 10^{45} erg s^{-1}, α_x k= 0.7, R = 10^{17} cm.

For values of the total column depth $N \approx 10^{22} - 10^{23}$ suggested by the single photoionized cloud model, the critical masses M_{Hx} and velocities u_x shown in Table 1 are comparable to expected or observed values. In order to produce appropriate line widths, however, the mean position $\langle R \rangle$ of the clouds may need to be somewhat smaller than predicted from canonical values of Γ on the single cloud photoionization model. However, the outward acceleration of optically thick clouds by X-radiation is likely to be larger than those in Table 1 for at least two reasons: (i) the values of $g_{r,xt}$ are based on solar abundances while super-metal-rich abundances appropriate to galactic nuclei could increase $g_{r,xt}$, and (ii) the acceleration by ultraviolet radiation and Balmer continuum have been ignored in calculating u_x in the table; somewhat higher velocities are expected under the combined acceleration of all relevant continua.

However, assuming M_H is sufficiently small so that gravity can be ignored, line profiles produced from UV and X-ray acceleration might be expected to differ since $g_{r,uv}$ and $g_{r,xt}$ are sensitive to different parameters. The acceleration of the partially ionized region by X-rays depends on the column density N, while the fully ionized region would be accelerated by ultraviolet photons sensitive to the plasma density. If this is the correct model, why do the observed C IV and Mg II lines have similar or roughly similar line widths? Apart from possible differences in the mean radius $\langle R \rangle$ associated with UV and X-ray accelerated clouds, the ratio of the line widths is proportional to

$$\frac{u_x}{u_{uv}} \propto \left(\frac{g_{r,xt}}{g_{r,uv}} \right)^{1/2} \propto \left(\frac{N_s}{N} \right)^{1/2} \propto \left(\frac{\Gamma}{N} \right)^{1/2} ,$$

where $g_{r,uv} N_s \ll g_{r,xt} N$ is assumed for clouds accelerated by X-rays. However, Γ is often regarded as being roughly constant among active galaxies and quasars, while N may be rather constant if clouds are produced largely by ablation of large parent clouds having $N \geq N_T$, the Compton column. Alternatively, if small fully-ionized clouds are ablated off large clouds accelerated by X-rays, both types of clouds will have the same velocity immediately following the ablation process.

Radiative ablation of large clouds is a natural result of differential radiative forces within the cloud structure. In particular, if the surface of a cloud irradiated to a depth N_{rad} experiences a strong radiation force, then this surface may be pushed around or through a cloud of radius r in a time $\delta t \approx (r/g_{rad})^{1/2}$, resulting in a complete ablation of the cloud in time $t_{ab} \approx \delta t N/N_{rad}$, where $N > N_{rad}$ is the total column density of the cloud. If, for example, $g_{r,uv} > g_{r,xt}$, as in the fully-ionized region, the irradiated layer to N_s can ablate the whole cloud in a time

$$t_{ab,uv} \approx \left(\frac{r}{g_{r,uv}}\right)^{1/2} \frac{N}{N_s} \approx 200 \frac{N_{24}^{3/2}}{n_{10}\Gamma_{-2}} \ yrs.$$

This may be comparable to the free fall time of a large cloud across the broad line region

$$t_{ff} \approx \left(\frac{R^3}{GM_H}\right)^{1/2} \approx 90 \frac{R_{18}^{3/2}}{M_{H9}^{1/2}} \ yrs.$$

In a like manner, the differential forces due to the momentum in the X-radiation absorbed to depth N_x can ablate very large clouds in time

$$t_{ab,x} \approx \left(\frac{r}{g_{r,xt}}\right)^{1/2} \frac{N_t}{N_x} \approx \frac{N_t^2 r R^2}{N_x N_o \kappa \ln(1 + N_x/N_o)}.$$

Specifically, a cloud having $N_t = 10^{25}$ cm^{-2} and radius $r = 10^{15}$ cm, if subjected to X-ray forces to depth $N = 10^{24}$ cm^{-2}, is ablated away by in $\approx$ 240 yrs, again comparable to the free fall time. These very approximate estimates of the ablation time apply equally well to clouds moving in both radial directions. Therefore if the broad line gas were to be supplied by infalling clouds of very large mass, or if such clouds were produced in the quasar atmosphere, smaller clouds with $N \approx 10^{23} - 10^{24}$ cm^{-2} can be expected to be ablated from the parent cloud and behave as separate dynamical entities (Weymann *et al.* 1982). Such clouds formed from ablated material are comparable in size to those required by detailed photoionization studies. However, it must be stressed that these estimates of the ablation time are extremely crude.

Recently Wandel and Yahil (1984) have discovered a weak inverse correlation between the velocity width of the $H\beta$

line and the ratio of X-ray to $H\beta$ luminosities, $\Delta u(FWHM) \propto (L_x/L_{H\beta})^{-0.17}$. A simple X-ray acceleration model would have predicted a positive correlation with power index 0.25, but the coefficient in this proportionality might well be an implicit model-dependent function of the luminosity ratio. Therefore, as Wandel and Yahil note, radiative acceleration cannot be ruled out by this observation.

iv) Concerns Regarding Radially-Moving Clouds

Models of the broad emission line region based on systems of radiatively accelerated clouds are attractive because emission line widths similar to those observed follow in a natural way from observed luminosities and observationally allowed densities and ionization levels. Following an initial transient, the acceleration is extremely coherent. Logarithmic line profiles, first predicted as a theoretical consequence of radiative acceleration (Blumenthal and Mathews 1975), have been found to be in excellent agreement with observations. Nevertheless, a number of additional attributes of this model should not be overlooked. The requirement that $L\alpha$ emitting clouds radiate isotropically implies not only that both optically thin $(N \leq N_s)$ and optically thick $(N > N_s)$ clouds move with roughly similar kinematics, but also that the mean ionization parameter Γ based on the "one-cloud photoionization model," and its attendant implication regarding the dimensions of the broad line region, must now be considered as only a rough approximation which may not be suitable for a significant part of the emitting gas. If C IV and Mg II lines or the $L\alpha$ and Balmer lines are produced in different cloud systems, as suggested by IUE Seyfert observations, then the flux ratios of these lines may depend more on the relative amount of gas in clouds of differing optical depths, than on the mean value of Γ required for the one-cloud photoionization model.

Unlike emission line models based on orbiting gas, for which the emitting gas can contribute to the line profile for more than one revolution, radially moving clouds imply an abundant and currently poorly-understood source of gas. In order to account for the observed H_β flux, about $2f_{sq}^2 M_\odot$ of emitting gas is required. If the size of the broad line region is $\sim 10^{18} f_{sq}$ cm, the time required for gas to move radially through the system is $\sim 100 f_{sq}$ yrs, and the implied rate that line-emitting mass is processed through the system is $\sim 3 \times 10^{-2} f_{sq}$ $M_\odot$ yr^{-1}. If the cloud-confining medium has a temperature $\hat{T} \leq 10^9$ K, then the radial mass flow in the intercloud medium could exceed that in the clouds. In some Seyferts, for example, we are seeing today entirely different gas than was observed 10 years ago, while the line profiles have not changed drastically for most objects. The source of broad line emitting gas most therefore be smooth and continuous in both space and time.

Successful cloud models for the broad emission line region probably require that drag forces exerted by the intercloud medium not be dominant. Not only can cloud velocities be limited by the drag, as discussed above, but outward moving clouds can pass through a maximum velocity which is less than the drag-related terminal velocity if the confining pressure varies as $\hat{P} \propto R^{-s}$, where $s \leq 1$ (Blumenthal and Mathews 1979; Weymann *et al.* 1982). In this situation, clouds of constant mass actually produce two overlapping line profiles as they are first accelerated then decelerated. In general the combined line profile in such cases is non-logarithmic, but log-like profiles can still be produced by choosing an appropriate source function for clouds originating at a variety of initial radii in the broad line atmosphere. Such complications, however, seem ill-suited to most of the broad line regions for which the line profiles are quite similar and logarithmic.

Finally, it is important to consider the influence of various dynamical instabilities and their consequences for the cloud model. The strongly directed nature of the nonthermal continuum in the fully ionized parts of the clouds can amplify sound waves moving parallel to the radiative flux by the action of radiation pressure on the compressions in the wave (Mathews 1976). Instability occurs whenever the Strömgren length r_s exceeds the growth distance $c_s t_{gr}$ of the travelling wave, where $t_{gr} \gtrsim 2c_s/g_{r,uv}$ for UV-accelerated clouds. This results in an upper limit on the radiation parameter for stability: $\Gamma < 2\alpha_B c_s^2/cB \approx 0.24$.

The Rayleigh-Taylor instability of broad line clouds has been discussed by Mathews and Blumenthal (1977), Krolik (1977, 1979), and Allen (1984). The conclusion of these studies, based largely on linear perturbation analyses, is that instabilities of an R-T nature do in fact exist, but they may not be important for clouds of most interest. As a simple example, consider a fully ionized cloud which is accelerated by UV-radiation. The condition for hydrostatic equilibrium in the noninertial frame within the accelerating cloud is

$$\frac{dP}{dr} = Mc_s^2\frac{dn}{dr} = Bn - g \equiv g_{eff},$$

where g, the instantaneous acceleration, is found by integrating the structure equation across the slab:

$$\Delta P = B \int_0^r n\,dr - gr = BN - gr.$$

If there is no drag force at either boundary of the cloud, $\Delta P = 0$, $g = Bn$, and $g_{eff} = 0$. Since the effective gravity vanishes throughout the cloud structure, there is no R-T instability. However, suppose there is a drag force at the nonirradiated surface of the cloud, then $\Delta P = \hat{\rho}u_r^2 = rg_{eff}$, where u_r is the velocity of the cloud relative to the intercloud medium. The effective gravity in this case

$$g_{eff} = (BN/r) - g$$

is positive and is directed from the dense cloud into the low density confining medium at the nonirradiated surface, which is therefore R-T unstable. The growth time for the instability, given in the nonlinear limit by the free fall time across the cloud in the effective gravity field, exceeds the UV acceleration time only for very small drag forces, requiring a highly relativistic confining medium: $\hat{T} \gtrsim 10^{12}$. However, for somewhat more optically thick, but still fully ionized, clouds the coefficient $B(r)$ decreases with r until $g_{eff} \to 0$ at the nonirradiated surface which then becomes neutrally stable. This pancake condition, discussed in detail by Blumenthal and Mathews (1979), is in fact a probable configuration for clouds moving in broad line environments such that the cloud confining pressure $\hat{P}$ decreases with radius faster than $R^{-6/5}$, so that $dN_s/dR < 0$. Similar stability arguments can be made for more massive clouds accelerated by X-radiation.

The pressure of resonance line radiation in the cloud can also have a destabilizing influence. In some situations, the radiation pressure in $L\alpha$ or Mg II radiation may exceed that of the gas in the clouds (Mathews 1976; Ferland and Elitzur 1984), and equilibrium cloud models are difficult or impossible to construct (Williams 1972; Weymann 1976). When the $Ly\alpha$ pressure is an appreciable fraction of the gas pressure, an additional term $-dP_\alpha/dr$ must be added to g_{eff}. Since P_α is always maximal at the center of the cloud (Weymann 1976), the gas pressure gradient and g_{eff} for a cloud not subjected to drag forces points away from the cloud at both surfaces, promoting R-T instability (Krolik 1979). Mg II $\lambda2800$ photons may play a similar role in more massive clouds having large partially-ionized zones. However, several additional considerations may reverse this conclusion. Equilibrium density gradients resulting from small drag forces on pancaked clouds could stabilize both surfaces. For example, a drag force on the nonirradiated edge of a cloud $\hat{\rho}u^2 > P_\alpha$ (corresponding to $\hat{T} \lesssim 3 \times 10^{10}\Gamma_{-2}^{-1}$ K for P_α/P estimated as in Mathews 1976) would produce an overall pressure gradient in the cloud which could neutralize the unstable resonance line pressure gradient at the irradiated surface. The nonirradiated surface could be stabilized if g_{rad} decreases sufficiently rapidly with N for the most optically thick, but still essentially fully-ionized, pancaked clouds.

It is also important to keep in mind that the interaction of the cloud with the intercloud medium may not occur at a mathematically precise boundary, as assumed in the studies above, but over a region given by the Larmor radius within the cloud corresponding to typical particles from the confining medium. Such a pressure transition region could incorporate a significant fraction of the cloud. For example, protons with energy $\gamma_4 = 10^{-4}E/Mc^2$ penetrate $r_L \approx 2 \times 10^{11}\gamma_4\beta^{1/2}n_{10}^{-1/2}$ cm into the cloud, where $\beta > 1$ is the ratio of gas to magnetic pressures. Pressure gradients produced in this manner at the surface of the cloud (by particles having neglible bulk inertia) oppose those established by dP_α/dr and would presumably be stabilizing. The question of cloud R-T instability for pancaked clouds, particularly in the important non-linear regime, although complex, requires further theoretical attention.

Except for cloud surfaces that are pancaked by radiation forces, R-T instabilities are always possible whenever clouds are accelerated or deaccelerated primarily by interactions with the intercloud medium. While such instabilities rearrange the cloud material and influence the total optical depth, they do not directly destroy the emitting gas, but disrupted cloud velocities are expected to be reduced since the cloud fragments suffer more drag force per gram.

V. BROAD LINE EMISSION FROM KEPLERIAN MOTIONS

a) Orbiting Clouds

Since the powerful continuum energy source in quasars and Seyferts is evidently produced by accretion onto a massive black hole, it is natural to consider orbital motions of gravitationally bound clouds as a possibility for explaining the broad emission lines. The mass supply rate to the broad line region, which is a difficult problem for radially moving clouds, is lessened if the gas can orbit many times, contributing to the line profile each time around.

Although it may be possible to design fully self-consistent models based on orbiting clouds, a number of potential difficulities with this model must be overcome.

As noted above, very large central masses, $M_H \sim 10^{10} M_\odot$, are required to account for observed line widths provided the emission line gas orbits at distances $R \sim 10^{18} f_{sq}$ regarded as typical for the emission line region. Typical orbital periods

$$t_{orb} \approx 2\pi \left(\frac{R^3}{GM_H} \right)^{1/2} \approx 173 \frac{(R_{18} f_{sq})^{3/2}}{M_{H10}^{1/2}} yrs$$

must be compared with the cloud collision time

$$t_{coll} = (n_c \pi r^2 u)^{-1}$$

if the clouds are moving roughly isotropically in random orbits around a central mass. The space density of clouds n_c can be interpreted in terms of the cloud covering factor

$$\Omega \approx (\pi/3) n_c r^2 R,$$

the fraction of the sky filled with clouds as seen from the small central source of radiation. Combining these expressions, the collision time is

$$t_{coll} \approx \frac{t_{orb}}{6\pi\Omega}.$$

Covering factors estimated from comparisons of continuum and line fluxes, $\Omega \sim 0.1/f_{sq}$, suggest that clouds with random orbits collide in about one orbital time. At typical broad line velocities, $u \sim 1000 - 10000$ km s^{-1}, colliding clouds are heated to temperatures $\geq 10^8$ K and are effectively destroyed. In this case clouds must be formed at rates comparable to the mass flux rates for radially moving clouds. Collisions among clouds are reduced if the clouds swarm like a school of fish around the central mass in the same direction in nearly circular orbits. This would in fact be expected if the clouds enter the broad line region from outside with a small net angular momentum. Emission lines generated by such a swarming cloud system can produce log-like profiles in a manner similar to those from continuous gaseous disks described below, even when individual clouds do not radiate isotropically (Hubbard and Puetter 1983).

Since the sound crossing time is so small, orbiting clouds must also be confined by a hot intercloud medium. Pressure confined clouds massive enough to be self-gravitating would be cold at their centers and would probably form into stars during contraction (Mathews 1982). Stars, however, are so condensed that their total surface area is unable to absorb an appreciable amount of the continuum flux and convert it into line radiation. Pressure-confined clouds moving through an intercloud medium may experience strong drag forces and spiral into the central mass in a time

$$t_{drag} \approx \frac{(1/2)mu^2}{u(\hat{n}Mu^2\pi r^2)} = 0.7\frac{\hat{T}_8 r_{12}}{T_4 u_9} \quad yr.$$

The orbital decay time is less than or comparable to the orbital time unless $\hat{T} \gg 10^8$ K or the cloud size considerably exceeds that required by photoionization models $r \sim 10^{12}$ cm .

If drag forces are very small and if gravity were the only force acting on orbiting clouds, the clouds would be appreciably distorted by Keplerian shear in time $\sim t_{orb}$. However, the uneven radial deposition of radiative momentum in the orbiting clouds causes a differential Poynting-Robertson shear which can greatly exceed Keplerian shear. Suppose, for example, that a small part δm_r of an orbiting cloud of mass $m \gg \delta m_r$ is irradiated. The radiative acceleration will have a component $g_{rad}(u_k/c)$ tangential to the orbit for a cloud moving at velocity $u_k = (GM_H/R)^{1/2}$. This irradiated part of the cloud will be sheared by one cloud diameter in a time

$$\delta t_r \approx \left(\frac{cr}{u_k g_{rad}}\right)^{1/2}.$$

The whole cloud is sheared by differential Poynting-Robertson forces in a time

$$\delta t_{pr} \approx (m/\delta m_r)\delta t_r \approx (N/N_r)\delta t_r,$$

where N_r is the column depth of the radiation in the cloud. For example, suppose g_{rad} arises mainly from UV photoionization and $N_r = N_s = c\Gamma/\alpha \approx 1.1 \times 10^{21}\Gamma_{-2}$, then a cloud of total column density $N = 10^{23}$ cm^{-2} is completely sheared by UV radiation in time

$$\delta t_{pr} \approx 42\frac{N_{23}^{3/2}}{n_{10}\Gamma_{-2}}\left(\frac{R_{18}f_{sq}}{M_{H10}}\right)^{1/4} \; yrs,$$

which is comparable to or less than the orbital period. The differential shearing effect of the radiative force rapidly converts an initially spherical cloud into an orbiting worm of fully ionized gas which no longer can radiate lines characteristic of the partially ionized zone (Mg II, $H\alpha$, Fe II, etc.). The influence of X-ray momentum will be to slightly prolong the shearing process but typical parameters do not allow a situation where $\delta t_{pr} \gg t_{orb}$. In view of this it may be advantageous to consider a continuous rotating gaseous disk as a source of broad line emission.

b) Line Emission from Continuous Gaseous Disks

Line profiles similar to observed logarithmic shapes can be generated by emission from a rotating disk provided the emissivity per unit area of the disk varies with disk radius as $\propto r^{-2\pm0.3}$ (Shields 1978; Capriotti, Foltz, and Byard 1980; Raine and Smith 1981; Gerbal and Pelat 1981; Mathews 1982; van Groningen 1983). In these models the outermost parts of the disk produce radiation near the core of the line profile, and unless the disks are quite large, the central part of the line profile is strongly depressed – appearing as if the line were self-absorbed. Such profiles are not observed in general. The velocity width of this central depression u_{cd} can be estimated from the surface area (at normal incidence) $R_{H\beta} \sim 10^{18}$ cm derived earlier which is needed to produce the observed $H\beta$ flux:

$$u_{cd} = (GM_H/R_{H\beta})^{1/2} = 11500(M_{H10}/R_{H\beta18})^{1/2} \ km \ s^{-1}.$$

Since the resolution limit of the observations is only $\sim 50 - 200$ km s^{-1}, the central depressions would be easy to observe unless the disks extend to $r_d \approx 10^{22}$ cm. A stellar component to the gravitational field could be expected at these large distances and this would tend to increase u_{cd} further. It is possible that the central depression is always just filled in with emission from the narrow line region, but such a conspiracy seems unlikely. In addition, either the ionizing radiation must be appropriately beamed to avoid the disk or the emissivity in the line-emitting disk must be reduced considerably below the Case B value in a uniform manner throughout the entire disk if $r_d > R_{H\beta}$. Shields (1978) has stressed that the approximate constancy of Γ across the disk, as implied by the first order similarity of line widths and profiles for all ions, requires that the electron density must vary with disk radius as $n \propto r^{-2}$, suggesting that semi-broad [O III] from the outer disk should be commonly observed, which it is not.

Rotating disk models for the broad line profiles generally require that the source of ionizing radiation be above the disk rather than localized near the central mass. Illumination from above may be necessary if the scale height of the disk decreases at large radii due to self-gravity (Sakimoto and Coroniti 1981), assuming this does not lead to star formation in the outer disk. This can be accomplished by scattered light from the central source or by beamed radiation from a jet, both of which could be adjusted to produce the observed ratio of line and continuum fluxes. In addition, a tilted jet (or differential line of sight absorption across the face of the disk) could lead to asymmetries in the line profiles. Such asymmetries would be expected to be randomly distributed between the blue and red wings, similar perhaps to the various asymmetries in Seyfert Balmer line profiles observed by Osterbrock and Shuder (1982). It would be difficult, however, to understand the enhanced blue wing asymmetry in the CIV line which is systematically observed in both quasars (Wilkes 1984) and Seyferts (Wu 1984).

There is also no widespread evidence as yet for X-ray continuum absorption (or Compton broadening of emission lines) by a disk illuminated in part or wholly by X-radiation from the far side of the disk. The transparency of accretion disks may in fact be an important parameter for interpeting all models of the broad line region. If a disk is largely neutral except for top and bottom layers of electron column density $N < \sigma_T^{-1}$, the Compton column density, radiation from the opposite side of the disk is visible. But if the electron column in the disk exceeds σ_T^{-1} by more than ~ 10, most radiation from the occulted backside is extinguished, including that of the occulted stars.

Statistics of emission line widths suggest that there are fewer narrow line objects than expected from a distribution of rotating line-emitting disks, and those relatively rare narrow line quasars (Foltz *et al.* 1984) and Seyferts (Stocke *et al.* 1982; MacAlpine *et al.* 1984) may have emission line flux ratios which differ from the norm.

VI. TIME VARIABILITY IN THE EMISSION LINES

Variability of the continua and line fluxes is a common property of many Seyferts and some quasars, but is most dramatic in those continuum-variable Seyferts with the smallest broad line regions in which the emission lines respond with the shortest time lag. If the continuum change is sufficiently abrupt, the emission properties of a photoionized broad line region will be mapped out both spatially, along paraboloids of constant time delay aligned with the line of sight, and in velocity space according to observed profile variations (Antokhin and Bochkarev 1983; Blandford and McKee 1982). Unfortunately, it has not been possible so far to obtain sufficiently frequent observations of variable Seyferts to permit an unambiguous interpetation of the kinematics. Nor can we be entirely certain that these highly variable Seyferts have episodes of normal kinematic behavior. In addition, even if an excellent set of observations were obtained, the interpetation of observed continuum and line variations for a particular ion is not straightforward (Gaskell 1984). The variable continuum observed near an emission line of a particular ion is not the relevant continuum responsible for producing the ion; the relevant continuum is usually in an observationally inconvenient part of the spectrum. Time and amplitude lags across the variable continuum could be a source of error or misinterpretation.

Some of the most spectacular line profile changes have been observed in NGC4151 (Penston *et al.* 1981; Ulrich *et al.* 1984) where different UV line fluxes and profiles exhibit markedly different responses and time lags following continuum flux variations. The rise time of the C III] line following increases in the ionizing flux were found to be much longer than that of MgII and C IV, and this has generally been interpreted as evidence of a stratification in the broad line region in which the C III] emitting regions are further from the central source of radiation. At the workshop, however, Gaskell reported on calculations (Gaskell and Sparke 1984) of time dependent emission line regions which indicate that line fluxes of different ions respond quite differently to continuum flux variations even if the clouds are all at the same distance from the central source. In particular, when the incident flux on a typical optically thick emission line region is suddenly increased, the C IV line responds by increasing much faster than the C III] and Mg II lines. This is in fact the pattern observed in NGC 4151. Furthermore, the paraboloid coincident with the line of sight is *immediately* aware of a sudden flare in the continuum flux, with no time delay. Gaskell stressed that the correct procedure to determine the spatial distribution of emitting gas around a flaring central source is a line-continuum cross-correlation analysis (Cherepashchuk and Lyuti 1973). In addition, a proper interpetation of a given profile variability observation may require a calculation of the time-dependent response of emitting regions (clouds) that are both optically thick and thin in the Lyman continuum. For example, C IV line emission from fully-ionized clouds may not vary with modest changes in the ionizing flux while that from optically thick clouds would.

Recent dramatic emission line variations in the Seyfert 1 galaxy Akn 120 were described at the workshop by Peterson *et al.* (1984). In addition to its variability, Akn 120 is very unusual in having double-peaked Balmer lines in which the emission peaks ($+1800$, ~ -1300 km s^{-1}) persist during the profile variations (Capriotti *et al.* 1982; Peterson *et al.* 1983). Such persistence may be difficult to understand on the radially moving cloud picture. Certainly, given our ignorance of the origin of the broad line gas, it is possible to imagine that a large number of asymmetrically arranged clouds might have a similar radial velocity at some time, producing a peak in the emission line. However, after a flow (or acceleration) time in the broad line region, $t_{fl} \sim 10$ yrs, the velocity of the peak would be expected to change, while the persistent features have been observed for over six years. Perhaps the peaks in this unusual object are more sensitive to the source function for the gas than its subsequent dynamical behaviour. For example, a sheared out massive gas cloud or star cluster orbiting the central mass could provide a long-lived, velocity-dependent source of broad line gas.

The $H\beta$ profile in Akn 120 is so variable that the mean profile peak has shifted from an overall red asymmetry to a blue asymmetry, and the sense of asymmetry – red or blue – relative to the $H\beta$ peak and relative to [O III] can in fact disagree at the same epoch. Capriotti *et al.* (1982) showed that such behavior can be a result of differential variability in excitation of outflowing clouds due to light travel time effects, even in a kinematical situation for which the emission line profile would be symmetric if the source of ionizing radiation were constant with time. According to Peterson, the integrated $H\beta$ flux in Akn 120 responds very rapidly to continuum variations, suggesting that the broad line region is less than a light month in size. With such a small emission line region, the ionization parameter $\Gamma \approx 0.2/(n_{10}R_{lm})$ is too large unless the density exceeds 10^{10} cm^{-3}, implying that the C III] emission comes from a separate region of lower density. Detailed photoionization calculations at plasma densities $\gtrsim 10^{10}$ cm^{-3} will ultimately be required to decide conclusively whether such regions contribute to the broad line region or not.

Peterson also pointed out that the $H\beta$ profile in Akn 120 at half maximum exhibits a redshift of ~ 400 km s^{-1} relative to the rest frame of [O III]λ5007. If this is interpreted as a gravitational redshift, a central mass of $\sim 10^8 M_\odot$ is indicated, which would be consistent with the observed emission line widths interpreted in terms of a model in which line broadening arises from gravitationally bound or orbiting radiating elements. Such a conclusion must be somewhat tentative, however, since the possibility of light travel time profile inhomogeneities is likely in Akn 120, and also de Bruyn and van Groningen (1984) have determined that the narrow [O III] λ5007 line is blue shifted by ~ 120 km s^{-1} relative to the rest velocity of the stars in Akn 120.

The most spectacular new variability observation reported at the workshop was the announcement by Lawrence that the entire broad line emission in NGC 4151 had completely disappeared! During such periods of low continuum flux, the emitting regions experience only inward gravitational forces, and, unless these forces are always dominant, it is hard to believe that a completely normal kinematical situation can be rapidly reestablished if and when the continuum turns on again. It must be emphasized therefore that observations of Seyferts having more moderate variability will provide the most trustworthy information about broad line kinematics and, conversely, that the structure and velocity field in objects such as NGC 4151 may provide little insight into steady state conditions that prevail in the majority of active galactic nuclei.

VII. MODELS PRESENTED AT THE WORKSHOP

In this final section we briefly summarize several models of the broad line region presented at the workshop which have not been already discussed above.

The most detailed and comprehensive dynamical model for the broad line region presented at the workshop was that of Kwan, produced in collaboration with Carroll. This model is an extension of the parabolic-orbital model (Kwan and Carroll 1982) including finite sized clouds and detailed calculations of emission line profiles for several strong lines. In this model large clouds are assumed to fall inward almost radially under the influence of the gravitational field of the condensed central mass. When they reach the broad line region, the clouds become trapped into nearly circular orbits by the action of the drag force of a relativistically hot intercloud wind, and eventually spiral in fragmented form into the central mass. In the optimum or standard model, 2×10^4 clouds having dimensions 1.5×4 pc are located at 1 kpc from a central mass of $10^{10} M_\odot$. Clouds having small angular momenta, approximately $u_{orb} \times 60$ km s^{-1} pc, where $u_{orb} \gtrsim 210$ km s^{-1} is the local orbital velocity at 1 kpc, fall almost radially toward the center in $\approx 2 \times 10^6$ yrs to within ~ 2 pc of the central mass. The high dynamical pressure in the intercloud wind at this small radius removes enough orbital energy so that the clouds becomes trapped into an inward spiralling orbit. The core of the line profile is produced by a spherically symmetric ensemble of clouds during their radial infalling trajectories, while the wings of the lines are generated by the spherical system of trapped clouds. The orbiting clouds speed up as they spiral in until they achieve a maximum velocity ($u \approx 14,000$ km s^{-1} at $R \approx 7 \times 10^{17}$ cm) at which point the clouds are assumed to be destroyed. During the infall, the clouds are assumed to have constant column densities, $N = 10^{23}$ A cm^{-2}, but their masses and crossectional areas decrease with radius as $\sim R^{-p}$. Model cloud systems with constant cloud masses give profiles which are too jagged and have stronger wings than those observed. A power law with $p = 0.5$ produces line profiles similar to the characteristic logarithmic shape and represents a nonconservation of cloud mass that might be expected if the clouds were ablated by the action of the intercloud wind. The initial cloud masses are $2400M_\odot$. At the moment the clouds become trapped, they are assumed to become strongly sheared by differential Keplerian forces; these sheared worm-shaped clouds, which extend to ~ 20 pc in length, may also be regarded as a large number of small cloud fragments with correlated velocities. In order to smoothly cover the full extent of the emission line profile, $-10,000$ to $+10,000$ km s^{-1} with $\sim$ tens of initial clouds, it is necessary to provide the clouds at 1 *kpc* with an internal velocity spread of ~ 10 km s^{-1} which becomes greatly magnified at ~ 2 pc, where the clouds become captured into circular orbits. The total accretion rate of clouds into the central black hole, $\sim 23M_\odot$ yr^{-1}, is somewhat larger than the mass outflow rate in the intercloud wind, $\sim 10M_\odot$ Å yr^{-1}, provided the wind is relativistically hot and rapidly expanding ($\hat{u} = 1.3 \times 10^9$ km s^{-1}).

The emission line profiles calculated by Kwan and Carroll for this model (using a random sample of clouds) are reasonably smooth, but intensity fluctuations remain at a ~ 10 % level across the line profile due to the finite (50-100) number of clouds contributing at each time to the profile. The He Iλ5876 line profile is much broader than that of $H\beta$, in agreement with observations (Shuder 1982), and Mg IIλ2798 is a bit narrower. Emission of $Ly\alpha$ is assumed to be nonisotropic in the cloud frame, with more emission directed toward the source of ionizing radiation. This necessarily produces a relative enhancement of the blue side of the $Ly\alpha$ profile, particularly in the core of the line, due to the

initial one-way radial infall of all the clouds. The centroid of the
*Ly*α profile is also shifted to the blue.

High resolution line profile observations of Akn 120 (at an
epoch in early October 1982) were presented by van Groningen and
interpreted as a result of two velocity systems, (i) an outflowing
region producing a nearly symmetric slightly blue-shifted profile,
and (ii) an emission-line producing rotating disk which generates a
double-peaked profile characteristic of finite disks (Mathews 1982;
van Groningen 1983). A two-component photoionized broad line
region has also been suggested by Collin-Souffrin *et al.* (1980,
1982). The high excitation lines of *Ly*α, C IV, and He II are
only represented in the nearly central profile component, while the
double-peaked emission line system contains most or all of the Fe II
emission and has a rather small $H\alpha/H\beta$, suggesting high densities
($\gtrsim 10^{10}$ cm^{-3}). A rotating disk illuminated from above could in
principle account for the velocity persistence of these peak-like features in Akn 120. However, the strength of the blueward displaced
peak is much greater than that of the redward component which
is submerged in the red shoulder of the nearly centrally symmetric profile. Even with light travel time inhomogenieties, the two
peaks would be expected to be essentially equal in strength on the
rotating disk hypothesis. Line asymmetries produced by disk illumination from a tilted jet might be more pronounced in the line
wings than in the core. Any ratio of peak intensities could result
from differential absorbtion across the disk, however.

According to de Bruyn and van Groningen, at least two
other active galaxies have spectra that show evidence of two redshift systems: the Seyfert 1 galaxy IC 3291 and Mkn 279. High
resolution observations of the Seyfert 1 galaxy Mkn 335 were also
reported by van Groningen. This galaxy has exceptionally strong
blue asymmetry in the broad lines. In the extreme red wing
$H\alpha/H\beta$ approaches unity. This is interpreted by van Groningen as an indication of very high densities ($n \gtrsim 10^{13}$ cm^{-3}). He
regards this component of the broad line system as emission from
a nearly face-on rotating accretion disk. Most of the *Ly*α and

C IV is explained as coming from a second outflowing system of lower density ($n \lesssim 10^9$ cm^{-3}) which produces the blue wing, while the red symmetric counterpart is assumed to be occulted by the disk.

De Robertis described a model for a non-spherically symmetric broad line region in which ionizing radiation from a central source is limited to a biconical region, the remainder being blocked by an optically thick accretion disk. This allows broad line clouds to be accelerated outward by radiation force within a conical regions surrounding the symmetry axes, while also permitting gravitationally dominated gas to flow inward near the plane of symmetry within or above the accretion disk. Some of this inflowing gas can be accreted, while some of it may provide a source for broad line gas by flowing in across the surfaces of the conical volumes where it can experience the radiation force. Line profiles calculated by De Robertis using a Monte Carlo technique for a system of outwardly accelerated isotropically emitting clouds provided line profiles in good agreement with observations when the opening angles in the conical outflow are not too small. Moderate opening angles often fit observed profiles better than the corresponding spherically symmetric models, however. Differences (inhomogeneities) in the mass injection rate between the two cones could result in asymmetries and variability similar to those observed in some broad line profiles.

Shlosman described a physical model for an accretion disk origin for the broad line gas (Shlosman, Vitello, and Shaviv 1984). Provided the cooler ($T \sim 10^4 - 10^5$ K) regions of the disk, located near $r \sim 10^{16}$ cm, are shielded by the inner disk from the hard power-law continuum in a quasar, a UV line-driven wind, similar to those which may occur in early type stars, can proceed vertically from the disk surface. The asymptotic velocity of the wind, $u \sim 10^9$ km s^{-1}, is comparable with broad line widths. As the wind rises from the disk surface, it eventually becomes illuminated and heated by the hard power law radiation from the vicinity of the central massive black hole. The gas flow becomes thermally unstable at the base of the broad line region, $R \sim 10^{16}$ *cm*, as the temperature rises through the range $10^{6.5} \lesssim T \lesssim 10^8$ K and forms into a two-phase medium (Krolik, McKee, and Tarter 1981) with dense phase clouds having rather large densities ($n \sim 10^{13}$) and column densities ($N \sim 10^{25}$). Subsequently, the clouds, confined by the hot Compton-heated wind pressure, are accelerated through the broad line region ($R \sim 10^{18}$ cm) by radiation forces. In this model, the emission line clouds are formed very close to the central mass and at densities $\gtrsim 10^{10}$ cm^{-3}, where no detailed photoionization and line emission calculations are currently available. Since the broad line outflow predicted in this model is axially, not spherically, symmetric, emission line profiles (including the possibility of broad absorption lines) may depend on the aspect angle of the line of sight with the rotation axis.

We are grateful to the National Science Foundation for partial support (AST83- 12971) during the preparation of this review.

REFERENCES

Allen, A. J. 1984, *M. N. R. A. S.*, **210**, 147.

Anderson, K. S. and Kraft, R. P. 1969, *Ap. J.*, **158**, 859.

Antokhin, I. I., and Bochkarev, H. G. 1983, *Sov. Astron.*, **27**, 261.

Baldwin, J. A. and Netzer, H. 1978, *Ap. J.*, **226**, 1.

Blumenthal, G. R. and Mathews, W. G. 1975, *Ap. J.*, **198**, 517.

_____ . 1979, *Ap. J.*, **233**, 479.

Blandford, R. D. and McKee, C.F. 1982, *Ap. J. (Letters)*, **255**, 419.

Braginskii, 1965, in *Reviews of Plasma Physics*, ed. M. A. Leontovich. (Consultants Bureau: New York), **1**,, 205.

Capriotti, E., Foltz, C., and Byard, P. 1980, *Ap. J.*, **241**, 903.

. 1981, *Ap. J.*, **245**, 396.

Capriotti. E. R., Foltz, C.B., and Peterson, B. M. 1982, *Ap. J.*, **261**, 35.

Carswell, R. F. and Ferland, G. J. 1980, *M. N. R. A. S.*, **191**, 55.

Cherepashchuk, A. M. and Lyuti, V. M. 1973, *Ap. J. (Letters)*, **13**, 165.

Clavel, J. and Joly, M. 1984, *Astr. Ap.*, **131**, 87.

Collin-Souffrin, S., Dumont, S. Heidmann, N., and Joly, M. 1980, *Astron. Ap.*, **83**, 190.

Collin-Souffrin, S., Dumont, S., and Tully, J. 1982, *Astron. Ap.*, **106**, 362.

Cowie, L. L. and McKee, C. F. 1977, *Ap. J.*, **211**, 135.

Crenshaw, D. M. and Peterson, B. M. 1984, *Ap. J.*, in press.

Cromwell, R. and Weyman, R. 1970, *Ap. J. (Letters)*, **159**, L147.

Davidson, K. and Netzer, H. 1979, *Rev. Mod. Phys.*, **51**, 715.

de Bruyn, A. G. and van Groningen, E. 1984, preprint.

De Robertis, M. 1984, talk at Santa Cruz Summer Workshop.

Ferland, G. J. and Elitzur, M. 1984, preprint.

Foltz, C., Weymann, R., Hazard, C., Turnshek, 1984, preprint.

Gaskell, C. M. 1981, Ph. D. thesis, University of California, Santa Cruz.

_____. 1982, *Ap. J.*, **263**, 79.

_____. 1984a, *Annals New York Academy of Sciences*, **422**, 350.

_____. 1984b, preprint.

Gaskell, C. M. and Sparke, L. 1984, in preparation.

Gaskell, C. M. 1984, talk at Santa Cruz Workshop.

Gerbal, D. and Pelat, D. 1981, *Astron. Ap, .,* 95 18.

Holt, S. S., Mushotzky, R. F., Becker, R. H., Boldt, E. A., Ser-lemitsos, P. J., Szymkowiak, A. E., and White, N.E. 1980, *Ap. J. (Letters),* **241**, L13.

Hubbard, E. N. and Puetter, R. C. 1983, *Ap. J.,* **265**, 35.

Junkkarinen, V. T., Burbidge, E. M., Smith, H. E. 1983, *Ap. J.,* **265**, 51.

Krolik, J. H. 1977, *Phys. Fluids,* **20**, 264.

_____. 1979, *Ap. J.,* **228**, 13.

Krolik, J. H., McKee, C. F., and Tarter, C. B. 1981, *Ap. J.,* **249**, 422.

Kwan, J. and Krolik, J. H. 1979, *Ap. J. (Letters),* **233**, L91

_____. 1981, *Ap. J,* **250**, 478.

Kwan, J. and Carroll, T. J. 1982 Ap. J. 261 25.

Kwan, J. 1984, preprint.

Levich, E. V. and Sunyaev, R. A. 1970, *Ap. J. (Letters),* **7**, 69.

_____. 1971, *Sov. Astron. Jour.,* **15**, 363.

MacAlpine, G. M., Davidson, K., Gull, T. R., Wu, C-C, l984, preprint.

Mathews, W. G. and Baker, J. C. 1971, *Ap. J.,* **170**, 241.

Mathews, W. G. 1974, *Ap. J.,* **189**, 23.

_____. 1976, *Ap. J.,* **207**, 351.

_____. 1982, *Ap. J.,* **258**, 425.

_____. 1983, *Ap. J.,* **272**, 390.

Mathews, W. G. and Blumenthal, G. R. 1977, *Ap. J.,* **214**, 10.

Mathews, W. G., Blumenthal, G. R., and Grandi, S. A. 1980, *Ap. J.*, **235**, 471.

McCray, R. A. 1979, in *Active Galactic Nuclei* ed. C. R. Hazard and S. A. Mitton (Cambridge: Cambridge University Press).

McKee, C. F. and Tarter, C. B. 1975, *Ap. J.*, **202**, 306.

Meyers, K. A., and Peterson, B. M. 1984, in preparation.

Miller, J. S. and Antonucci, R. R. J. 1983, *Ap. J. (Letters)*, **271**, L7.

Mushotzky, R. F., Serlemitsos, P. J., Becker, R. H., Boldt, E. A., and Holt, S. S. 1978, *Ap. J.*, **220**, 790.

Mushotzky, R. F. 1982, *Ap. J.*, **256**, 92.

_____. 1984, paper at Workshop on "Future of UV Astronomy Based on Six Years of IUE Research," Goddard Space Flight Center, April 1984.

Netzer, H. 1978, *Ap. J.*, **219**, 822.

Oke, J. B. and Korycansky, D. G. 1982, *Ap. J.*, **255**, 11.

Osmer, P. 1979, *Ap. J.*, **227**, 18.

Osterbrock, D. E., and Shuder, J. M. 1982, *Ap. J. Suppl.*, **49**, 149.

Penston, M. V. *et al.* 1981, *M. N. R. A. S.*, **196**, 857.

Peterson, B. M., Foltz, C. B., Miller, H. R., Wagner, R. M., Crenshaw, D. M., Meyers, K. A., and Byard, P. L. 1983, *A. J.*, **88**, 926.

Peterson, B. M., Meyers, K. A., Capriotti, E. R., Foltz, C. B., Wilkes, B. J., and Miller, H. R. 1984, Ap. J., in press.

Raine, D. J. and Smith, A. 1981, *M. N. R. A. S.*, **197**, 339.

Reichert, G., Mushotzky, R. F., Petre, R., and Holt, S. S. 1984, in preparation.

Reichert, G. A. 1984, talk at Santa Cruz Workshop.

Richstone, D. D., Ratnatunga, K., and Schaeffer, J. 1980, *Ap. J.*, **240**, 1.

Sakimoto, P. J., and Coroniti, F. V. 1981,, *Ap. J.*, **247**, 19.

Shields, G. A. 1978, in *Pittsburgh Conference on BL Lac Objects*, ed. A. M. Wolfe (Pittsburgh: University of Pittsburgh Press), p. 257.

Shlosman, I., Vitello, P. A., and Shaviv, G. 1984, preprint.

Shuder, J. M. 1982, *Ap. J.*, **259**, 48.

Shull, M. 1983, *Ap. J.*, **264**, 446.

_____. 1984, talk at Santa Cruz Summer Workshop.

Smith, H. E. 1980, *Ap. J. (Letters)*, **241**, L137.

Smith, M. G. *et al.* 1981, *M. N. R. A. S.*, **195**, 437.

Soltan, A. 1982, *M. N. R. A. S.*, **200**, 115.

Stocke, J., Liebert, J., Maccacaro, T., Griffiths, R. E., and Steiner, J.E. 1982, *Ap. J.*, **252**, L9.

Ulrich, M. H. and Boisson, C. 1983, *Ap. J.*, **267**, 515.

Ulrich, M. H., *et al.* 1984, *M. N. R. A. S.*, **206**, 221.

Van Groningen, E. 1983, *A. A.* , **126**, 363.

Verbunt, F., Fabian, A. C., and Rees, M. J. 1984, *Nature*, **309**, 331.

Wandel, A. and Yahil, A. 1984, preprint.

Weymann, R. 1976, *Ap. J.*, **286**, 78.

Weymann, R. J., Scott, J. S., Schiano, A. V. R., and Christianson, W. A. 1982, *Ap. J.*, **262**, 497.

Wilkes, B. J. and Carswell, R. F. 1982, *M. N. R. A. S.*, **201**, 645.

Wilkes, B. J. 1984, *M. N. R. A. S.*, **207**, 73.

Williams, R. E. 1972, *Ap. J.*, **178**, 105.

Wills, B. J., Netzer, H., and Wills, D. 1980, *Ap. J. (Letters)*, **242**, L1.

Wu, C. C., Boggess, A., and Gull, T. R. 1983, *Ap. J.*, **266**, 28.

Wu, C. C. 1984, talk given at Santa Cruz Workshop

Young, P. J., Sargent, W. L. W., and Boksenberg, A. 1982, *Ap. J. Suppl*, **48**, 455.

ACTIVE GALAXIES VIEWED FROM THE INFRARED

G. H. Rieke

Steward Observatory
University of Arizona
Tucson, AZ

ABSTRACT

Infrared studies tend to emphasize continuum processes in active galaxies and QSOs: stellar populations and star formation; thermal reradiation of absorbed optical and ultraviolet photons by dust; and the extension of the nonthermal spectra of these sources from the optical toward the radio. In many cases, a new perspective also results from the ability of infrared photons to penetrate dense clouds of interstellar dust. This review suggests areas where these tools need to be applied to advance our understanding of active galaxies. Starburst models must be developed that account for realistic triggering mechanisms, accurate tracks of stellar evolution, and the interactions of supernova remnants with themselves and the interstellar medium. The role of starbursts in LINERs in late type, dusty galaxies needs further clarification. The importance of dust in contributing to the infrared continuum of Seyfert galaxies (and in reddening the optical and ultraviolet continua) is still not clear, after 15 years of controversy. A similar situation holds for the role of dust in broad line radio galaxies and QSOs. Coordinated with other measurements, infrared observations of the nonthermal continua of violently variable objects can trace the development of their spectral components. Finally, infrared astronomy is beginning to play an important role in the identification and classification of counterparts to members of complete samples of radio sources.

I. INTRODUCTION

Different spectral regions either attract people with different outlooks or create them. As was appropriate for the occasion and location of the Santa Cruz Workshop on Active Galaxies and QSOs, the optical region was discussed most intensively. Because of the rich emission line spectra in the optical and the mature technology to observe it, the result was an emphasis on the ionized gas around active nuclei and the ultraviolet continuum that excites it.

Near 1 micron, a number of transitions occur that bring a different perspective. Longward of this wavelength, atomic transitions are relatively weak and active galaxy spectra have few bright lines. The technology for observing these lines is less well developed; in any case, until the advent of SIRTF the background fluxes will seriously impair studies of the faint lines available. However, continua can be studied readily without interference from spectral lines or interstellar reddening.

The nonthermal continuum of the nuclear source must join to the radio through the infrared. Dust around sources of visible or ultraviolet luminosity becomes enormously visible in the infrared through thermal reradiation. The continua of normal galactic stellar populations peak beyond 1 μm. Consequently, this review will be concerned primarily with the nature of the infrared continua in active sources, with reddening, and with stellar populations, including the presence of starbursts that either accompany or mimic active nuclei. Other fruitful investigations have concerned the rich optical spectra of objects at sufficiently high redshift to shift them into the infrared, and comparison of infrared line strengths with the predictions of models developed to fit the optical and ultraviolet lines.

We prepared a comprehensive review of this general topic about six years ago (Rieke and Lebofsky 1979); related reviews have been written by Soifer and Neugebauer (1981), Stein and Soifer (1983), and Smith (1984a; 1984b). Taken together, these articles give a much more detailed and historical account than will be provided here. This review is an update with an emphasis on topics discussed at the workshop.

The review is organized by type of galaxy activity, in order of increasing dominance of nonthermal nuclear activity over stellar and other thermal emission processes. One advantage of this order is it naturally poses the question of what similarities and evolutionary links bridge the gaps imposed by the section headings in the text. The rapid growth in observational and analytic capabilities relevant to the infrared promises real progress on this fundamental question, for example, by studies in the near infrared where galaxy nuclear activity can be observed largely free of reddening effects and by observations at longer wavelengths which can detect nuclear activity that may be hidden from optical studies either by reddening, by the surrounding stars, or because of a steeply falling nonthermal spectrum.

II. STARBURST GALAXIES

Prior to 1980, a number of investigators had suggested that certain aspects of powerful galaxy activity could arise from episodes of extremely intense formation of massive stars (e.g. Harwit and Pacini 1975; Rieke and Low 1975; Larson and Tinsley 1978). Rieke *et al.* (1980) combined these suggestions into a comprehensive first-order theory of a starburst. This theory takes as boundary conditions 1) the bolometric luminosity, 2) the ionizing flux deduced from extinction-corrected recombination line intensities, 3) the flux in the near infrared generated by red giants and supergiants, 4) the relative proportions of red giants and supergiants as indicated by the depth of the CO absorption bands, 5) the nuclear mass, 6) the nonthermal radio emission (assumed generated by supernova remnants), and 7) the X-ray emission (assumed generated by stellar remnants, Compton scattering, or supernova remnants). For galaxies such as M82, NGC 253, and MGC 2903, starburst models were shown to be successful at meeting these conditions so long as the initial mass function is weighted strongly toward massive stars compared with the IMF in the solar neigh-

borhood. A beautiful confirmation of this model is the detection of
the predicted high density of supernova remnants in M82 (Kronberg, Biermann, and Schwab 1984). The model has also been
applied successfully to other galaxies: NGC 7714 (Weedman *et al.*
1981), NGC 3690 (Gehrz, Sramek, and Weedman 1983), and NGC
6240 (Rieke *et al.* 1984), and re-examined and confirmed for NGC
2903 (Wynn-Williams and Becklin 1984).

The first order starburst model assumes, without consideration of the required conditions, that star formation at the
necessary rates can occur. It follows the progress of each star along
a simplified evolutionary track through the supernova stage, computing the integrated properties of the starburst as the sum of the
contributions of the stars without regard to possible interactions.
Given the success of such models, more sophisticated models need
to be developed.

In extreme cases (e.g., NGC 6240; Rieke *et al.* 1984),
massive stars must be forming in galactic nuclei at a rate of 100
$M_\odot$/yr over a period of the order of 10^8 years. Means must be
found to explain such large mass flows, and the appropriate conditions must be imposed on the starburst models. The original
suggestion by Larson and Tinsley (1978) that galaxy interactions
seem to play an important role in triggering starbursts seems am-
ply confirmed by infrared studies (Rieke *et al.* 1980; Joseph *et al.*
1984; Soifer *et al.* 1984; Lonsdale, Persson, and Matthews 1984;
Cutri and McAlary 1985), which further imply that interactions
may be nearly essential for the most energetic starbursts (Cutri
and McAlary 1985; Rieke *et al.* 1984). Mechanisms for initiating
and feeding starbursts should reflect this observation. However,
at least 40% of bright spiral galaxies show reasonably strong nuclear infrared excesses approximately independent of Hubble type
(Rieke and Lebofsky 1978; Scoville *et al.* 1983; de Jong *et al.*
1984). The triggering and feeding mechanisms must therefore
work efficiently at lower levels in most galaxies. A good beginning
at understanding these processes has been made by a number of

authors, such as Loose, Krugel and Tutukov (1982), Nozakura and Ikeuchi (1984), and Scalo and Struck-Marcell (1984).

Advances can also be made in understanding the stellar populations in starburst galaxies. One approach, taken by Terlevich and Melnick (1984), is to improve the stellar evolutionary tracks in the starburst models to include short-lived phases which can have a significant effect on the conditions in the galactic nucleus. A second approach is to carry out a detailed synthesis of the stellar populations in starburst galaxies by simulating their spectra through the combination of the spectra of appropriate Galactic stars. Because of the strong extinction of the star-forming regions, such a study needs to be conducted in the infrared; fortunately, infrared spectrometers have now reached the necessary sophistication to do this work.

Starburst models have been most criticized from the viewpoint of radio astronomy. For example, Heckman *et al.* (1983b) express skepticism that starbursts would exhibit nonthermal radio spectra; a number of authors have commented on differences in the radio and 10 μm structure in some starburst nuclei; and Ulvestad (1982) remarks that the starburst galaxies have steeper radio spectra than would an ensemble of normal supernovae. In evaluating these arguments and others, it is useful to remember the conditions in a starburst nucleus. The star forming activity is frequently confined to within a few hundred to a thousand parsecs of the galactic nucleus. It seems unlikely that star formation was triggered simultaneously over this entire region; hence, one might expect varying levels of supernova activity relative to the populations of newly formed and forming hot stars and hence relative to the infrared flux density. However, the timescales for evolution to the supernova stage ($< 10^7$ yrs) are shorter than those associated with the nuclear starbursts (about 10^8 yrs). The nuclear gravitational potential therefore confines the supernovae to the same general region as the starburst, unlike extranuclear H II regions where the hot stars tend to dissipate the gas before they evolve to supernovae. Finally, one should take note of the density of supernova remnants. Taking M82 as an example and assuming that each remnant has a lifetime of about 10^5 yrs, there is only a volume of about 1000 pc^3 per active supernova remnant. Hence, the older remnants will tend to overlap and coalesce, producing an extended region filled with energetic particles.

None of these points answers directly the problems in understanding the radio spectra of starburst galaxies. They do indicate areas where the assumptions of the first order starburst calculations oversimplify in taking the rate of star formation to be uniform over the nucleus and in treating each star's evolution independently. More sophisticated models are needed!

III. LINERS

One would like to distinguish starburst from active galaxies – those which derive most of their nuclear energy from nonstellar processes. Attempts to extend the first order starburst model to account for Seyfert manifestations (Condon *et al.* 1982) appear to be unsuccessful because of the absence of exceptionally strong stellar fluxes from the nuclei of Seyfert galaxies (Ulvestad 1982). However, it has been suggested that more sophisticated starburst models can produce Seyfert and LINER (Heckman 1980) characteristics, at least during brief intervals in their evolution. As discussed below, the starburst or non-starburst nature of some LINER characteristics is uncertain at present. Thus, this fundamental distinction is elusive; if a clear distinction is to be made, it will probably derive from a more precise understanding of LINERs than we have now.

We choose to distinguish between early and late type galaxies in discussing LINERs. When observed at adequate sensitivity, modern spectrometers detect LINER characteristics in about 50% of early type galaxies (Heckman 1984; Phillips 1984). These galaxies tend to have very compact nuclear radio sources, a general lack of any indicators of recent episodes of star formation, and relatively weak ultraviolet excesses which can frequently be attributed directly to a nuclear source. Thus, it is expected that the LINER spectrum is produced by a weak active nucleus. Only a few examples have been studied in the infrared, and more work is required to define the properties of a representative selection of sources. The prototype, NGC 1052, has a strong infrared excess which is strongly polarized near 2 μm and appears to be non-variable (Rieke, Lebofsky, and Kemp 1982) and compact at 10 μm (Becklin, Tokunaga, and Wynn-Williams 1982); this behavior agrees with the arguments from optical data that this class of source contains a weak, non-thermal source that photoionizes the surrounding gas. For NGC 1052, it remains unclear whether the nonthermal spectrum dominates longward of 2 μm fluxes arise from dust heated by the central source (Becklin, Tokunaga, and Wynn-Williams 1982). The other early type LINERs observed beyond 2.2 μm tend to have infrared excesses (NGC 4278, M87; Heckman *et al.* 1983a), but sufficiently weak that detailed studies will be very difficult.

LINER spectra are also observed in some late type and irregular galaxies, where substantial interstellar material is available and recent star formation is hence a possibility. In these cases the origin of the excitation is less clear. A number of examples have been studied particularly thoroughly. In the cases of NGC 253 and NGC 6240, the 10 μm source is extended, implying an extended luminosity source, and other infrared properties, such as abnormally deep stellar CO absorption bands, demand the presence of a powerful starburst (Rieke and Low 1975; Rieke *et al.* 1980; Rieke *et al.* 1984). For NGC 3079, the 10 μm source is also extended (Lawrence *et al.* 1984); although this galaxy has not yet been studied thoroughly, it seems likely that the extended luminosity also requires a starburst. NGC 2110 and 5033, on the other hand, apperar to share many characteristics with type 1 Seyfert galaxies and NGC 4826 has a 10 to 20 μm excess with a higher color temperature than is typical of starbursts (Lawrence *et al.* 1984). The available evidence appears to implicate starburst activity as one of the possible origins of LINER spectra, but the

physical connection between starbursts and the excitation is unclear. The original suggestion that LINER spectra represent shock
excitation (Heckman 1980) has fallen into disfavor compared with
photoionization models based on a power law ultraviolet spectrum
from an active nucleus (Rose and Tripicco 1984 and references
therein). Shock excitation could be a frequent development from
starburst activity, when a high rate of supernovae releases large
amounts of mechanical energy into the interstellar medium, or it
could arise from large-scale cloud collisions that lead to enhanced
star formation. Shock models deserve reconsideration, in view of
the discovery of huge amounts of shock heated molecular hydrogen
in the starburst LINER galaxy NGC 6340 (Becklin, DePoy, and
Wynn-Williams 1984; Joseph, Wright, and Wade 1984; Rieke *et
al.* 1984).

IV. SEYFERT GALAXIES

Since the discovery of the strong infrared excess of NGC
1068 (Pacholczyck and Wisniewski 1967), there has been a running debate regarding whether Seyfert galaxies emit in the infrared
predominantly by thermal reradiation by dust grains, or whether
we see their nuclear nonthermal continua directly. At stake in this
debate is an understanding of how reddening affects the observable properties of these galaxies, such as emission line strengths,
and a correct picture of the underlying continuum of the nuclear
source, free of the influence of both reddening and components
arising from thermal reradiation. The potential effects of dust in
Seyfert 1 galaxies and related objects have been discussed recently
by Rudy (1984).

A fairly large number of bright Seyferts have been studied spectrophotometrically in the infrared with an aim to find the
emission and absorption features associates with Galactic thermal
sources (such as emission bands at 3.3, 7.7, 8.6, and 11.3 μm and
the silicate feature at 10 μm – see, e.g., Aitken and Roche, 1984;
Roche *et al.* 1984; Jones *et al.* 1984; and references therein).

Perhaps a quarter to a third of the galaxies do show such features (the exact percentage depends on whether one includes the heavily obscured X-ray discovered active galaxies, which tend to have features relatively often). These features indicate that a least some of the infrared flux from these galaxies is thermal reradiation. In general, the measurements do not address how dominant this component is; in addition, because of selection effects the exact percentage of Seyferts with infrared features is not well determined [e.g., the galaxies bright enough for spectrophotometry in the infrared tend to have steep spectra which may themselves indicate thermal emission – on the other hand, it is expected that the known sample of Seyfert galaxies is deficient in infrared-bright examples (Rieke 1978)].

Where spectral features are not found, the nature of the continuum can be constrained by its shape and behavior during variations. For these less definitive arguments, it is worthwhile to separate carefully what is known observationally from the interpretations that have been attached to it.

As pointed out by Neugebauer *et al.* (1976) and reinforced by the more extensive data of Rieke (1978), there is a tendency for the infrared spectra of type 2 Seyfert galaxies to fall rapidly toward higher frequencies and to be very steep near 3 μm (after the stellar spectral component has been removed), whereas the non-stellar spectra of type 1 galaxies tend to be relatively strong in the 1 to 3 μm region and frequently can be fit by power laws of modest slope over most of the 1-20 μm range. The continuum shape for the type 2 galaxies suggests strongly that the excess emission is reradiation by dust, a result that is consistent with indications of reddening from the emission line ratios (e.g., Koski 1978; Rieke 1978; Lacy *et al.* 1982). The continuum shape of type 1 galaxies suggests the presence of a dominant nonthermal, power law source.

More detailed studies of type 1 galaxies have utilized multi-aperture photometry (e.g., McAlary 1981) and accurate variability studies (Lebofsky and Rieke 1980) to examine the intrinsic spectral behavior of type 1 galaxies near 1 μm. In virtually every case, careful subtraction of the stellar component has indicated that the nuclear spectrum steepens dramatically going from 3 to 1 μm. In addition, the infrared component is variable but with different amplitude and phase from the variability in the optical and ultraviolet. In no case has a single power law spectrum accounted satisfactorily for the behavior of the nuclear source over the entire 0.3 to 20 μm region accessible in these groundbased observations.

This conclusion has been questioned by Malkan and Sargent (1982) and Malkan and Fillipenko (1983), who have revived arguments for a unified optical-infrared power law spectrum. To consider their arguments, we will discuss NGC 4151 since it has been studied particularly thoroughly by their methods and in the infrared. Malkan and Fillipenko (1983) use SIT area photometry to construct a model of this galaxy as an unresolved nuclear source embedded in an extended distribution of stars. They also obtained high resolution spectra to estimate the stellar flux from the equivalent widths of stellar absorption lines. The stellar spectrum estimated by either method can be subtracted from spectrophotometry to obtain the nuclear spectrum. Malkan and Fillipenko state that "Rieke's estimate of the stellar flux in NGC 4151 is 50% too high. Consequently, the nonstellar spectrum of NGC 4151 is not qualitatively different from that at maximum brightness: both fall smoothly from 2-3 μm to the visible, roughly with a power law slope of -1.1 to -1.2. There is no short-wavelength break near 1 μm." The statement about lower stellar flux is based on their Table 1, where a flux of 14 mJy (with an error of 10 to 20%) is listed in a 10" beam at 5400 Å, compared with Rieke and Lebofsky's (1981) estimate of 19$\pm$2 mJy in an 11" beam at 5600 Å. However, in comparing these estimates, one should correct them to equivalent wavelengths and beam diameters; doing so for Malkan and Fillipenko gives a flux of 17$\pm$2 mJy for comparison with the result of Rieke and Lebofsky (1981). These values are in general agreement although somewhat lower than that obtained by McAlary (1981) from multi-aperture photometry. We conclude that all the methods employed find consistent estimates of the stellar flux, a very encouraging result.

If estimates of the stellar component agree, why is there disagreement on the nuclear spectrum? Part of the answer is that the spectrum seems to approximate a power law when the source is bright but develops an inflection near 1 μm and eventually a steep cutoff as the source becomes fainter. The beginning of this behavior is apparent in the data of Malkan and Fillipenko (1983) as presented in their Figure 8; the "faint" spectrum *is* qualitatively different from the "bright" one, falling below a power law connecting 3 μm and the visible by a factor of at least 1.45 near 1 μm. This behavior is even more obvious in the data of Rieke and Lebofsky (1981), which trace the nuclear source to levels at least five times weaker than the "faint" level reported by Malkan and Fillipenko. The data leave little question that the source cuts off steeply when it is at its faintest. It is less clear whether the apparent power law at brighter levels is the superposition of two components, one of which still cuts off near 1 μm, or is a true unified power law. However, the differing variability amplitudes and phases across this wavelength support the former possibility.

Although observed less thoroughly than NGC 4151, the available data indicate that a number of other Seyfert galaxies exhibit spectral components with steep cutoffs near 1 μm and with distinct behaviors on either side of this weavelength during variations. Additional measurements of variability and infrared area photometry – becoming possible with the advent of sensitive infrared arrays – would be extremely useful in probing this behavior more thoroughly and in a larger sample of galaxies.

The underlying cause of this spectral behavior is less clear than its existence. Both the variability and the spectral cut off are consistent with the near infrared spectrum arising through thermal reradiation by very hot dust (Penston *et al.* 1974; Lebofsky and Rieke 1980; Rieke and Lebofsky 1981; Puschell 1981). A possible difficulty with this interpretation is that the spectral features frequently found in Galactic thermal sources are only seen in a minority of type 1 Seyferts, as already mentioned. In particular, spectral features are absent or of marginal detectability in NGC 4151 (Jones *et al.* 1984). An additional puzzle is the correlation between 3.5 μm and X-ray fluxes for Seyfert 1 galaxies (Elvis *et al.* 1978; McAlary, McLaren and Crabtree 1979; Malkan 1984); this correlation is not an obvious prediction of thermal reradiation models. Additional measurements that could test for the presence of very hot dust would include more detailed spectral information near 1 μm and detailed variability studies of a range of sources – thermal reradiation would require that the minimum variability timescale go as the square root of the source luminosity.

Puetter and Hubbard (1984) suggest that the near infrared excess may be free-free emission from exceedingly dense, hot gas. Compared with thermal reradiation, the spectrum of such a source would cut off less abruptly toward the blue and variations would occur more rapidly, probably on a timescale similar to variations in the strengths of the broad emission lines. It is also conceivable that the observations refer to complex behavior by a single nuclear source; in this case, the similarities in cutoff frequency and variability behavior seen among the galaxies observed to date are probably to be ascribed to coincidence. Observations of a larger number of galaxies should reveal a larger range of behavior.

For the brighter Seyfert galaxies, it is possible to measure infrared line spectra. Nearly all such studies have tried to determine to what extent the departures from theoretical emission line ratios in the optical and ultraviolet are due to radiative transfer effects or can be attributed to reddening by dust. An extensive survey of Paα strengths by Lacy *et al.* (1982) found that reddening accounts for the line strength anomalies satisfactorily in most cases, but that a few galaxies have exceptionally weak Paα

for their Balmer decrements and Hβ stregnths (see also Rudy and Willner 1983). More extensive sets of hydrogen recombination line measurements for NGC 1068 (Neugebauer *et al.* 1980), NGC 4151 (McAlary and McLaren 1981; Rieke and Lebofsky 1981), and NGC 3783 (Ward 1984) reinforce this conclusion. LeVan *et al.* (1984) have observed the He 10830A line for comparison with the strength of the line at 5876A. For type 2 Seyferts, they find that the ratio can be explained adequately by reddening, but they must invoke radiative transfer effects to account for the ratio seen in type 1 galaxies.

Recent observations of Brγ/Paα in Seyfert galaxies with extremely steep Balmer decrements show this ratio to be much smaller than predicted by simple theoretical models (Cutri, Rieke, and Lebofsky 1985; McAlary, Rieke, and Lebofsky 1984). It is thought that this result demands exceedingly high densities (n $>$ 10^{11}) in the broad line emitting regions of the galaxies (Puetter and Hubbard 1984). Additional theoretical modeling of the relative strengths of the weak infrared hydrogen recombination lines would be highly desirable.

V. RADIO GALAXIES

In principle, the term "radio galaxies" includes virtually every object discussed in this review. As commonly used to describe a radio source with a measurable optical extent, the class is to a large extent defined by selection effects, the more so now that many relatively nearby QSOs have been found to lie within extended optical images that presumably are surrounding galaxies. A more satisfactory classification might be based on spectral characteristics. A galaxy could be defined to be an object whose integrated light is dominated by stars in the red and near infrared, near the peak of a normal galaxy spectrum. Such a definition would recognize certain nearby objects with visible extent but extremely powerful nuclei – e.g., 3C120, Markarian 231 – as nearby QSOs. However, on historical grounds I discuss under this heading a variety of nearby objects divided into those with narrow nuclear emission lines (NLRG) and those with broad lines (BLRG).

Recent infrared studies of NLRG have examined their suitability as probes of galaxy evolution and cosmological parameters. Out to 3 μm, it has been found that the majority of these sources have similar colors and luminosities to those of radio quiet galaxies (e.g. Lebofsky 1981; Lilly and Longair 1982; Lebofsky and Eisenhardt 1985). Hence, their red and near infrared light is in fact dominated by starlight and the properties of the stellar population are not significantly modified by the presence of the radio source. This result provides the foundation for application of these galaxies in cosmological studies.

At wavelengths longward of 3 μm, NLRG have been studied by Heckman *et al.* (1983a) and Elvis *et al.* (1984). The galaxies with strong *nuclear* radio sources nearly all show excess infrared emission with strength roughly proportional to the strength of the compact radio source (Heckman *et al.* 1983a).

Photometry of BLRG has also been summarized by Heckman *et al.* (1983a) and Elvis *et al.* (1984). These objects tend to have very strong excesses, which dominate their entire optical-infrared spectra. By our proposed spectral classification scheme, they would be nearby QSOs. Elvis, *et al.* (1984) measured three BLRGs with extremely steeply falling infrared spectra; they discuss whether these excesses arise from intrinsically steep nonthermal spectra or from reradiation from dust. A number of arguments favor the latter explanation, particularly since two of these galaxies, 3C445 (Rudy and Tokunaga 1982) and 3C234 (Carleton *et al.* 1984), have been shown to have large Paα/Hα flux ratios, indicative of very high levels of extinction to their emission line regions. A number of BLRGs are also known with relatively flat infrared spectra. In three of these cases, III Zw 2 (Lebofsky and Rieke 1980), 3C120 (Rieke and Lebofsky 1979), and 3C382 (Puschell 1981), it has been shown that the infrared variations are decoupled from the optical ones. As with type 1 Seyfert galaxies, this observation suggests that reradiation by dust dominates the infrared spectra.

VI. "QUIESCENT" QSOs

By quiescent QSOs, we refer to non-violently-variable sources, including classical QSOs such as 3C273. Infrared studies of these sources have concentrated on the nature of their continuum emission and on measuring their emission line spectra, particularly to study the strengths of the familiar optical lines in objects at high redshift.

The optical-infrared continua of a number of these sources were studied in detail by Neugebauer *et al.* (1979). They found a general tendency for the spectra to steepen from the longer infrared towards 1 μm, and then to flatten dramatically through the visible and ultraviolet. A similar tendency was deduced from near infrared photometry by Hyland and Allen (1982). Both sets of authors suggested that this behavior could arise if the near infrared fluxes included a significant contribution from heated dust. Capps, Sitko, and Stein (1982) call attention to a subset of QSOs with very steep infrared spectra, strongly suggestive of thermal spectra connected with circumnuclear dust. However, on balance Stein and Soifer (1983) concluded that the evidence on thermal components in QSO infrared spectra was inconclusive.

Additional information on this question can be obtained from variability studies. 3C273 has been monitored extensively for more than 10 years (Rieke and Low 1972; Neugebauer *et al.* 1979; Rieke and Lebofsky 1979; Cutri *et al.* 1985). Other than a brief infrared outburst, described by Rieke and Lebofsky (1979), for most of this time the source remained relatively constant across the optical-infrared spectrum. Recently, 3C273 has brightened significantly over its entire optical infrared spectrum, (Robson *et al.* 1983; Cutri *et al.* 1985). A thermal source of the luminosity of 3C273 would have serious difficulty varying with the observed timescale; at least the variable portion of the spectrum of this

QSO must arise nonthermally.

In addition to 3C273, Cutri *et al.* (1985) report simultaneous UBVRIJHK monitoring of six other "quiescent" QSOs. All six were seen to vary in the optical, yet none was found to change in the infrared. This behavior mimics that found for type 1 Seyfert galaxies, and its possible explanation as the presence of thermally reradiating dust, excited gas, or a complex continuum source has been discussed above. The usual occurrence of a spectral inflection near 1 μm favors explanations that invoke the presence of heated dust aroud the QSO nucleus.

QSO emission lines were first studied in the infrared by Grasdalen (1976) and subsequently by a number of authors as summarized by Puetter *et al.* (1981) and Soifer *et al.* (1981). Note that in many cases these studies are of the optical lines in the QSO rest frame, shifted into the infrared. The conclusions of these studies are described by Stein and Soifer (1983): optical depth effects are required to explain the relative line strengths, but a modest amount of reddening cannot be ruled out as a further contributor to the observed departures from theoretical line ratios.

VII. VIOLENTLY VARIABLE QSOs

A collection of attributes tend to occur together in a subset of QSOs: violent and rapid variability, strong continuum polarization, and relatively steep continuum spectra of powerlaw shape or with smooth downward curvature. Some of these objects have emission lines (OVV QSOs), some do not (BL Lac type sources) and some have lines when the continuum is faint and no lines when it is bright. These objects appear to be closely related and are discussed together in this section.

Because of the rapid variability across the entire electromagnetic spectrum, it has been difficult to determine the interrelation of different spectral components and to trace the development of outbursts in these objects. Recent efforts have addressed this problem by the organization of large groups of observers with access to instruments covering the spectrum from the radio to the X-ray. In general, the results of these campaigns have been compatible with the conventional synchro-compton models, if relativistic beaming toward the observers is included. A consequence of the model fits is a suite of values for the source parameters, such as magnetic fields, degree of beaming, etc. Examples of these programs can be found in Bregman *et al.* (1984a and references therein) and Worrall *et al.* (1984b and references therein).

A campaign on BL Lac itself by Moore *et al.* (1980) indicated from extensive polarimetry that the source undergoes continuous outbursts in a stochastic fashion. From the variable dependence in amount and position angle of polarization with wavelength (Rieke *et al.* 1977; Impey, Brand, and Tapia 1982; Puschell *et al.* 1983; Sitko, Stein, and Schmidt 1984), it appears that these outbursts can have somewhat distinct spectral shapes and decay rates, so that different outbursts can dominate the spectrum simultaneously at different wavelengths.

A different perspective on these sources was provided by the discovery that many flat spectrum radio sources with very faint optical identifications are violently variable and have spectra falling exceedingly steeply between the infrared and optical (Rieke, Lebofsky, and Kinman 1979). A systematic study of a sample of 200 flat spectrum radio sources shows that nearly all of the 15 optically faintest members fall into this category (Kuhr *et al.*, in preparation). Detailed monitoring is not available for all of the brighter members of the sample. However, if the number of violent variables is estimated from the number of objects classified spectroscopically as of BL Lac type, the "empty field" objects constitute a significant fraction (30 to 40 %) of this category. IUE spectra of traditional BL Lac type sources frequently show them to fall steeply in the UV even when their optical-infrared spectra are relatively flat (Maraschi *et al.* 1984; Bregman *et al.* 1984b; Worrall *et al.* 1984a). Thus, some of these objects are probably similar to those found in "empty fields," but their spectral cutoffs occur at higher frequencies. On the other hand, a percentage of these objects show simple power law spectra extending from the near infrared through the highest observed UV frequency. Evidently, a steep spectral cutoff is a very frequent, but not universal, characteristic of violently variable QSOs. Other characteristics of these sources, for example their X-ray spectra, may correlate with this spectral dichotomy.

VIII. CONCLUSIONS

As this review is being completed, the trickle of results from IRAS is about to become a flood with the release of the point source catalog. This review is hopefully the last one that will be prepared on this subject without some understanding of the true unbiased contents of the infrared sky, although many IRAS discoveries will remain unappreciated until the fainter sources can be detected and studied again with SIRTF.

Two overriding problems confront studies of active galaxies and QSOs: how do they derive and emit their energy, and what relation do sources of different types and ages have to each other. Current infrared studies have addressed primarily the first of these questions, having achieved major successes with the widespread application of the starburst concept, with the drawing of attention to the role of dust in reddening active galaxy continua and reradiating the absorbed energy at longer wavelengths, and with the extension of measurements of nonthermal optical continua including the discovery of extreme forms of continua that had been largely overlooked in optical studies. With the IRAS source lists and the continued improvements in infrared instrumentation, the problem of source evolution and interrelations will receive much more attention. Because of the efficiency of dust in absorbing ultraviolet energy, virtually any active source in a spiral galaxy calls attention to itself in the infrared. The IRAS catalog will therefore provide an unbiased census of nearby galaxy activity. In addition, with the newest near infrared instrumentation on large, groundbased telescopes we are beginning to study the rest frame optical morphology and spectra of sources at large redshift, fundamental information to understand source evolution over a cosmic timescale.

It is a pleasure to thank J. Miller and Lick Observatory for their efforts in organizing a very interesting and successful workshop. A number of participants helped with the preparation of this review by sending preprints. My attendance at the workshop and the preparation of the review were supported by the National Science Foundation.

REFERENCES

Aitken, D. K., and Roche, P. F. 1984, preprint.

Becklin, E. E., Depoy, D., and Wynn-Williams, C. G. 1984, presented at the Infrared Detector Workshop, Laramie, Wyoming, May 15-16.

Becklin, E. E., Tokunaga, A. T., and Wynn-Williams, C. G. 1982, *Ap. J.*, **263**, 624.

Bregman, J. N., *et al.*, 1984a, *Ap. J.*, **276**, 454.

_____ . 1984b, this conference.

Capps, R. W., Sitko, M. L., and Stein, W. A. 1982, *Ap. J.*, **255**, 413.

Carleton, N. P., Rudy, R. J., Willner, S. P., and Tokunaga, A. T. 1984, *Ap. J.*, **284**, 523.

Condon, J. J., Condon, M.A., Gisler, G., and Puschell, J. J. 1982, *Ap. J.*, **252**, 102.

Cutri, R. M., and McAlary, C. W. 1985, submitted to Ap. J.

Cutri, R. M., Rieke, G. H., and Lebofsky, M. J. 1985, Ap. J., in press.

Cutri, R. M., Wisniewski, W. Z., McAlary, C. W., Rieke, G. H., and Lebofsky, M. J. 1985, preprint.

de Jong, T., Clegg, P. E., Soifer, B. T., Rowan-Robinson, M., Habing, H. J., Houck, J. R., Aumann, H. H., and Raimond, E. 1984, *Ap. J. (Letters)*, **278**, L67.

Elvis, M., Maccacaro, T., Wilson, A. S., Ward, M. J., Penston, M. W., Fosbury, R. A. E., and Perola, G. C. 1978, *M.N.R.A.S*, **183**, 129.

Elvis, M., Willner, S. P., Fabbiano, G., Carleton, N. P., Lawrence, A., and Ward, M. 1984, *Ap. J.*, **280**, 574.

Gehrz, R. D., Sramek, R. A., and Weedman, D. W. 1983, *Ap. J.*, **267**, 551.

Grasdalen, G. L. 1976, *Ap. J. (Letters)*, **208**, L11.

Harwit, M., and Pacini, F. 1975, *Ap. J. (Letters)*, **200**, L127.

Heckman, T. M. 1980, *Astr. Ap.*, **87**, 152.

_____ . 1984, this conference.

Heckman, T. M., Lebofsky, M. J., Rieke, G. H., and van Breughel, W. 1983a, *Ap. J.*, **272**, 400.

Heckman, T. M., Van Breugel, W., Miley, G. K., and Butcher, H. R. 1983b, *A. J.*, **88**, 1077.

Hyland, H. R., and Allen, D. A. 1982, *M.N.R.A.S.*, **199**, 943.

Impey, C. D., Brand, P. W. J. L., and Tapia, S. 1982, *M.N.R.A.S.*, **198**, 1.

Jones, B., Worrall, D. M., Rodriguez-Espinosa, J. M., Stein, W. A., and Gillett, F. C. 1984, *Pub. A.S.P.*, **96**, 692.

Joseph, R. D., Meikle, W. P. S., Robertson, N. A., and Wright, G. S. 1984, *M.N.R.A.S.*, **209**, 111.

Joseph, R. D., Wright G. S., and Wade, R. 1984, *Nature*, **311**, 132.

Koski, A. T. 1978, *Ap. J.*, **223**, 56.

Kronberg, P. P., Biermann, P., and Schwab, F. 1984, preprint.,

Lacy, J. H., Soifer, B. T., Neugebauer, G., Matthews, K., Malkan, M., Becklin, E. E., Wu, C.-C., Boggess, A., and Gull, T. R. 1982, *Ap. J.*, **256**, 75.

Larson, R. B., and Tinsley, B. M. 1978, *Ap. J.*, **219**, 46.

Lawrence, A., Ward, M., Elvis, M., Fabbiano, G., Willner, S. P., Carleton, N. P., and Longmore, A. 1984, preprint.

Lebofsky, M. J. 1981, *Ap. J. (Letters)*, **245**, L59.

Lebofsky, M. J., and Eisenhardt, P. R. M. 1985, preprint.

Lebofsky, M. J., and Rieke, G. H. 1980, *Nature*, **284**, 410.

LeVan, P. D., Puetter, R. C., Smith, H. E., and Rudy, R. J. 1984, *Ap. J.*, **284**, 23.

Lilly, S. J., and Longair, M. S. 1982, *M.N.R.A.S.*, **199**, 1053.

Lonsdale, C. J., Persson, S. E., and Matthews, K. 1984, Ap. J., in press.

Loose, H. H., Krugel, E., and Tutukov, A., 1982, *Astr. Ap.*, **105**, 342.

McAlary, C. W. 1981, unpublished Ph.D. thesis, Univ. of Toronto.

McAlary, C. W., and McLaren, R. A. 1981, *Ap. J*, **250**, 98.

McAlary, C. W., McLaren, R. A., and Crabtree, D. R. 1979, *Ap. J.*, **234**, 471.

McAlary, C. W., Rieke, G. H., and Lebofsky, M. J. 1984, this conference.

Malkan, M. A. 1984, this conference and preprint.

Malkan, M. A., and Fillipenko, A. V. 1983, *Ap. J.*, **275**, 477.

Malkan, M. A., and Sargent, W. L. W. 1982, *Ap. J.*, **254**, 22.

Maraschi, L., Tanzi, E. G., and Treves, A. 1984, in *COSPAR/IAU Symposium*, Rojen, Bulgaria.

Moore, R. L., et al. 1980, *Ap. J.*, **235**, 717.

Neugebauer, G., Becklin, E. E., Oke, J. B., and Searle, L. 1976, *Ap. J.*, **205**, 29.

Neugebauer, G., et al. 1980, *Ap. J.*, **238**, 502.

Neugebauer, G., Oke, J.B., Becklin, E. E., and Matthews, K. 1979, *Ap. J.*, **230**, 79.

Nozakura, T., and Ikeuchi, S. 1984, *Ap. J.*, **279**, 40.

Pacholczyck, A. G., and Wisniewski, W. Z. 1967, *Ap. J.*, **147**, 394.

Penston, M. V., Penston, M. J., Selmes, R. A., Becklin, E. E., and Neugebauer, G. 1974, *M.N.R.A.S.*, **169**, 357.

Phillips, M. M. 1984, this conference.

Puetter, R. C. and Hubbard, E. N. 1984, preprint.

Puetter, R. C., Smith, H. E., Willner, S. P., and Pipher, J. L. 1981, *Ap. J.*, **243**, 345.

Puschell, J. J. 1981, *Ap. J.*, **247**, 28.

Puschell, J. J., Jones, T. W., Phillips, A. C. Rudnick, L., Simpson, E., Sitko, M., Stein, W. A., and Moneti, A. 1983, *Ap. J.*, **265**, 625.

Rieke, G. H. 1978, *Ap. J.*, **226**, 550.

Rieke, G. H., Cutri, R. M., Black. J. H., Kailey, W. F., McAlary, C. W., Lebofsky, M. J., and Elston, R. 1984, Ap. J., in press.

Rieke, G. H., and Lebofsky, M. J. 1978, *Ap. J. (Letters)*, **220**, L37.

_____. 1979, *Ann Rev. Astr. and Ap.*, **17**, 477.

Rieke, G. H., Lebofsky, M. J., and Kemp, J. C. 1982, *Ap. J. (Letters)*, **252**, L53.

Rieke, G. H., Lebofsky, M. J., Kemp, J. C., Coyne, G. V., and Tapia, S. 1977, *Ap. J. (Letters)*, **218**, L37.

Rieke, G. H., Lebofsky, M. J., and Kinman, T. D. 1979, *Ap. J. (Letters)*, **213**, L151.

Rieke, G. H., Lebofsky, M. J., Thompson, R. I., Low, F. J., and Tokunaga, A. T. 1980, *Ap. J.*, **238**, 24.

Rieke, G. H., and Lebofsky, M. J. 1981, *Ap. J.*, **250**, 87.

Rieke, G. H., and Low, F. J. 1972, *Ap. J. (Letters)*, **177**, L115.

_____. 1975. *Ap. J.*, **197**, 17.

Robson, *et al.* 1983, *Nature*, **305**, 194.

Roche, P. F., Aitken, D. K., Phillips, M. M., and Whitmore, B. 1984, *M.N.R.A.S*, **207**, 35.

Rose, J.A., and Tripicco, M. J. 1984, *Ap. J.*, **285**, 55.

Rudy, R. J. 1984, *Ap. J.*, **284**, 33.

Rudy, R. J., and Tokunaga, A. T. 1982, *Ap. J. (Letters)*, **256**, L1.

Rudy, R. J., and Willner, S. P. 1983, *Ap. J. (Letters)*, **267**, L69.

Scalo, J. M., and Struck-Marcell, C. 1984, submitted to Ap. J. (Letters).

Scoville, N. Z. Becklin, E. E., Young, J. S., and Capps, R. W. 1983, *Ap. J.*, **271**, 512.

Sitko, M. L., Stein, W. A., and Schmidt, G. D. 1984, *Ap. J.*, **282**, 29.

Smith, M. G. 1984a, in *Proc. XVI ESLAB Symposium on Galactic and Extragalactic Infrared Spectroscopy*.

Smith, M. G. 1984b, in *Active Galactic Nuclei*, ed. J. E. Dyson (Manchester), preprint.

Soifer, B. T., and Neugebauer, G. 1981, in *IAU Symposium 96 on Infrared Astronomy*, ed. Wynn-Williams and Cruikshank (Reidel , Dordrecht), p. 329.

Soifer, B. T., et al. 1984, *Ap. J. (Letters)*, **278**, L71.

Soifer, B. T., Neugebauer, C., Oke, J. B., and Matthews, K. 1981, *Ap. J.*, **243**, 369.

Stein, W. A., and Soifer, B. T. 1983, *Ann. Rev. Astr. and Ap.*, **21**, 177.

Terlevich, R., and Melnick, J. 1984, cited in Smith (1984b).

Ulvestad, J. S. 1982, *Ap. J.*, **259**, 96.

Ward, M. 1984, this conference.

Weedman, D. W., Feldman, F. R., Balzano, V. A., Ramsey, L. W., Sramek, R. A., and Wu, C.-C. 1981, *Ap. J.*, **248**, 105.

Worrall, D. M., *et al.*, 1984a, *Ap. J.*, **278**, 521.

_____. 1984b, *Ap. J.*, **284**, 512.

Wynn-Williams, C. G., and Becklin, E. E. 1984, submitted to Ap. J.

DUST IN ACTIVE GALACTIC NUCLEI AND QUASARS

Gordon M. MacAlpine

Department of Astronomy
University of Michigan, Ann Arbor

ABSTRACT

Radiation from many active galaxies and possibly quasars shows evidence of dust extinction. Much of the obscuring material is apparently located close to the line-emitting gas. Then an asymmetric geometrical configuration viewed from various angles could explain observed differing amounts of reddening suffered by broad-line regions, narrow-line regions, and continua. Because active galaxy dust characteristics may differ significantly from those of interstellar material in our Galaxy, it is advisable to base extinction corrections on actual observations across relevant spectral ranges. Potential procedures for establishing useful corrections and inferred dust distributions are discussed in this chapter.

I. INTRODUCTION

The possibility that radiation from active galaxies and quasars has been altered significantly by wavelength dependent obscuration must be carefully considered if we are to understand the observed emission-line and continuum spectra. Accurate line ratios, corrected for differential extinction if necessary, are required to investigate gas physical conditions such as temperature and density and to address the question of relative chemical abundances. In addition, corrected line and continuum luminosities and continuum spectral characteristics are essential for photoionization calculations and for the investigation of energy sources or radiation production mechanisms. In this chapter, "active galaxies" will refer to Seyferts (classes 1 and 2), broad and narrow-line radio galaxies (BLRGs and NLRGs), and X-ray galaxies. Some galaxies to be discussed may overlap among these groups.

Early quantitative measurements showed that Seyfert galaxies have steep Balmer line decrements, but it was recognized that the ratios could not be simultaneously explained simply in terms of recombination and interstellar reddening (e.g., Osterbrock and Parker 1965; Oke and Sargent 1968). To test for unambiguous evidence of dust in the line of sight, Wampler (1968, 1971) measured the [S II] λ10320 and λ4072 blends, which arise from the same upper level and have a ratio insensitive to gas physical conditions (Miller 1968). He derived substantial reddening for the nuclei of NGC 1068 and NGC 1275, with inconclusive results for several other Seyfert galaxies. However, McKee and Petrosian (1974) searched the observed continua in a number of quasars for broad absorption corresponding to the λ2200 extinction "bump" characteristic of most interstellar dust in our Galaxy, and they looked for dust-caused deviations from assumed power-law continua. No evidence for dust was found. Hence, the idea developed early that maybe Seyfert galaxies, especially Seyfert 2s like NGC 1068, are reddened while quasars are not.

Concern about the possible importance of reddening in Seyfert 1 galaxies and quasars increased following Baldwin's (1977) discovery of considerably lower than expected Lyα (and other ultraviolet lines) to Balmer line ratios, which was subsequently confirmed by many investigators. Furthermore, International Ultraviolet Explorer (IUE) satellite data showed that: a) dust in active galaxies may have extinction properties different from those of interstellar material in our Galaxy, in particular with respect to the possible lack of a prominent λ2200 feature (e.g., Neugebauer *et al.* 1980); and b) the continuous spectra of quasars cannot be completely described by simple power laws (e.g., Richstone and Schmidt 1980). Therefore, it was realized that arguments against quasar reddening, based on apparent continuum characteristics, may not be valid. Shuder and MacAlpine (1977, 1979), Baldwin *et al.* (1978), and Netzer and Davidson (1979) pointed out certain line ratios (to be discussed later) which imply significant differential extinction due to dust in the line of sight, while London (1979) emphasized the case for dust destruction of trapped Lyα emission. Still, the idea of reddening in broad-line objects was not popular because the observed Paα/Hβ ratio in 3C 273 (Grasdalen 1976; Puetter *et al.* 1978) posed an apparent dilemma, being too low for straight-forward recombination or collisions modified by substantial differential extinction. Subsequent measurements of Paα/Hβ in other Seyfert galaxies and quasars were also recognized as being incompatible with a simple reddening interpretation of the observed ultraviolet to Balmer line ratios (Puetter *et al.* 1981; Soifer *et al.* 1981). Whereas Puetter *et al.* (1978) reported very high Paα/Hβ in the quasar PG0026+129 [providing the principal argument for dust by Baldwin *et al.* (1978) and encouraging Shuder and MacAlpine (1979) to publish their results], this particular measurement was later revised considerably downward.

It is now widely recognized that reddening does not provide the only means for changing initially emitted hydrogen line ratios and that optical-depth effects are also important. Of particular consequence are the very large optical depths possible for extended partially ionized regions past the "Strömgren distance," where strong Lyα trapping and subsequent collisional Balmer line enhancement from the n=2 level can decrease both the Lyα/Hβ and Paα/Hα ratios (Kwan and Krolik 1979, 1981; Canfield and Puetter 1980, 1981; Mathews, Blumenthal, and Grandi 1980; Weisheit, Shields, and Tarter 1981). The most complete of these calculations, which includes heavy elements, is the Kwan and Krolik "standard model" (see also Kwan 1984).

Does the optimized "standard model" account for typical observed Seyfert 1 galaxy or quasar spectra without any recourse to differential extinction? The requirement of some reddening is explicitly noted by Kwan and Krolik (1981), who pointed out that constraints on the allowable gas column density limit their model prediction for Lyα/Hβ to about 10.4, whereas ratios as low as 2 or 3 are sometimes measured. The "typical" observed Lyα/Hβ for Seyfert 1 galaxies is near 5 (Wu, Boggess, and Gull 1983). In addition, Shuder and MacAlpine (1979), Netzer and Davidson (1979), and MacAlpine and Feldman (1982) found that differential extinction factors of four or more still appear necessary to account for observed He II $\lambda 1640/\lambda 4686$ and OI $\lambda 1304/\lambda 8446$ ratios derived from average composite spectra. MacAlpine (1981) also suggested that observed He II $\lambda 4686/H\beta$ may be used to set limits on the possible amount of $H\beta$ collisional enhancement. Then the He II $\lambda 4686$ measurements of Osterbrock (1977) for Seyfert 1 galaxies appear to require substantial reddening as part of an explanation for observed $Ly\alpha/H\beta$, although $\lambda 4686$ is relatively weaker in quasars. Finally, the revealing analysis by Lacy *et al.* (1982) of hydrogen lines in Seyfert galaxies and quasars suggests that *both* optical-depth effects and reddening are required to account for all points in the $Pa\alpha/H\alpha$ vs. $H\alpha/H\beta$ diagram. A large range of reddening is indicated, corresponding to values of E(B-V) between 0 and 0.5 or more (excluding the unusually heavily reddened Seyfert 2 galaxy Mkn 348).

Other evidence for dust in active galactic nuclei (AGNs) comes from polarization and infrared observations. The similar polarization of emission lines and underlying continuum in some Seyfert 1s (*e.g.,* Thompson *et al.* 1980; Martin *et al.* 1982) and in BLRGs (*e.g.,* Rudy *et al.* 1983, 1984) have been interpreted in terms of dust scattering or transmission. In addition, Rudy *et al.* (1983) reported a correlation between measured polarizations and broad-line Balmer decrements; and numerous AGNs show an apparent increase in continuum polarization toward shorter wavelengths, which may be indicative of dust scattering. On the other hand, Miller and Antonucci (1983) have cautioned that apparent blueward increases in polarization may also result from dilution by unpolarized starlight. In addition, Antonucci (1984) and Antonucci and Miller (1985) suggested that observed polarization of lines and nonstellar continuum in the BLRG 3C 234 and in the Seyfert 2 galaxy NGC 1068 (cf. Angel *et al.* 1976) results from electron scattering. This interpretation could be applied to other AGNs as well, but some of them show indications of dust besides polarization. Infrared observations (of which strong thermal emission, 3.3 μm emission, and 10 μm silicate absorption are good indications of dust) are discussed in the workshop proceedings chapter by Rieke. Numerous polarization and infrared investigations have also bee reviewed by Stein and Soifer (1983).

Even though the conclusion that dust is associated with many AGNs seems inescapable, some investigators appear to have advocated the idea that observed spectra must be explainable in terms of either reddening or optical-depth effects, but not a combination of both. One major cause for this philosophy may be a lingering belief in the requirement of a prominent λ2200 signature if dust is present in the line of sight. However, this feature is not characteristic of all dust in our Galaxy (Bless and Savage 1972; Meyer and Savage 1981; Clayton and Martin 1985), it is not prominent for stars in the LMC (Nandy *et al.* 1981; Koornneef and Code 1981) or the SMC (Prévot *et al.* 1984), and it is not always detected in Seyfert galaxies otherwise known to have significantly reddened line emission (Neugebauer *et al.* 1980; Malkan and Oke 1983). Even its cause is somewhat controversial (e.g., MacLean, Duley, and Millar 1982; Andriesse 1977). Simply stated, we cannot rely on the λ2200 feature as a test for reddening (which may not have a similar effect on continuum and line emission anyway; see § IV), except possibly for that reddening caused by material in our own Galaxy. Another often used, but misleading argument against any role for reddening has been its well documented inability to account for all broad hydrogen lines without recourse to optical-depth effects. Contrary to some apparent misunderstandings, Netzer and Davidson (1979) and Shuder and MacAlpine (1979) never asserted that dereddened hydrogen lines should have case B recombination ratios. In fact, the inadequacy of simple recombination for Balmer lines in Seyfert galaxies, with or without reddening, was recognized prior to Baldwin's 1977 discovery of low ultraviolet to optical line ratios. The main effects that modify the Balmer lines had already been proposed long before that date (Osterbrock and Parker 1965; and numerous references cited in

§IV.C of Davidson and Netzer 1979).

Still another potential barrier to understanding dust is a tendency to disregard its effects as being too hard to establish reliably in quantitative terms or as being inconsequential by comparison with more heavily reddened objects. In his valuable, thought-provoking discussion of the reddening problem, Grandi (1983) attributed little weight to the analysis by Lacy *et al.* (1982) because predictions of Kwan and Krolik (1981) and Canfield and Puetter (1981) model calculations were used in deducing that numerous objects exhibit substantial reddening. Whereas Grandi was correct in pointing out that the calculations may be inadequate, they are in fact encouragingly accurate. These and other models along with our related (albeit incomplete) understanding of relevant physical processes provide a framework for investigation of gas conditions; and, although we should proceed with caution, it is better to heed a comparison between theory and observations than to ignore possible reddening simply because of distrust in the theory. The other point mentioned above may be illustrated by Malkan's (1983) heroic analysis of [O II] and [S II] lines in 47 AGNs. He reported typical derived reddenings corresponding to "only" several tenths of a magnitude in E(B-V). Note that, for E(B-V) = 0.3, a Galactic extinction law (Seaton 1979) would result in a substantial differential extinction factor of nearly 8 between Lyα and Hα.

Clearly, we must make every possible effort to understand the roles played by dust for a full appreciation of active galaxy and quasar phenomena; and it is becoming apparent that reddening will have to be considered on a case by case basis. Numerous articles in the literature and recent investigations discussed at this workshop suggest that different classes of sources may be reddened by different amounts, with widely varying degrees of obscuration within each class. In addition, emission arising from separate regions suffers different amounts of extinction. And, to make matters still more interesting, because the obscuring material in an active galaxy environment is probably not identical to that in the interstellar medium of our Galaxy, we should be wary of standard interstellar extinction curves. The remainder of this chapter is devoted primarily to these issues, as they were discussed by various participants in the workshop.

II. PROPERTIES OF AGN AND QSO DUST

Can we make a reasonable *a priori* guess what reddening characteristics to expect? This seems presumptuous in view of the fact astronomers do not all agree on what produces the interstellar extinction curve in the Milky Way (see Savage and Mathis 1979). On the other hand, most pundits favor some mixture of graphite and silicate particles (e.g., Mathis, Rumpl, and Nordsieck 1977; Hong and Greenberg 1980). Recently, Draine and Lee (1984) used an improved treatment of dielectric functions for graphite and silicate to demonstrate that the Mathis, Rumpl, and Nordsieck particle distributions account satisfactorily well for the average Galactic interstellar extinction curve from ultraviolet through infrared wavelengths. However, altered grain sizes can have pronounced effects on extinction characteristics (Mathis 1978; Bode and Evans 1982); and Martin *et al.* (1982) reported that modeling of observed polarization in the Seyfert 1 galaxy IC 4329A shows the responsible grains to be typically 3 times smaller than Galactic polarizing grains. Also, different size and mixture distributions of graphite and silicates would be required to account for the weakness of the λ2200 feature and steep rise to the ultraviolet seen for stars in the Magellanic Clouds. And, whereas we might imagine that some galaxies without a detectable λ2200 feature (e.g., NGC 1068) may be characterized by very steep SMC-type extinction curves, others (e.g., 3C 120 and Mkn 79; Oke and Zimmerman 1979) show what appear to be strong λ2200 signatures like that for dust in our Galaxy. Any preconceived notions may turn out to be wrong, and reddening corrections over any spectral range will be more reliable if based on actual observations.

III. TOWARD OBTAINING APPLICABLE
EXTINCTION PARAMETERS

So how can we establish an extinction curve for an individual active galaxy or quasar? The most direct way is to use
measurable emission lines with predictable intensity ratios span-
ning the infrared to optical to ultraviolet parts of the spectrum.

a) Infrared-Optical Reddening Corrections

i) Broad-Line Regions

For infrared and optical wavelengths, the hydrogen Paschen and Balmer series lines may be useful, provided important
broad-line region (BLR) optical depth and collisional effects are
adequately understood. In addition to the $Pa\alpha/H\alpha$ and $Pa\alpha/H\beta$
ratios already mentioned, Ward and Morris (1984) have suggested
using efficient red-sensitive CCD detectors to measure the Paschen
8, 9, and 10 lines between 9000A and 9500A for comparison with
corresponding Balmer lines arising from the same upper levels.
They applied this technique for the bright Seyfert 1 galaxy NGC
3783 and found the results to be consistent, for a Galactic reddening law, with extinction derived by other methods over other
wavelength ranges. As Ward and Morris pointed out, the above
Paschen lines are difficult to measure and must, in some cases,
be deblended from other features. They also noted that optical
depths, especially for transitions ending on n=2, are causes for
concern; although the effects will be smaller than for lower series
transitions. The $Br\alpha/H\gamma$ ratio, studied in NGC 4151 by McAlary
and McLaren (1981), would be more disposed to optical depths.

We should probably consider He I $\lambda 10830/\lambda 5876$ only as a
potential test for evidence of reddening, but not to measure it. As
pointed out by MacAlpine 1976 (see also Feldman and MacAlpine
1978, but be aware of a revised 2^3S to 2^3P collision rate coefficient
published by Barrington, Fon, and Kingston 1982) and illustrated
by LeVan *et al.* (1984), this ratio is sensitive to gas density and

optical depth induced collisional enhancement of the λ5876 line, especially for Seyfert 1 and quasar broad-line gas. LeVan *et al.* have suggested the use of He I λ10830/λ5876 in combination with Lyα/Hα and model calculations as a test for reddening.

The He II λ10126 (Piα) and λ4686 (Paα) recombination lines should be relatively free from both collisional and optical depth effects (see MacAlpine 1981 and below). A problem, however, is the difficulty of measuring the broad components for these lines, especially Pickering α, which may be blended with hydrogen Paschen 7 at λ10049. Also, density-dependent angular momentum (ℓ-state) redistribution in He$^+$ might be important in establishing the intrinsic ratio (see Seaton 1968).

ii) Narrow-Line Regions

The above techniques for deriving reddening corrections may be more successfully applied to lower-density narrow-line regions (NLRs) (which we take to include Seyfert 2 emission-line gas), because optical depths are lower and features are more easily measured. Unfortunately, it is often difficult or impossible to distinguish between broad and narrow-line components when *both* are present in strength. Particularly suitable cases where this has been attempted with some success are the BLRG 3C 390.3 (Netzer 1982) and the low-redshift quasar 3C 351 (Netzer, Wills, and Wills 1982), but observations were not performed in the infrared.

The possibility of estimating reddening from the ratio of [S II] blends near λ10320 and λ4072, as suggested by Miller (1968), has already been mentioned. Although measurement of the red blend with lines at λ10287, λ10320, λ10336, and λ10370 presents a special challenge, this technique could be very profitable and should receive more attention.

A general comment is in order here. Even if a Galactic extinction law is valid for a particular active galaxy or quasar, it may not apply at infrared wavelengths. Mathis (1970, 1983) has shown that, for cases with dust mixed with or close to the line-emitting gas (see §IV): a) line ratios can lead to a serious underestimate of the total amount of dust present, and b) the usual procedure using E(B-V) will lead to significant undercorrections for lines longward of about 7000A.

b) Optical Red-Blue Reddening Corrections

i) Broad-Line Regions

Reddening estimates across the visual part of the spectrum for BLRs can present a real problem. Balmer decrements are not particularly suitable because of collisional and optical-depth effects, although extremely steep decrements may indicate that reddening is unusually heavy. Gas physical conditions also influence observable He I lines (Feldman and MacAlpine 1978). The He II λ3204 (Paβ) and λ4686 (Paα) lines should have a predictable recombination ratio of about 0.54 (see Seaton 1968, 1978). Unfortunately, however, λ3204 lies in a very cluttered wavelength region and is virtually impossible to measure accurately in most broad-line spectra.

ii) Narrow-Line Regions

It was originally believed that steep NLR Balmer decrements imply reddening (e.g., Osterbrock and Miller 1975; Costero and Osterbrock 1977), but Netzer (1982) argued that self-absorption steepens the NLR decrement in the BLRG 3C 390.3. On the other hand, Gaskell (1982, 1984) has shown that NLR reddenings derived from Balmer lines are consistent with those estimated from other methods. And recent detailed theoretical calculations (Halpern and Steiner 1983; Gaskell and Ferland 1984) indicate that intrinsic Hα/Hβ is unlikely to be far from 3.1 under NLR conditions. Gaskell and Ferland also presented an NLR Lyα/Hα/Hβ diagnostic diagram that may permit one to separate out other effects from those of reddening. This method has been used by Ferland and Osterbrock (1984) to estimate the reddening in NLRGs. For these objects and some Seyfert 2s, they found the data to be consistent with reddened "normal" line ratios, with extinction corresponding to E(B-V) = 0.1 to greater than 0.6 of a magnitude.

The He II $\lambda 3204$ and $\lambda 4686$ lines provide an excellent means for correcting the optical spectra of NLR or Seyfert 2 galaxy gas (e.g., Shuder and Osterbrock 1981). The only potential drawback is the requirement of a blue-sensitive detector or modest object redshift.

As suggested by Allen (1979), one can also compare the [O II] $(\lambda\lambda 7320+7330)/(\lambda\lambda 3726+3729)$ and [S II] $(\lambda\lambda 4069+4076)/(\lambda\lambda 6716+6731)$ ratios, which are reputed to be a powerful reddening indicator for consistent values of electron density and temperature (see Malkan 1983). However, as always, perfection eludes us; and Mihalszki and Ferland (1983) have questioned whether this method might be too sensitive to other parameters such as chemical composition and ionization structure.

c) Optical-Ultraviolet Reddening Corrections

i) Broad-Line Regions

Finally, let us consider whether well-determined, measurable emission-line ratios link the important ultraviolet and optical parts of the spectrum, between which reddening corrections may be very large. Again, the broad hydrogen lines (e.g., Lyα/Hβ) are unreliable and recognized as being sensitive to gas physical conditions. Both Shuder and MacAlpine (1979) and Netzer and Davidson (1979) placed considerable emphasis on the importance of He II $\lambda 1640$ (Hα)/$\lambda 4686$ (Paα), and Netzer and Davidson also pointed out the potential for using O I $\lambda 1304/\lambda 8446$. Grandi (1983) has challenged the use of both these ratios as reddening indicators; and MacAlpine and Netzer spoke in defense of the methods at this workshop.

MacAlpine (1981) carefully examined possible line-production alternatives and concluded that the He II $\lambda 1640/\lambda 4686$ ratio probably has an intrinsic broad-line recombination value of

8-10 if the gas physical conditions and optical depths are not significantly more extreme than implied by the Kwan and Krolik (KK) standard model. Grandi (1983) argued that MacAlpine underestimated the contribution to $\lambda4686$ resulting from He^+ ($n=2$ to $n=4$, 1215.19A) pumping by diffuse hydrogen Lyα (1215.68A), the latter line profile having been very much broadened by scattering through large optical depth. However, as discussed in detail by MacAlpine, Davidson, Gull, and Wu (1985), this criticism was apparently based on a misunderstanding. By concentrating the Lyα radiation 5.9 thermal Doppler widths on either side of line center [reaching into the He^+ (2-4) absorption profile], MacAlpine attempted to maximize the pumping effect which could take place in the KK model, and it still was not enough to be important. Use of a perhaps more realistic, somewhat flatter Lyα emission profile as advocated by Grandi would only *decrease* the amount of pumping. (Grandi also quoted a considerably higher optical depth than that from which Lyα emission would be available in the KK model.) As pointed out by MacAlpine (1981) and stressed by Grandi (1983), if the gas density is much higher than 5×10^9 cm^{-3}, then pumping effects could begin to dominate recombination [see MacAlpine's 1981, eq. (10)], thereby lowering intrinsic emitted $\lambda1640/\lambda4686$. But this seems unlikely from other observational evidence (e.g., the C III] $\lambda1909$/C III $\lambda977$ ratio discussed by Shuder and MacAlpine 1979).

Bechtold *et al.* (1984) also challenged MacAlpine's (1981) He II line analysis, contending that it predicts an anomalous ratio of $\lambda1640$ and $\lambda4686$ line equivalent widths. However, their discussion involves a calculative error due to neglect of a λ^2 factor, and known equivalent width measurements do not appear to present any problems.

Finally, Netzer and Ferland (1984) questioned whether the importance of density-dependent angular momentum redistribution and its effect on He II $\lambda4686$ have been adequately considered. The answer is yes. This is why MacAlpine (1981) suggested an intrinsic recombination ratio of 8-10 for He II $\lambda1640/\lambda4686$ in Seyfert 1 galaxy and quasar broad-line gas, while the ratio would be about 7-7.5 (Seaton 1978) for lower-density Seyfert 2s and narrow-line galaxies.

Original estimates of the observed He II $\lambda1640/\lambda4686$ ratio, implying differential extinction factors of 4 or more, were based upon non-simultaneous measurements or composite spectra for high and low redshift objects (Shuder and MacAlpine 1979; Netzer and Davidson 1979). Observations by Oke and Goodrich (1981) of the Seyfert 1 galaxies Mkn 9 and Mkn 10 and the BLRG 3C 390.3 illustrate the challenge of measuring $\lambda1640$ with IUE. They derived $\lambda1640/\lambda4686$ ranging from 1.7 to 11, or 3.0 to 20 after correcting for $E(B-V) = 0.14$ assumed to result from our Galaxy. Not only are these lines often confused by low signal-to-noise, but they may also be contaminated by Fe II emission (Wills, Netzer, and Wills 1980). MacAlpine, Davidson, Gull, and Wu (1985) used 900 minutes of integration with IUE to measure an accurate $\lambda1640$ intensity for the exceptionally narrow-lined, Fe II-free Seyfert 1 galaxy Mkn 359. Comparison with nearly simultaneous ground-based observations of $\lambda4686$ suggests only slight reddening, which could be accounted for by our Galaxy. However, Mkn 359 is extraordinary in that it also exhibits a near case B recombination value of 29 for $Ly\alpha/H\beta$. This galaxy does not show evidence for either substantial reddening or extended high-optical-depth regions in the line-emitting gas. MacAlpine, Kirshner, and Henry (unpublished) have also observed several $z \approx 1$ quasars in an effort to obtain accurate measures of *both* $\lambda1640$ and $\lambda4686$ from the ground. The $\lambda1640$ line redshifted to the blue-visible does not present a problem, but $\lambda4686$ falls in a part of the spectrum with particularly strong atmospheric absorption; and we have not yet gotten a reliable ratio. More quasar observations of this type, with careful attention to suitable standard stars at nearly the same positions as the program objects, are needed.

Netzer reaffirmed his belief in the O I $\lambda1304/\lambda8446$ ratio as a valid reddening indicator. As pointed out by Netzer and

Davidson (1979), these lines, which result from hydrogen Lyβ fluorescence, are produced with equal numbers of photons. Therefore, the predicted intensity ratio, in the absence of secondary effects, is 6.5. Subsequently, Kwan and Krolik (1981) showed that collisional processes and line trapping could lower the above ratio to about 5. More recently, Grandi (1983) noted that all previous calculations neglected a potentially important transition from the 3s $^3S_1^\circ$ level (upper level of the λ1304 line) to the 2p^4 $^1D_2$ level (upper level of the [O I] λ6300 line). This intercombination transition (Einstein $A = 2.2 \times 10^3$ s^{-1}; Garstang 1961), which results in a line at λ1641, can be important in situations where the optical depth in λ1304 ($A = 5.4 \times 10^8$ s^{-1}) is large. Indeed, Kwan's (1984) new model calculations with allowance for the λ1641 transition yield a λ1304/λ8446 ratio nearer to 3. However, Netzer's re-examination of this process suggests that the λ1641 transition will *not* have a large effect on either the O I λ1304/λ8446 or He II λ1640/λ4686 ratios. First, the optical depth in λ1641 must be taken into account since the $^1D_2$ metastable level is thermally coupled to the ^3P ground term. Very large $\tau(\lambda1304)$ may result in $\tau(\lambda1641) \sim 1$, and this would affect the escape probability in the latter transition. Secondly, the *total* $\tau(\lambda1304)$ is not the important factor, since the temperature in the back of the cloud may be too low for efficient Lyβ fluorescence to occur. Instead, the value of $\tau(\lambda1304)$ at the point where most of the Lyβ pumping is taking place must be considered; and this is not large enough, in most cases, to produce significant λ1641 emission. Netzer reported that his detailed photoionization calculations, including the above considerations, yield an intrinsic line ratio in the range

$$4.5 < OI\ \lambda1304/\lambda8446 \le 6.5$$

for most cases of interest. Ratios less than 4.5 probably indicate reddening. As noted previously, composite spectra suggest a substantial differential extinction factor based on these lines (Netzer and Davidson 1979; MacAlpine and Feldman 1982). However, they need to be observed simultaneously for individual Seyfert 1 galaxies and low-redshift quasars. Unfortunately, IUE satellite measurements of $\lambda 1304$ are very difficult, even for relatively bright objects like NGC 4151 and 3C 273 (see Boksenberg *et al.* 1978).

There are no known easily predictable emission lines farther into the ultraviolet and observable in high-redshift quasars with existing instrumentation. Potential candidates, however, are He II $\lambda 1304$, and its Bowen fluorescence products, the O III lines at $\lambda 374$, $\lambda 644$, and $\lambda 703$. Predicted relative emitted intensities of these lines, for a variety of detailed models, are given by Eastman and MacAlpine (1985). Although accurate lmeasurements are not practical with IUE (especially if the far ultraviolet spectral region is obscured), detections with instruments like the Space Telescope or Hopkins Ultraviolet Telescope for such quasars as PG1115+080 (see Green *et al.* *1980*) could be very informative. It should be pointed out that the inferred "extinction" in this case would probably be due to more than dust. The observed continua of Seyfert 1 galaxies and quasars are known to exhibit a spectral turn-down shortward in wavelength from roughly the rest-frame position of Lyα (e.g., Bechtold *et al.* 1984). It has been argued that this does not represent the intrinsic continuum (MacAlpine 1981; MacAlpine, Davidson, Gull, and Wu 1985; Netzer 1985). Some of the obscuration may be caused by dust, but much of it probably results from the combined effects of gas near the source (Eastman, MacAlpine, and Richstone 1983) and intervening cosmological gas (Oke and Korycanski 1982; Bechtold *et al.* 1984).

ii) Narrow-Line Regions

One may consult the NLR Lyα/Hα/Hβ diagnostic diagram of Gaskell and Ferland (1984) to sort out an appropriate ultraviolet reddening correction based on measured hydrogen lines. Also, He II $\lambda 1640$, $\lambda 3204$, and $\lambda 4686$ may be compared without fear of collisional or optical-depth effects. As noted above, the NLR or Seyfert 2 galaxy intrinsic recombination $\lambda 1640/\lambda 4686$ ratio should be about 7-7.5 (Seaton 1978).

Strong forbidden lines generally arise from transitions within a given electron configuration, and it is difficult to find suitable ones for measurement in the ultraviolet. However, Draine and Bahcall (1981) have called attention to some interesting possibilities involving transitions from the same upper metastable levels leading to lines well separated in wavelength. Some of the more promising pairs are [O III] λ2322 and λ4363, [Ne V] λ1572 and λ2973, and [Mg V] λ1325 and λ2418. A practical problem is that these lines are very weak, most having never been reported, and some of them fall within other broader, stronger emission features (e.g., [O III] λ2322 would be within C II] λ2326 and an Fe II blend). Nevertheless, it will be worthwhile to keep the above lines in mind, as individual objects might turn up where they are strong enough for reliable measurement.

iii) Other Regions

It may eventually be possible to set limits on the absolute amount of obscuration near λ2430 in nearby, bright AGNs. McClintock (1984) pointed out that the photon fluxes from positronium recombination Lyα λ2430 and the positronium annihilation feature at 511 keV should be about equal. The latter has been reported in a handful of sources, including the Galactic center (Leventhal, MacCallum, and Stang 1978); and it may be detectable with the Gamma Ray Observatory in some of the brightest active galactic nuclei. If so, one could compare with Space Telescope observations at λ2430.

IV. LOCATION OF OBSCURING MATERIAL

Suppose we can obtain reliable measurements of a particular reddening indicator, say [S II] λ10320/λ4072. Does the derived differential extinction necessarily apply not only to the NLR, but also to the BLR; and is it reasonable to assume the continuum is reddened by the same amount? This depends on the location and distribution of the obscuring material. Several workshop contributions addressed these questions, suggesting strongly that the various spectral components should be considered independently and that the most effective dust is located very near to the emitting gas.

Filippenko reported on his study of NGC 7314 (Filippenko 1984). This narrow-line X-ray galaxy shows a faint, broad component of Hα, but the corresponding Hβ component is extremely weak. The broad Hα/Hβ ratio is about 48, whereas Hα/Hβ for the narrow lines is approximately 5.1. Filippenko concluded that, although self absorption and related collisional effects are more important in the broad-line emitting gas, it is very likely that the BLR is also reddened considerably more than the NLR. For reference purposes, the Hα/Hβ ratio in the Kwan and Krolik (1981) broad-line standard model is 4.16, and the largest ratio obtained by Kwan (1984) while varying parameters is about 10. Osterbrock (1981), Rudy and Willner (1983), and Rudy *et al.* 1985 have also investigated similar, if not so extreme, situations (so-called Seyfert 1.8 or 1.9 galaxies). Whereas Osterbrock and Rudy *et al.* concluded that reddening may be particularly important for the BLRs, Rudy and Willner stressed that the strength of Paα in V Zw 317 indicates that reddening alone cannot account for the observed Hα/Hβ ratio.

Filippenko postulated an edge-on view of a disk-like or flattened geometry for the BLR of NGC 7314, with the obscuring dust more associated with this gas than with the NLR, which has larger dimensions. Example schematic drawings of gas configurations which resemble this picture are given by Osterbrock (1979, 1984).

Carleton presented evidence that obscuring material has a larger effect on the BLR than on the NLR in the BLRG 3C 234 (Carleton *et al.* 1984). Measurement of the Paα line shows a relative intensity strong enough to imply reddening with $A_v = 2.65^{+0.6}_{-1.0}$ magnitudes for the broad hydrogen lines. Since the NLR appears strongly photoionized and only slightly reddened, most of the obscuring material is not in our line of sight to this region, nor between this region and the (assumed) central source. A high resolution profile of the [O III] $\lambda5007$ line shows attenuation of the red wing, which may be indicative of preferential obscuration of emitting material with higher positive velocities (see Heckman *et al.* 1981). Extrapolation of the observed optical continuum cannot provide the necessary ionization for even the observed narrow lines, but a continuum corrected for the reddening above with a Galactic extinction law can provide sufficient ionizing photons to account for the dereddened broad and narrow emission-line spectra. (See Antonucci and Miller 1985 for a somewhat different interpretation.)

Carleton also discussed recent work on the Seyfert 1 galaxy NGC 5548. He noted that the broad-line spectrum permits only a small amount of reddening ($A_v < 1.0$) and requires none (Lacy *et al.* 1982). Forbidden line profiles show strongly increasing asymmetry (and width) with increasing critical quenching density of the parent ion. The low-density lines are essentially symmetrical, while [Fe VII] lines ($n_c \approx 5 \times 10^7$ cm^{-3}) hardly show any positive velocities at all. This may imply that there is dense obscuring material ($A_v \gg 1$) in our line of sight to the "back half" of the [Fe VII] region.

To account for the characteristics of 3C 234 and NGC 5548, Carleton considered a disk-like or toroidal dust distribution, with dimensions of order 10-20 times the flattened BLR radius. Then, in the case of 3C 234, we would be viewing the system edge-on or in the plane containing the broad-line gas and dust. A larger, less flattened NLR receives radiation from the central source that does not pass through much dust, whereas broad lines, continuum, and some forbidden-line emission from the far side suffer substantial extinction. NGC 5548 could have a similar configuration viewed nearly face-on. Then there would be less reddening of the broad lines but the inner part of the back half of the forbidden-line gas could be obscured by the dust disk. The high polarization

($\sim$ 14%) of 3C 234 broad lines and continuum (Antonucci 1984) and much lower polarization ($\sim$0.7%) in NCG 5548 (Martin *et al.* 1983) are consistent with the above interpretation.

It is unlikely that a substantial amount of dust actually lies *within* the ionized, line-emitting BLRs. Rudy and Puetter (1982) (see also Hyland and Allen 1982) have concluded that dust would be warmed and possibly destroyed in the highly-ionized part of a Seyfert galaxy or quasar gas cloud; and Gaskell, Shields, and Wampler (1981) found that gas-phase abundances of refractory elements in quasar BLRs suggest that significant amounts of dust have not formed there. This is not surprising because dust mixed with line-emitting gas would effectively destroy resonance lines, which scatter and traverse large path lengths. Observed strengths of resonance lines compared with non-resonance lines suggest a BLR dust to gas ratio about 10% that of the Galactic interstellar medium (Shuder and MacAlpine 1979). Furthermore, Shuder and MacAlpine pointed out that appreciable amounts of dust within the broad-line-emitting gas would be expected to lead to an inverse correlation of C IV λ1549 equivalent width and continuum luminosity (the Baldwin effect) which is much stronger than observed. Other photoionization calculations incorporating dust in the line-emitting gas have been carried out by Baldwin and Netzer (1978), Ferland and Netzer (1979), and Martin and Ferland (1980), but the first two of these studies assumed unrealistically high dust extinction cross sections at high photon energies.

Rudy (1984) has argued that substantial amounts of dust must be associated with narrow-line gas in AGNs and quasars to account for correlation between mid-infrared emission and [O III] line intensities. The previously mentioned NLRG and Seyfert 2 galaxy observations of Ferland and Osterbrock also call for obscuring material in or near NLRs. Although they reported measuring hydrogen line reddening with E(B-V) = 0.1 to 0.6 of a magnitude or greater, they found the optical to ultraviolet continua to be nearly flat, with little evidence of any correlation between reddening and spectral index. A similar effect was noticed by Costero and

Osterbrock (1977) for NLRGs and by Koski (1978) for Seyfert 2s. A conclusion is that the source of extinction of the line-emitting region does not also necessarily cover the continuum source. Ferland inferred a disk geometry for the NLR gas and associated dust, which could present a relatively unobscured line of sight to a central source when viewed from appropriate angles. Another possibility is a less flattened distribution with gaps between clouds.

Although alignment of flattened emitting gas and associated dust with the host galaxy plane is not necessary on theoretical grounds (Tohline and Osterbrock 1982), it has been suggested to account for correlation between galaxy inclinations and Hβ to X-ray luminosity (Lawrence and Elvis 1982). This could also indicate that some of the obscuration is contributed by interstellar dust distributed in the galaxy. Other evidence for alignment or galactic plane interstellar dust are correlations between observed Seyfert galaxy axial ratios and broad-band colors (Cheng, Danese, and de Zotti 1983) and between axial ratios and BLR Balmer decrements (Gaskell and de Zotti 1983), although the latter correlation was not confirmed by Rudy (1984). Gaskell and de Zotti found Seyfert galaxy *narrow-line* Balmer decrements to be only weakly correlated with axial ratios, suggesting that the scale height of the absorbing layer is smaller than the size of the NLR in most cases.

Other possible locations for dust in the line of sight are the intergalactic medium or intervening galaxies. We might expect increasing obscuration at high redshifts because of longer light paths, shorter observed wavelengths, and cosmological crowding (see Ostriker and Heisler 1984). Although this does not produce a large apparent effect for AGNs, it may be important for some quasars.

V. RELATIVE DUST CONTENTS OF AGNs AND QSOs

The preponderance of evidence for dust in quasars is not as great as for some AGNs. Stein and Soifer (1983) reviewed infrared and polarization observations and concluded that "...the question of the existence of dust in QSOs remains open." However, a recent study by Stockman, Moore, and Angel (1984) indicates that polarization properties for *typical* bright quasars and Seyfert galaxies may be similar, and that some quasars exhibit the lack of variability and increasing polarization toward shorter wavelengths which may be attributed to dust scattering by a flattened configuration. Also, whereas the quasar and active galaxy Paα/Hα and Hα/Hβ data available to Soifer and Neugebauer (1981) suggested that quasars are not as subject to reddening as active galaxies, the subsequent larger data set in Lacy *et al.* (1982) shows more of a mixture of inferred characteristics, especially between Seyfert 1 galaxies and quasars. Other evidence for quasar reddening includes the composite spectral He II λ1640/λ4686 and O I λ1304/λ8446 ratios already mentioned. And, although there are few specific examples of apparently highly reddened quasars [e.g., 3C 68.1 with z = 1.24, an observed $f_\nu \propto \nu^{-6.1}$ continuum, and apparently normal equivalent widths for C IV λ1549 and C III] λ1909 lines (Boksenberg, Carswell, and Oke 1976)], we might expect selection effects to work against indentification of such objects. For instance, Rudy *et al.* (1984) have pointed out that luminous objects with heavily reddened nuclei are more likely to be classified as galaxies because the comparatively unreddened galactic stellar component will be easier to detect. Still, there may be something to the idea that quasars are less likely to be reddened; several investigators have noticed a possible trend toward less extinction with increasing luminosity (above what would be expected for simply comparing obscured and unobscured objects).

Malkan argued that continua in very-high-luminosity AGNs or quasars may not be substantially reddened. Using available data, he prepared plots of f_ν (λ4220)/f_ν (λ1460) and f_ν (λ4220)/f_ν (λ1770) vs. Log L_ν (λ4220) in erg s^{-1} Hz^{-1} (Malkan 1984). The observed flux density ratios were corrected for reddening along the line of sight through the Milky Way using the Burstein and Heiles (1982) method. Although there is considerable scatter in these ratios below Log L_ν (λ4220) = 30, above this point those objects with simultaneous measurements and considered as non-highly-variable exhibit a total scattering amplitude which would correspond with ΔE(B-V) = 0.1 magnitude or less for a standard Milky Way reddening law. Malkan stated that "the narrow range of colors for more luminous AGNs sets a tight empirical upper limit on the amount of continuum reddening in these objects."

Cheng, Danese, and de Zotti (1983) and Gaskell and de Zotti (1983) also presented suggestive evidence for a decrease in extinction with increasing luminosity in Seyfert 1 galaxies. However, Rudy *et al.* (1984) have cautioned that there are numerous exceptions to this rule, especially when intercomparing different object classes, and that available samples are incomplete because of selection effects (in the sense of not having enough heavily reddened sources). Still, according to Gaskell (1984), active galaxies without BLRs (e.g., lower luminosity sources like Seyfert 2s) have systematically higher NLR reddening (by E(B-V) $\approx$ 0.18 magnitude) compared with galaxies which contain detectable BLRs. And Rudy (1984) has suggested a relationship between decreasing obscuration and weakening of NLR emission with increasing luminosity. Among BLR objects, the *apparent* ranking, in terms of presently accumulated observations, for decreasing dust content is: BLRGs, Seyfert 1 galaxies, and quasars (see Rudy *et al.* 1983).

The above reddening progression with quasars at the bottom of the list is consistent with the idea of a decade ago, but we have to wonder whether this means that we were correct before or that we still just do not have enough information about quasars. We need good He II line intensities and measures of emission-line polarization in quasars.

VI. SUMMARY

I had two major objectives in writing this chapter. The first was to emphasize that recombination, collisions, optical-depth effects, *and* dust extinction may all be important contributors to observed active galaxy and quasar spectra. We should recognize the potential significance of dust and make every possible effort to understand it. Whereas there are some indications that quasars have lower dust content than AGNs, this idea needs confirmation or rejection, rather than tacit acceptance.

My second objective was to address the practical issues of making quantitative corrections for dust reddening or obscuration. This was done largely within the context of contributions at the workshop, and I would like to thank D. Burstein, N. Carleton, R. Eastman, G. Ferland, A. Filippenko, M. Gaskell, M. Malkan, P. Martin, H. Netzer, and M. Ward for speaking or supplying me with information. I did not stress the very important results of infrared and X-ray observations because they are the subjects of other chapters.

The consensus of opinion among workshop contributors was that many BLRGs, NLRGs, and Seyfert 1, 1.9, and 2 galaxies contain nuclear dust near the line-emitting regions, possibly with a disk-like or flattened configuration. The obscuring material can shield the BLR (or line-emitting gas in Seyfert 2 galaxies), while the extinction suffered by the NLR or continuum may be similar or considerably less, depending on the viewing aspect angle. Therefore these spectral components should be considered separately for reddening purposes. And, because the dust may have extinction properties different from the interstellar medium in our Galaxy, the applied extinction corrections will be more reliable if based on actual observations over the relevant spectral ranges. I have critically discussed various possible methods for doing this. NLRs, if measurable, and Seyfert 2 galaxy emission-line gas are most readily corrected for reddening from infrared through ultraviolet wavelengths; then come BLRs, which although more prone to measurement errors and optical-depth effects, do have potential reddening indicators; and finally the continuum may require an educated guess or extinction estimates based on X-ray measurements (see chapter by Elvis and Lawrence). In spite of apparent complications, workshop participants agreed that the measurement and understanding of reddening are sufficiently important that we must make the necessary efforts. Also, dust has more than a dark side. Not only does it make the study of AGNs and quasars a little more challenging, but it also provides valuable and unique information about geometrical characteristics.

REFERENCES

Allen, D. A. 1979, *M.N.R.A.S.*, **186**, 1P.

Andriesse, C. D. 1977, *Vistas Astron.*, **21**, 107.

Angel, J.R.P., Stockman, H.S., Woolf, W. J., Beaver, E. A., and Martin, P. G. 1976, *Ap. J. (Letters)*, **206**, L5.

Antonucci, R. R. J. 1982, *Nature*, **299**, 605.

_____. 1984. *Ap. J.*, **278**, 499.

Antonucci, R. R. J., and Miller, J. S. 1985, preprint.

Baldwin, J. A. 1977, *M.N.R.A.S.*, **178**, 67P.

Baldwin, J. A., and Netzer, H. 1978, *Ap. J.*, **226**, 1.

Baldwin, J. A., Rees, M. J., Longair, M. S., and Perryman, M. A. C. 1978, *Ap. J. (Letters)*, **226**, L57.

Barrington, K. A., Fon, W. C., and Kingston, A. E. 1982, , **M.N.R.A.S.**, 200 347.

Bechtold, J., Green, R. F., Weymann, R. J., Schmidt, M., Estabrook, F. B., Sherman, R.D., Wahlquist, H. D., and Heckman, T. M. 1984, *Ap. J.*, **281**, 76.

Bless, R. C., and Savage, B. D. 1972, *Ap. J.*, **171**, 293.

Bode, M. F., and Evans, A. 1982, *Ap. J.*, **254**, 263.

Boksenberg, A., Carswell, R. F., and Oke, J. B. 1976, *Ap. J. (Letters)*, **206**, L121.

Boksenberg, A. *et al.* 1978 *Nature*, **275**, 404.

Burstein, D., and Heiles, C. 1982, *A. J.*, **87**, 1165.

Canfield, R. C., and Puetter, R. C. 1980, *Ap. J. (Letters)*, **236**, L7.

_____. 1981, *Ap. J.*, **243**, 390.

Carleton, N. P., Willner, S. P., Rudy, R. J., and Tokunaga, A. T. 1984, *Ap. J.*, **284**, 523.

Cheng, F. Z., Danese, L., and de Zotti, G. 1983, *M.N.R.A.S.*, **204**, 13P.

Clayton, G. C., and Martin, P. G. 1985, *Ap. J.*, **288**, 588.

Costero, R., and Osterbrock, D. E. 1977, *Ap. J.*, **211**, 675.

Davidson, K., and Netzer, H. 1979, *Rev. Mod. Phys.*, **51**, 715.

Draine, B. T., and Bahcall, J. N. 1981, *Ap. J.*, **250**, 579.

Draine, B.T., and Lee, H. M. 1984, *Ap. J.*, **285**, 89.

Eastman, R. G., and MacAlpine, G. M. 1985, submitted to Ap. J.

Eastman, R. G., MacAlpine, G. M., and Richstone, D. O. 1983, *Ap. J.*, **275**, 53.

Feldman, F. R., and MacAlpine, G. M. 1978, *Ap. J.*, **221**, 486.

Ferland, G. J., and Netzer, H. 1979, *Ap. J.*, **229**, 274.

Ferland, G. J., and Osterbrock, D. E. 1984, *Ap. J.*, in press.

Filippenko, A. V. 1984, preprint.

Garstang, R. H. 1961, *Proc. Cambridge Phil. Soc.*, **57**, 115.

Gaskell, C. M. 1982, *P.A.S.P.*, **94**, 891.

_____. 1984, *Ap. J. (Letters)*, **24**, 43.

Gaskell, C. M., and de Zotti, G. 1983, *Bull. A.A.S.*, **15**, 988.

Gaskell, C. M., and Ferland, G. J. 1984, *P.A.S.P.*, **96**, 393.

Gaskell, C. M., Shields, G. A., and Wampler, E. J. 1981, *Ap. J.*, **249**, 443.

Grandi, S. A. 1983, *Ap. J.*, **268**, 591.

Grasdalen, G. L. 1976, *Ap. J. (Letters)*, **208**, Lll.

Green, R. F., Pier, J. R., Schmidt, M., Estabrook, F. B., Lane, A. L., and Wahlquist, H. D. 1976, *Ap. J.*, **239**, 483.

Halpern, J. P., and Steiner, J. E. 1983, *Ap. J. (Letters)*, **269**, L37.

Heckman, T. M., Miley, G. K., van Breugel, W. J. M., and Butcher, H. R. 1981, *Ap. J.*, **247**, 403.

Hong, S. S., and Greenberg, J. M. 1980, *Astr. Ap.*, **88**, 194.

Hyland, A. R., and Allen, D. A. 1982, *M.N.R.A.S.*, **199**, 943.

Koornneef, J., and Code, A. D. 1981, *Ap. J.*, **247**, 860.

Koski, A. T. 1978, *Ap. J.*, **223**, 56.

Kwan, J. 1984, *Ap. J.*, **283**, 70.

Kwan, J., and Krolik, J. H. 1979, *Ap. J. (Letters)*, **233**, L91.

_____. 1981, *Ap. J.*, **250**, 478.

Lacy, J. H. *et al.*, 1982, *Ap. J.*, **256**, 75.

Lawrence, A., and Elvis, M. 1982, *Ap. J.*, **256**, 410.

LeVan, P. D., Puetter, R. C., Smith, H. E., and Rudy, R. J. 1984, *Ap. J.*, **284**, 23.

Levanthal, M., MacCallum, C. J., and Stang, P. D. 1978, *Ap. J. (Letters)*, **225**, L11.

London, R. 1979, *Ap. J.*, **228**, 8.

MacAlpine, G. M. 1976, *Ap. J.*, **204**, 694.

_____. 1981, *Ap. J.*, **251**, 465.

MacAlpine, G. M., Davidson, K., Gull, T. R., and Wu, C. C. 1985, *Ap. J.*, in press.

MacAlpine, G.M., and Feldman, F. R. 1982, *Ap. J.*, **261**, 412.

MacLean, S., Duley, W. W., and Millar, T. J. 1982, *Ap. J. (Letters)*, **256**, L61.

Malkan, M.A. 1983, *Ap. J. (Letters)*, **264**, L1.

_____. 1984, proceedings of symposium on *X-ray and UV Emission from Active Galactic Nuclei*, held at Garching, West Germany.

Malkan, M. A., and Oke, J. B. 1983, *Ap. J.*, **265**, 92.

Martin, P. G., and Ferland, G. J. 1980, *Ap. J. (Letters)*, **235**, L125.

Martin, P. G., Stockman, H. S., Angel, J. R. P., Maza, J., and Beaver, E. A. 1982, *Ap. J.*, **255**, 65.

Martin, P. G., Thompson, I. B., Maza, J., and Angel, J. R. P. 1983, *Ap. J.*, **266**, 470.

Mathews, W. G., Blumenthal, G. R., and Grandi, S. A. 1980, *Ap. J.*, **235**, 971.

Mathis, J. S. 1970, *Ap. J.*, **159**, 263.

_____. 1978, *IAU Symp. No. 76: Planetary Nebulae, Theory and Observations*, ed. Y. Terzian (D. Reidel: Dordrecht), p. 281.

_____. 1983, *Ap. J.*, **267**, 119.

Mathis, J. S., Rumpl, W., and Nordsieck, K. H. 1977, *Ap. J.*, **217**, 425.

McAlary, C. W., and McLaren, R. A. 1981, *Ap. J.*, **250**, 98.

McClintock, J. E. 1984, *Ap. J.*, **282**, 291.

McKee, C. F., and Petrosian, V. 1974, *Ap. J.*, **189**, 17.

Meyer, D. M., and Savage, B. D. 1981, *Ap. J.*, **248**, 545.

Mihalszki, J. S., and Ferland, G. J. 1983, *M.N.R.A.S.*, **205**, 1279.

Miller, J. S. 1968, *Ap. J. (Letters)*, **154**, L57.

Miller, J. S., and Antonucci, R. R. J. 1983, *Ap. J. (Letters)*, **271**, L7.

Nandy, K., Morgan, D. H., Willis, A. J., Wilson, R., and Gondhalekar, P. M. 1981, *M.N.R.A.S.*, **196**, 955.

Netzer, H. 1982, *M.N.R.A.S.*, **198**, 589.

_____. 1985, preprint.

Netzer, H., and Davidson, K. 1979, *M.N.R.A.S.*, **187**, 871.

Netzer, H., and Ferland, G. J. 1984, *Pub. A.S.P.*, **96**, 593.

Netzer, H., Wills, B. J., and Wills, D. 1982, *Ap. J.*, **254**, 489.

Neugebauer, G. *et al.* 1980, *Ap. J.*, **238**, 502.

Oke, J. B., and Goodrich, R. W. 1981, *Ap. J.*, **243**, 445.

Oke, J. B., and Korycanski, D. G. 1982, *Ap. J.*, **255**, 11.

Oke, J. B., and Sargent, W. L. W. 1968, *Ap. J.*, **151**, 807.

Oke, J. B., and Zimmerman, B. 1979, *Ap. J. (Letters)*, **231**, L13.

Osterbrock, D. E. 1977, *Ap. J.*, **215**, 733.

_____. 1979, *A. J.*, **84**, 901.

_____. 1981, *Ap. J.*, **249**, 462.

_____. 1984, *Q. Jl. R. Astr. Soc.*, **25**, 1.

Osterbrock, D. E., and Miller, J. S. 1975, *Ap. J.*, **197**, 535.

Osterbrock, D. E., and Parker, R. A. R. 1965, *Ap. J.*, **141**, 892.

Ostriker, J. P., and Heisler, J. 1984, *Ap. J.*, **278**, 1.

Prévot, M. L., Lequeux, J., Maurice, E., Prévot, L., and Rocca-Volmerange, B. 1984, *Astr. Ap.*, **132**, 389.

Puetter, R. C., Smith, H. E., Soifer, B. T., Willner, S. P., and Pipher, J. L. 1978, *Ap. J. (Letters)*, **226**, L53.

Puetter, R. C., Smith, H. E., Willner, S. P., and Pipher, J. L. 1981, *Ap. J.*, **243**, 345.

Richstone, D. O., and Schmidt, M. 1980, *Ap. J.*, **235**, 377.

Rudy, R. J. 1984, *Ap. J.*, **284**, 33.

Rudy, R. J., Cohen, R. D., and Puetter, R. C. 1985, *Ap. J. (Letters)*, **288**, L29.

Rudy, R. J., and Puetter, R. C. 1982, *Ap. J.*, **263**, 43.

Rudy, R. J., Schmidt, G. D., Stockman, H. S., and Moore, R. L. 1983, *Ap. J.*, **271**, 59.

Rudy, R. J., Schmidt, G. D., Stockman, H. S., and Tokunaga, A. T. 1984, *Ap. J.*, **278**, 530.

Rudy, R. J., and Willner, S. P. 1983, *Ap. J. (Letters)*, **267**, L69.

Savage, B. D., and Mathis, J. S. 1979, *Ann. Rev. Astr. Ap.*, **17**, 73.

Seaton, M. J. 1968, *IAU Symp. No. 34: Planetary Nebulae*, ed. D. E. Osterbrock and C. R. O'Dell (D. Reidel: Dordrecht).

_____. 1978, *M.N.R.A.S.*, **185**, 5P.

_____. 1979, *M.N.R.A.S.*, **187**, 73P.

Shuder, J. M., and MacAlpine, G. M. 1977, *B.A.A.S.*, **9**, 431.

_____. 1979, *Ap. J.*, **230**, 348.

Shuder, J. M., and Osterbrock, D. E. 1981, *Ap. J.*, **250**, 55.

Soifer, B. T., and Neugebauer, G. 1981, *IAU Symp. No. 96: Infrared Astronomy*, ed. C. G. Wynn-Williams and D. P. Cruikshank (D. Reidel: Dordrecht), p. 329.

Soifer, B. T., Neugebauer, G., Oke, J. B., and Matthews, K. 1981, *Ap. J.*, **243**, 369.

Stein, W. A., and Soifer, B. T. 1983, *Ann. Rev. Astr. Ap.*, **21**, 177.

Stockman, H. S., Moore, R. L., and Angel, J. R. P. 1984, *Ap. J.*, **279**, 485.

Thompson, I., Landstreet, J. D., Stockman, H. S., Angel, J. R. P., and Beaver, E. A. 1980, *M.N.R.A.S.*, **192**, 53.

Tohline, J. E., and Osterbrock, D. E. 1982, *Ap. J. (Letters)*, **252**, L49.

Wampler, E. J. 1968, *Ap. J. (Letters)*, **154**, L53.

_____. 1971, *Ap. J.*, **164**, 1.

Ward, M., and Morris, S. 1984, *M.N.R.A.S.*, **207**, 867.

Weisheit, J. C., Shields, G. A., and Tarter, C. B. 1981, *Ap. J.*, **245**, 406.

Wills, B. J., Netzer, H., and Wills, D. 1980, *Ap. J. (Letters)*, **242**, L1.

Wu, C. C., Boggess, A., and Gull, T. R. 1983, *Ap. J.*, **266**, 28.

X-RAY SPECTRA OF ACTIVE GALAXIES AND QUASARS

Martin Elvis

Harvard-Smithsonian Center for Astrophysics
Cambridge, MA

and

Andrew Lawrence*
Royal Greenwich Observatory
Hailsham, England

ABSTRACT

We review the existing X-ray spectral data for active galaxies and quasars. These exist mainly for type 1 Seyferts, quasars, and BL Lacs. There is little data yet for radio galaxies, type 2 Seyferts or LINERS. A variety of different power-law slopes exist for quasar and Seyfert 1 spectra, implying that several different emission mechanisms can make X-rays in AGN. Material within the active nucleus causes low energy X-ray absorption, primarily for low luminosity objects. Absorption can be used to constrain the physical state, abundance, and geometry of this nuclear material. The prospects for future X-ray satellite missions are outlined, with an emphasis on high resolution spectroscopy from AXAF.

I. INTRODUCTION

a) X-rays from AGN

Strong X-ray emission has been an accepted general property of active galaxies and quasars for several years now (Elvis *et al.* 1978, Tananbaum, *et al.* 1979). Over 500 such objects have detected X-ray emission and most of these were discovered by the identification of a newly found X-ray source (Gioia *et al.* 1984; Reichert *et al.* 1982; Kriss and Canizares 1982). It could even be

---

*   Current Address: Queen Mary College, London

claimed (*pace* Margon *et al.* 1982; Arnaud *et al.* 1984) that the intense output of X-rays is the *only* property shared by all 'active' objects: They may or may not possess broad emission lines, double radio sources, blue optical continua, rapid variability, or strong polarization but, from LINERS and absorption line radio galaxies to BL Lacs and high redshift quasars, they all show strong X-ray emission.

The realization that strong kilovolt X-ray emission was a widespread feature of active galaxies prompted the investigation of optically thick ionization models for broad line clouds where X-ray heating in the interiors becomes important (see chapter by Shields and Ferland). Also, the uniform flat slopes found in the first X-ray spectra stimulated work on Synchrotron Self-Compton and other models which could produce a 'universal slope.' However of the large number of X-ray detected AGN, only a relative handful have any spectral information in the X-ray band. These spectra are further limited almost entirely to type 1 Seyfert galaxies selected to be hard X-ray sources.

X-ray spectra are now beginning to become available from a wider selection of AGN. In this review we try to give extra emphasis to these areas of X-ray work on AGN. Section II concentrates on the variety of continuum properties now being uncovered and their importance to the several emission mechanisms occurring (see §IId). These data also bear on the photoionization models mentioned above, and on the formation of the emission line clouds (see §IIe). Although most of a quasar's energy output may well emerge in the hard X-ray/soft γ-ray regime (100 keV-1 MeV, Bezler *et al.* 1984), in some cases the very soft XUV photons may dominate (see §IId).

The integrated X-ray emission of all quasars cannot yield a surface brightness larger than that of the diffuse X-ray background. This can significantly limit the evolution rates allowed for quasars and AGN. A great deal of work has gone into this topic (e.g., Avni 1978; Zamorani *et al.* 1981; Marshall *et al.* 1984;

Elvis, Soltan, and Keel 1984). However, spectral slopes had to be assumed in these papers. Even stricter limits apply when the spectral shapes of the X-ray background and of AGN are considered (deZotti *et al.* 1982) and the new results both on the continuum and on luminosity dependent absorption are likely to affect the previous results quite strongly (see §IIf).

Low luminosity AGN have a tendency to be strongly obscured X-ray sources. Through photoelectric absorption of its low energy X-rays (0.1-6 keV) the X-ray continuum gives us a powerful means of studying the structure, abundances, and physical conditions of intervening material in the active nucleus. The existing observations are discussed in §III.

A wide variety of AGN – Radio galaxies, type 2 Seyferts, LINERS and Starbursts – have almost no X-ray spectral information to date. In §IV we discuss the expectations for these objects and how X-ray spectra will be important diagnostics.

All these results depend on a relatively small number of past, present, and future X-ray astronomy satellite missions. To complete our introduction, we summarize the major instruments used to give the data for this review (§Ib). We complete our review (§V) by outlining the prospects for expanding the X-ray spectroscopy of AGN and quasars in the future.

b) Sources of X-ray Spectra

Almost all the X-ray spectra published so far come from the two HEAO satellites using non-dispersive detectors with intrinsic energy resolution: HEAO-1 provided the A-2 proportional counters with an energy resolution of $E/\Delta E \sim 6$ at 6 keV with energy coverage from 2-60 keV (Rothschild *et al.* 1979), and the A-4 Phoswich scintillator which was sensitive at high energies, 12-165 keV, with an energy resolution $E/\Delta E \sim 4$ at 100 keV (Matteson 1978). Both of these instruments were non-imaging and had fields-of-view of several square degrees. Thus, because of the strong diffuse X-ray background, and the particle background in-orbit, they had limited sensitivity and could only yield spectra of the brightest objects in the sky in their energy range. Most of the A-2 results are summarized in Mushotzky (1984b) and Urry (1984). The A-4 results are mainly included in Rothschild *et al.* (1983). HEAO-1 operated from 1977-1979.

The HEAO-2, satellite, or *Einstein Observatory,* carried the Solid State Spectrometer (SSS) and the Imaging Proportional Counter (IPC). It operated from 1978-1981. The SSS had relatively good energy resolution ($E/\Delta E$ ~12 at 2 keV) in the energy range 0.75-4.5 keV but had a high background rate (Joyce *et al.* 1978). It therefore was used mainly to observe HEAO-1 sources in a lower energy range (0.75-4.5 keV). SSS spectra of AGN are published in Holt *et al.* (1980), Petre *et al.* (1984), and Reichert *et al.* (1985). The *Einstein* IPC on the other hand had a very low background due to its small (~1 arcminute) beam size but only limited energy resolution ($E/\Delta E$ ~1 at 1 keV; Gorenstein, Harnden, and Fabricant 1981). It covered the softer 0.1-4.5 keV energy band. Its much greater sensitivity made the IPC the workhorse instrument for surveys of optical and radio selected objects with quasars figuring prominently. Recently a good calibration has been derived for the energy scale of the IPC (Harnden *et al.* 1984; Harnden and Fabricant 1985) so that IPC "spectra" of quasars are now becoming available. The first IPC quasar spectra resulting from this recalibration are presented in Elvis, Wilkes, and Tananbaum (1985). Other results presented here are in preparation (Elvis *et al.* 1985, and others).

At the time of writing, EXOSAT is collecting more spectra of bright active nuclei. The medium energy (ME) experiment is similar in sensitivity and resolution to HEAO1-A2. The imaging Channel Multiplier Array (CMA) samples a lower energy range (0.05-2 keV) than the IPC but with much lower sensitivity. Crude X-ray "colors" are available from the CMA by inserting various filters.

By comparison with optical spectroscopy these are all low

resolution instruments and are more akin to UBV photometry. Indeed the energy resolution is usually so broad that a model fitting procedure is needed to characterize the data. Thus, even a measurement of flux is a derived model dependent quantity.

II. HIGH LUMINOSITY AGN: CONTINUUM PROPERTIES

a) The "Universal" Spectrum

Ignoring for the moment effects of low energy absorption (§III), there is seen to exist a characteristic spectral form for medium energy (2-20 keV) *X-ray selected* emission line AGN, i.e., those seen in all sky surveys.

The (2-20 keV) spectra of 20 active galaxies reported by Mushotzky *et al.* (1980), Mushotzky and Marshall (1980) and Mushotzky (1982) can all be described by a power law with differing amounts of low energy absorption. The spectral index * seems always to be the same, $\alpha_E \sim 0.7$. The observed dispersion in α is ~ 0.1, and is consistent within the errors with zero intrinsic dispersion. This result holds for both high and low luminosity AGN, and for both radio loud and radio quiet objects. Also, for the 11 active galaxies detected by HEAO-A4 (Rothschild *et al.* 1983, Figure 1), the high-energy spectra are consistent with the same slope continuing out to 120 keV. *Einstein* SSS observations (Petre *et al.* 1984; Reichert *et al.* 1985) appear to confirm this slope in the softer (0.75-4.5 keV) region. New EXOSAT data (Pounds, McHardy, and Warwick 1984) using simultaneous spectral fitting of the ME and CMA experiments, show the same slope down to ~ 0.1 keV. Thus the "universal slope" seems to hold over ~ 4 decades of luminosity, and ~ 3 decades of photon energy for

---

* We shall use the 'energy index' throughout. This is the same as that in log (flux density) versus log frequency plot ($F_\nu \propto \nu^{-\alpha}$). X-ray astronomers often use the 'photon index', which is one power steeper, since this is closer to the observed quantity, counts.

this type of AGN.

The "universal spectrum" seems to be a good general rule for AGN selected by instruments sensitive in the range (2-20 keV), although occasional observations seem slightly discrepant. (The spectrum of 3C273 has $\alpha = 0.41\pm.02$ according to Worrall *et al.* 1979.) A different story emerges from X-ray observations of quasars and Seyfert galaxies selected by other means.

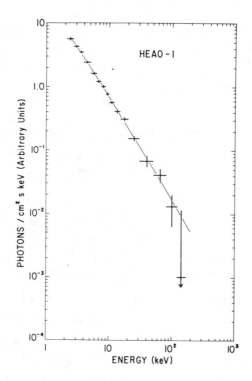

Figure 1: The mean 2-120 keV power-law fit for Seyfert galaxies. Best fit slope is 0.62±0.04 (Rothschild *et al.* 1983).

b) A Variety of Spectra in Quasars

At X-ray luminosities greater than 10^{44} erg s $^{-1}$ (2-10 keV *) low energy photoelectric absorption is rarely seen. This

---

* L_x (2-10 keV) = L_x (0.5-4.5 keV) for $\alpha_E = 0.7$ with no low energy cut-off.

allows the study of the X-ray continuum of quasars with detectors sensitive to low energies, such as the IPC.

The new IPC data (Elvis *et al.* 1985 and in preparation) have now shown that the 'universal spectrum' picture is too simple. For quasar X-ray spectra there is no universal power law slope. The three quasar spectra published by Elvis, Wilkes, and Tananbaum (1985) show slopes of α_E ~0.6, ~1.2, and ~2.2 (Fig. 2). Further quasar spectra so far analysed (Elvis *et al.*, in preparation) cover a similar range in spectral indices. It is not clear yet whether there are three distinct groups or whether a continuous distribution of slopes exists. In at least one case no single power law gives an acceptable fit.

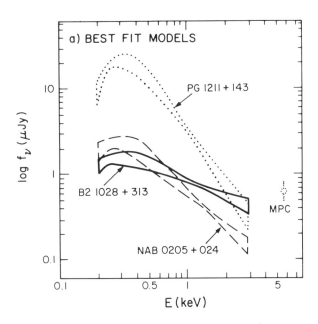

Figure 2: IPC (0.2-3.0 keV) power-law spectral fits for three quasars. Best fit slopes are 0.6, 1.2, and 2.2 (Elvis, Wilkes, and Tananbaum 1985).

Why is there this striking contrast with other data? We can imagine three reasons:

1. The lower energy boundary of the IPC is ~0.1 keV, well below the 0.75 keV of the SSS. This might take the IPC into

the region where the X-ray continuum turns up to meet the UV-continuum. It has to do this at some point near 0.1 keV since the UV continuum typically has 100 times the flux density of the hard X-ray continuum and lies only one and half decades below in frequency;

2. The extra sensitivity of the IPC allows it to see more distant and more luminous quasars. There might be some luminosity, or redshift, dependence of the X-ray spectral index;

3. The AGN measured by the SSS come from the sources found in HEAO-A2 all sky survey and are thus selected to be strong *hard* X-ray (2-10 keV) sources. To have a spectrum measured by the IPC an AGN needs to give about 1000 counts in one observation. These AGN are thus typically strong *soft* (0.3-3.5 keV) X-ray sources. Thus selection effects may be biasing the two data sets toward flat and steep spectra respectively.

The lower energy range of both the IPC and SSS compared to HEAO-A2 does seem to be important. The IPC and SSS spectral indices for Seyfert galaxies agree to *better than* the quoted SSS errors (Fig. 3). If 0.7 were really a universal slope for these data we would see a scatter diagram. Instead there is a clear correlation. A comparison of the SSS results with the higher energy HEAO-A2 data shows no such correlation (Petre *et al.* 1984). Even hard X-ray selected galaxies, then, show some diversity in their low energy spectra.

Luminosity effects are probably not important. A comparison of the luminosity ranges of the two samples shows that the current IPC sample has a mean luminosity only a factor three higher than the SSS sample. None of the quasars have a redshift greater than 0.2 so that any evolutionary effect would have to be very strong to be significant.

Probably the most important effect is that of sample selection. In Figure 4 radio- and optically-selected quasars are shown distributed according to their X-ray spectral index. Although the numbers are small there is a clear separation between the two

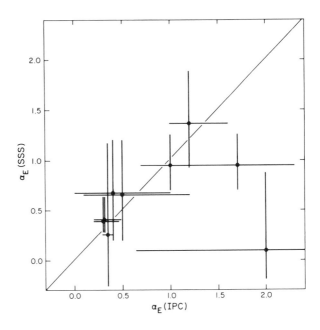

Figure 3. Comparison of IPC and SSS spectral indices for Seyfert galaxies (Harnden and Fabricant 1985).

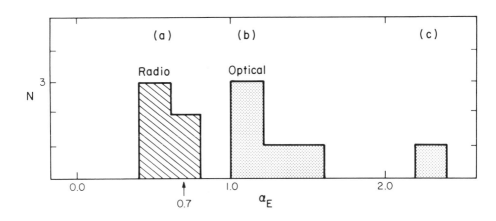

Figure 4. Histogram of IPC power-law indices for radio- and optically-selected quasars.

types. The radio-selected quasars have slopes near to the formerly canonical $\alpha = 0.7$, while the optically-selected quasars are steeper and cluster around $\alpha = 1.1$-1.2. (The object with $\alpha = 2.2$ is PG1211+143 discussed in §IId.) This is not a trivial answer. More likely it contains significant astrophysics since it implies that different families of quasars produce X-rays via different processes (see §IId).

There have been earlier hints of a soft component in some Seyfert galaxies also. Soft excesses around 0.2 keV have been suggested in 3C273 and NGC 5548 (Halpern 1982). The discovery of a transient "soft excess" in ESO 141-G55 (Mushotzky *et al.* 1980) has been retracted by the Goddard group (Tennant 1984). Subsequently, however, two Seyferts discovered by their *soft* X-ray emission were found to be bright enough to obtain measurable spectra with the HEAO-A2 experiment (Pravdo *et al.* 1981; Pravdo and Marshall 1984). They are steeper than the "normal" Seyferts, with $\alpha \sim 1.5$. Another case is NGC 4051 a well known "classical" Seyfert galaxy which was never detected in the 2-20 keV sky surveys of UHURU and Ariel V. NGC 4051 was studied by Marshall *et al.* (1983) with the IPC who found not only that it was remarkable for showing very fast variability ($\sim 1/2$ hour), but also that the spectrum, based on the IPC hardness ratio, seemed unusually soft. Both of these properties are confirmed by EXOSAT observations (Lawrence *et al.* 1985a). A spectrum jointly fitted through the ME experiment (2-10 keV) and three CMA filters gives $\alpha \sim 1.5$.

Finally several AGN are known to show a heavily absorbed medium energy spectrum coupled with a low energy excess. This phenomenon is probably better explained by partial covering (§IIIc), but could also be the result of a physically distinct unabsorbed soft component.

c) Two Component Spectra in BL Lacs

The BL Lac objects have never had a single canonical

power-law to describe their X-ray spectra. The first reports of their spectra (Mushotzky *et al.* 1978a) showed a soft excess below 2 keV on top of a hard $\alpha \sim 0.4$ spectrum from 2-20 keV. A more explicit 2-component spectrum was found for PKS0548-322 (Fig. 5, Agrawal, Riegler, and Mushotzky 1979). There are now five BL Lacs that have well-studied X-ray spectra (Urry 1984). These are, understandably, the five brightest BL Lacs in the X-ray sky. In each case both hard and soft spectral components have been found, although not always simultaneously. Indeed, unlike Seyfert galaxies, BL Lacs show substantial spectral changes. The data are mostly consistent with two independently varying components for all given objects. However, a single component of variable index is preferable in the case of PG($\equiv$2A) 1219+305 which changes its spectral slope with little or no change in flux (Urry 1984).

d) Emission Processes

The range of IPC spectra implies a variety of soft X-ray emission mechanisms. This can be seen most clearly from an infrared-to-X-ray log f_ν vs. log ν plot for three cases (Fig. 6).

(i) Quasars with a power-law index $\alpha \sim 0.7$ (Fig. 6a) have a characteristic break to a steeper spectrum below a few tenths of a kilovolt (0.1 keV = 124 Å), implying different emission mechanisms for X-ray and optical continua. Models are often made which link the two mechanisms in the two wavelength regions. For instance, the X-ray emission could be Inverse Compton emission of photons upscattered from the far infrared/millimeter region of a synchrotron spectrum while the optical continuum could be the loss-steepened tail of the synchrotron emission (Urry and Mushotzky 1982; Bregman *et al.* 1983). A continuous injection model for the primary electrons predicts the observed ~0.5 break in spectral index (0.7 to 1.2)(Kardashev 1962). The slope of 0.7 is very similar to that seen in the radio spectra of 3CR galaxies, in radio jets, and in the radio emission from the disks of spiral galaxies (see discussion in Rothchild *et al.* 1983).

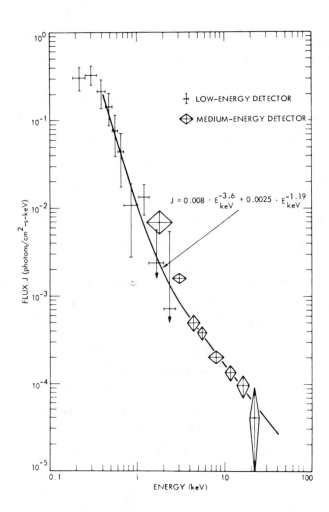

Figure 5: Two-component spectrum in the BL Lac PKS0548-322 (Agrawal, Riegler, and Mushotzky 1979).

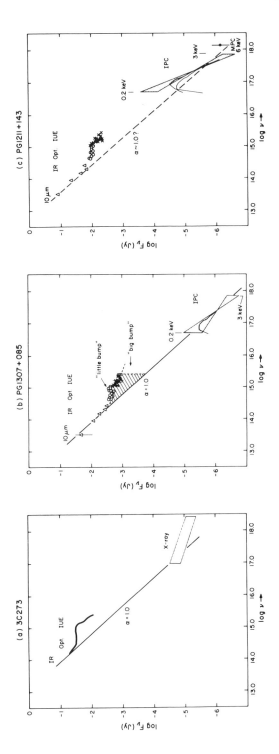

Figure 6: Infrared to X-ray continua for three quasars illustrating the different cases seen in the IPC spectra: (a) $\alpha \sim 0.7$, 3C273; (b) $\alpha \sim 1.2$, PG1307+085; (c) $\alpha \sim 2.2$, PG1211+143.

This strongly suggests a common mechanism, and one which is insensitive to the precise physical conditions; e.g., relativistic particles accelerated by shocks. However, no compelling theoretical explanation exists for the constancy of slope, and viable alternatives exist, such as a Comptonized thermal spectrum (Mezaros 1983).

(ii) For a power-law slope, α of $\sim$1.2 (Fig. 6b) there are a number of quasars which show a surprising continuity between the infrared 1-1.0 μm and the X-ray 0.2-3 keV continua both in slope and normalization. This suggests that a single mechanism produces the entire five decades of power-law continuum. The first candidate mechanism that comes to mind is direct synchrotron emission. There are alternatives. For instance, Comptonized cyclotron emission from an accretion flow (Maraschi, Roasio, and Treves 1982; Ipser and Price 1983). Because the X-rays can originate in an extended accreting region, this possibility may avoid the problems of predicting extreme variability.

If the infrared and X-ray continua are two ends of the same power law, then the optical and ultraviolet continuum forms a large excess which must be due to some other process. Part of this excess, the 3000 Å bump (Grandi 1982, labelled 'little bump' in Fig. 6b), is undoubtedly due to a combination of Balmer continuum and broad Fe II emission (Wills, Netzer, and Wills 1985). Although this 'little bump' looks small on logarithmic plots (e.g., Fig. 6b) it can carry significant luminosity. The more prominent component of the excess (labelled 'big bump' in Fig. 6b) was first pointed out by Shields (1978) and explored in detail by Malkan and Sargent (1982) and Malkan (1983) on the basis of an extrapolation of the infrared continuum alone. The join-up of the infrared-to-X-ray continua puts their decomposition of the spectrum on a firmer basis. They suggested that the 'big bump' was blackbody emission from an accretion disk at a range of temperatures.

(iii) The observation of a very steep, $\alpha \sim$ 2.2, X-ray spectrum in at least one quasar (Fig. 6c) may give a new perspective to this 'big bump' component. Figure 6c shows how any underlying power-law continuuum leaves a large excess at soft X-ray energies. When these same data are plotted in log νf_ν vs. log ν space the excess becomes clearer (Fig. 7), as does the similar excess in the UV. There is no necessary connection between these two excesses. It is, however, tempting to connect the two and suggest that they show the two ends of a single, highly luminous, excess. The luminosity from the excess is equivalent to that in the sketched-in power-law component in Figure 6c even when that power law is extrapolated over 10 decades (i.e., from 5 GHz to 1 MeV). If the 'big bump' is thermal then the maximum temperature, given by the IPC spectrum, is $\sim 1\text{-}2\times10^6$ K. Such temperatures can be expected from the inner regions of optically thick accretion disks around massive black holes. These spectra may be useful in determining the structure of these inner regions (Maraschi 1984). The IPC observations are insensitive to temperature below $\sim 0.5\times10^6$ K and so cannot rule out slightly cooler 'big bumps' in other quasars. The observations of soft excesses have insufficient resolution to determine any details. The UV-excess in quasars may, at least in some cases, be an XUV-excess and may carry the bulk of the luminosity in these quasars.

That the different X-ray spectra are displaying different emission mechanisms is supported by Figure 4 where radio-loud quasars can be seen to have a flatter slope than radio-quiet quasars. Zamorani *et al.* (1981) had already noted that radio-loud quasars are on average 3 times more X-ray luminous than radio-quiet quasars of the same optical magnitude. Their flat spectra suggest that this is due to a stronger inverse-Compton component. This would arise from either a more compact emission region or a weaker magnetic field. One caution: the radio-selected quasars have greater luminosities than the optically-selected ones in Figure 4 so that this change in α could be a luminosity effect.

The variety of spectra shapes seen over the whole radio-X-ray frequency range could arise from several physically distinct components of varying relative strengths: for example, (a) a region of relativistic particles producing a relatively steep synchrotron spectrum, (b) an accretion flow producing thermal radiation, and (c) a compact relativistic particle region with a strong Inverse

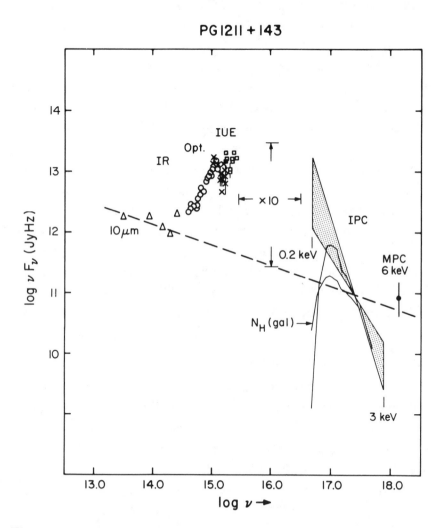

Figure 7: Energy distribution (ν F_ν vs. ν plot) for PG1211+143, infrared to X-ray. Note the UV and soft X-ray excesses. They may well contain more luminosity than the power-law continuum.

Compton component and substantial variability. In such a picture, and any similar one, important information could come from studying the relative variability properties in the different spectral regions, and between different quasars.

Finally, an interesting comparison has been made (White, Fabian, and Mushotzky 1984) of the spectra of black hole X-ray binary candidates (e.g., Cyg X-1) and AGN. In its low state Cyg X-1 has a hard spectrum similar to the $\alpha = 0.7$ power law of many Seyfert galaxies. In its high state it has a soft spectrum very much like those often seen in BL Lac objects. White, Fabian, and Mushotzky suggest that this may reflect the same underlying physics and that the critical point is whether a source exceeds 1% of its Eddington limit. This corresponds to the point at which X-ray photons with $E > 511$ keV cannot escape the source close due to pair production by γ-γ collisions. This produces a re-distribution of emergent photon energies towards softer X-rays (Guilbert, Fabian, and Rees 1983; Lightman, Giacconi, and Tananbaum 1978).

e) Energy Input to the Emission-line Regions

Photoionization codes which seek to explain line ratios seen in quasars must necessarily assume some form for the ionizing continuum (see the chapter by Shields and Ferland). In the optically thick clouds of the broad line region much of the Balmer line ionization is effectively produced by the soft X-ray continuum at about 1 keV (Kwan and Krolik 1981). Other strong lines (e.g., CIV, He II) are sensitive to the XUV flux above the helium edge at 228 Å, i.e., the range 0.05-0.10 keV (Kwan and Krolik 1981). These energies are now directly observable (after allowing for local interstellar absorption). The varied soft X-ray spectra of quasars (see §IIb) require that photoionization models be tailored to use the continua of individual quasars. No single generic quasar will be enough.

In a two-phase medium model (Krolik, McKee, and

Tarter 1981) the soft X-ray spectrum also affects the stability of the emission-line region clouds by determining the Compton temperature. A steep ($\alpha \gtrsim 2$) X-ray spectrum will lower the Compton temperature sufficiently to remove the two-phase instability (Guilbert, Fabian, and McCray 1983). This is an appealing explanation for the difference between quasars and BL Lacs. Such steep spectra are sometimes seen in quasars (Elvis, Wilkes, and Tananbaum 1985, see §IIb). Some additional energy input, such as adiabatic compressional heating from accretion, may be required in order to explain the existence of broad emission lines in these objects.

f) Evolution and the X-ray Background

The local population of Seyfert galaxies contributes $\sim$ 20% to the diffuse X-ray background (Piccinotti *et al.* 1982). Since quasars evolve strongly in number and/or luminosity with cosmic look-back time (see chapter by Weedman; Schmidt 1968; Schmidt and Green 1983) they have the potential to comprise the entire X-ray background (Setti and Woltjer 1973; Marshall *et al.* 1984).

The summed spectra of any sources which dominate the X-ray background must, of course, match that of the background itself. From 3-50 keV the background spectrum is very well fit by thermal bremsstrahlung at 40 keV (Marshall *et al.* 1980). The constraint that this implies for power law sources in the 2-20 keV range are surprisingly tight. Any dispersion of spectral index, α, must be less than $\sim$0.2 (deZotti *et al.* 1982).

The observation of steep IPC spectra in bright quasars (§IIb) has important implications for existing X-ray background calculations. Since these were largely based on X-ray measurements of quasars with no spectral information, they were forced to assume a spectrum (usually a flat, $\alpha = 0.5$, slope). Steepening the assumed slope alters both the derived flux density and k-correction in such a way as to lower the expected quasar contribution to the X-ray background. Furthermore, the observed steep spectra in soft X-rays do not even approximate the background spectrum seen at (3-50 keV), so that it is clearly unwise to predict the hard X-ray background from soft X-ray observations. This further suggests that the soft extragalactic X-ray background (Nousek *et al.* 1982) may have a steep spectrum.

The X-ray spectrum enters implicitly into the large body of survey work, both optical and X-ray, which has been used to determine the quasar contribution to the X-ray background and, using this, limit the quasar evolution parameters. The quantity α_{ox} is conventionally used to connect optical and X-ray observations (Tananbaum *et al.* 1979). It is the slope on a log f_ν vs. log ν plot of the line joining the 2500 Å and the 2 keV flux points. It can provide a means of using optical luminosity functions to predict X-ray ones. The mean value of α_{ox} derived from X-ray- and optically-selected samples however disagree (Zamorani 1982). There also appears to be a dependence of α_{ox} on optical luminosity in the sense that optically luminous quasars are less X-ray luminous than predicted by a mean α_{ox} (Avni and Tananbaum 1982). The situation is confused.

It is possible that the resolution of these problems will come from spectral data. Kriss and Canizares (1985) have investigated the effects of intrinsic reddening, both in the optical and the X-ray, on α_{ox} as a function of redshift. At high redshifts the effective X-ray column is reduced while the optical is more strongly affected. Since X-ray selected samples (Gioia *et al.* 1984) do contain red AGN, the different α_{ox} distributions may be explicable in this way. Luminosity dependent reddening can furthermore explain a difference between hard- and soft-X-ray selected AGN luminosity functions (Maccacaro, Gioia and Stocke 1984; Reichert *et al.* 1985). The varied spectral indices found for quasar X-ray spectra (see §IIb) offer another route for investigating these anomalies.

III. LOW LUMINOSITY AGN: ABSORPTION EFFECTS

a) Absorption a Function of Luminosity

The work of Lawrence and Elvis (1982) and Mushotzky (1982) showed that, for those (largely radio-quiet) AGN for which we have spectra, the degree of low energy absorption seems to be a systematic function of luminosity, being confined to low luminosity ($L_X \lesssim 10^{43.5}$ erg s^{-1}) objects. Exceptions to the rule have appeared since. The quasar MR2251-179 has a large and variable column (Halpern 1984; see all §IIIb). Also some low luminosity Seyferts do not have a large column (e.g., N7213 and N4593; Reichert *et al.* 1985). Nevertheless a statistical effect seems secure. Above 10^{44} erg s^{-1}, an AGN is very unlikely to be absorbed; below $10^{43.5}$ erg s^{-1} it is about equally likely to be heavily absorbed or unabsorbed (Fig. 8). It is not clear whether there are really two 'branches' or whether further observations will fill in the 'wedge.'

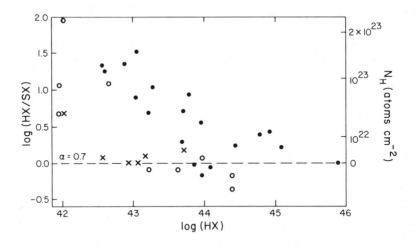

Figure 8: X-ray absorption versus 2-10 keV luminosity (HX) (after Lawrence and Elvis 1982, solid circles, updated with the data of Reichert *et al.* 1985, crosses, and private communications, open circles). HX/SX is the ratio of (2-10)/(0.3-3.5) keV X-ray luminosities and for spectral index $\alpha = 0.7$ corresponds to the column densities, N_H, indicated on the right.

Such large columns (up to $\sim 10^{23}$ atoms cm^{-2}) cannot arise in normal, cool, dust-bearing gas surrounding the Seyfert nucleus as a whole, because of the absence of the implied enormous optical reddening. An $A_v \sim 20$ corresponds to $N_H \sim 10^{23}$ atom cm^{-2} (Mushotsky *et al.* 1978b; Maccacaro, Perola, and Elvis 1982; Lawrence and Elvis 1982). The favored candidate for the absorbing material is the emission line cloud material of the Broad Line Region (BLR). The X-ray observed column densities of the order 10^{23} atoms cm^{-2} provide just the right optical depth in recombination lines to match model predictions for optical spectra (see the chapter by Shields and Ferland). Several further features, as described below, support this view, but it is by no means proven.

b) Variable Absorption

Barr *et al.* (1977) reported spectral variability of NGC 4151 on a timescale of months. An extreme change occurred between January and December 1976. The column increased from 5×10^{22} atoms cm^{-2} to 2×10^{23} atoms cm^{-2}. The slope and normalization of the underlying spectrum remained the same. Mushotzky *et al.* (1978b) reported a flare on a timescale of days in NGC4151 when the column was 7.5×10^{22} atoms cm^{-2}. While the flux changed, the slope and column remained constant.

Variability on a timescale of a few days has been seen in a large fraction of X-ray selected Seyfert 1 galaxies (Marshall, Warwick, and Pounds 1981). This suggests an X-ray source size $\sim 10^{15}$ cm. If a characteristic timescale of a few months is typical for absorption changes and is due to an occulting cloud than this implies a transverse velocity of $\sim 10^{3-4}$ km s^{-1} for the cloud, a typical broad line region velocity. Moreover as most of the absorption measurements are consistent with cold absorbers the occulting clouds cannot be too near the source, again consistent with broad line region absorption.

Not all absorption changes need be due to occultation. Halpern (1984) observed a large column change towards the quasar

MR2251-179 between measurements with the *Einstein* Monitor Proportional Counter (2-10 keV) in January 1979 and May 1980. At the same time a "soft excess" was seen in the *Einstein* High Resolution Imager. Halpern argued that this could be explained by a partially ionized absorber, transparent below the O VII edge at 0.75 keV, and that the change in apparent column was actually a change in ionization state. This requires clouds 10 times nearer to the X-ray/UV source than the standard BLR clouds. Such clouds would not be observed as optical emission line clouds.

c) Partial Covering

The SSS observation of NGC 4151 (Holt *et al.* 1980) found the expected low-energy turnover; however, the spectrum began to rise again below 1 keV (Fig. 9). Potentially this could be explained by a hot absorber, by abundance effects, by an incomplete covering of the X-ray source or by an additional source of X-rays outside the absorbers. The HEAO-A2 data on the Fe edge (see §IIId) imply a relatively cool absorber. Using this assumption, Holt *et al.* were able to fit their spectrum for the column, the covered fraction, and the relative abundance of $Z > 14$ and $Z < 10$ elements. They required the X-ray source to be $\sim 10\%$ uncovered, and the $z > 14$ elements (Fe, Si, S) to be overabundant by a factor 2. The partial covering is particularly pleasing in the context of the conventional picture of the BLR described by Lawrence and Elvis (1982) as being like "a swarm of glowing marbles." If many clouds cover the face of the X-ray source, to an average depth of 2-3 clouds, Poisson fluctuations would require $\sim 10\%$ of the possible lines of sight to have zero intervening clouds. Alternatively, highly variable column densities suggest a small number of large clouds in which case partial covering corresponds to partial overlap of one or a few clouds with an X-ray source of similar size.

Three further AGN have now been seen to possess columns together with soft excesses that are probably explainable by partial covering: NGC 2992, 3227, and 3783 (Reichert *et al.* 1985). All four "partially covered" objects are low luminosity AGN. This is not altogether surprising, as a large column is needed to be able to detect a covering factor effect. In terms of the "marble" picture, a connection between low luminosity and partial covering could occur, for example, if the overall size of the BLR scaled with L_x in a different way from the size of the X-ray source. In terms of the 'large cloud' picture, it could arise if the X-ray source size scales with L_x, whereas the size of a typical BLR cloud remains constant.

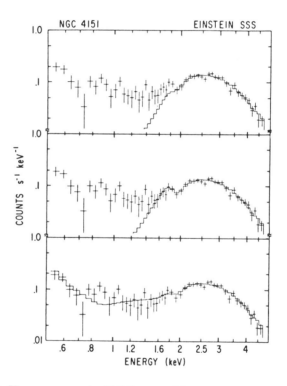

Figure 9: Soft X-ray excess in NGC 4151 (Holt *et al.* 1980) may indicate partial covering of continuum source (solid line in top frame is 100% covered, in bottom frame ~90% covered).

NGC 4151 displays some extended soft X-ray emission on a scale of $10''$ ~ 1 kpc (Elvis, Briel, and Henry 1983). This extended component supplied ~20% of the soft excess observed in the wide field of view SSS detectors, so while being a significant correction, does not in itself remove the arguments for partial covering. Nonetheless it reminds us of the remaining possibility that in all the above cases, some independent soft component (cf. §IIb) could be responsible for the excess. A crucial test would be a search for simultaneous hard and soft X-ray variability.

d) Atomic Features

Observation of atomic features can constrain the geometry, abundances, and ionization state of the absorbing material. The first observation of an Iron absorption edge at 7 keV was reported by Barr *et al.* (1977), for NGC 4151. As one might expect, it was only visible in the observation with the largest overall column density. Even so, its strength implied an overabundance (relative to the CNO group, which determines the overall column, and with respect to solar abundances) of a factor 2. The OSO-8 observation of iron features in NGC 5128 (Cen A, Mushotzky *et al.* 1978c) implied a factor 2 *underabundance* (of course, NGC 4151 is a spiral galaxy and NGC 5128 is an elliptical galaxy). In this case both an Fe edge at 7.1 keV, and an emission line at 6.4 keV, were observed. The line and edge were in the expected fluorescence ratio, suggesting that the clouds completely surround the X-ray source, and do not just lie along our line of sight. The position of the edge in the NGC 5128 data, and in the superior HEAO-A2 data on NGC 4151 (Holt *et al.* 1980), imply that in these cases the absorbing material is not highly ionized.* (Halpern 1984 postulated a highly ionized absorber in the case of MR2251-179, but had no spectral evidence to support this directly). The ratio of line to edge in NGC 4151 allowed Holt *et al.* (1980) to place a limit on the nonsphericity of the absorbing medium - - b/a>2/5. This however is still consistent with the kind of flattened but fat BLRs envisaged by Osterbrock (1979) and Lawrence and Elvis (1982).

---

* Not highly ionized, that is, by comparison with, for example, the solar corona but quite consistent with BLR clouds in which hydrogen is stripped, but heavy elements are in a relatively low ionization state.

The superior spectral resolution and lower energy range of SSS have brought other features into view. The NGC 4151 data (Holt *et al.* 1980) show features probably due to Si, S, and Ar. Reichert *et al.* (1985) have some indication of Si and S edges in N2992 and N3783. Again their positions imply relatively neutral material.

In all the above cases, absorption and emission is seen together with a large column density. Thermal or fluorescent emission lines could however occur without a large column. There are two possible instances in the literature: (i) A spectrum of NGC 5548 taken with Experiment C on Ariel V (Hayes *et al.* 1980) showed an extremely strong Fe line, eight times larger than the upper limit placed by HEAO-A2 (Mushotzky *et al.* 1980). This could be a fluorescence line from the BLR if the BLR surrounds most of the X-ray source, but we see it through a hole, and a large X-ray flare occurred a month before the Exp. C. observations. (ii) Petre *et al.* (1984) generally found no sign of any features in the spectrum of high luminosity AGN. An exception was 3C 120, which shows emission line features that could be explained by the addition of a 10-20% component from a T $\sim$ 1 keV plasma to the usual power law spectrum (Fig. 10, Mushotzky 1984b).

e) The Lack of Absorption in Quasars

For some years argument has raged over the reddening in quasars (see the chapter by MacAlpine). The degree of extinction in contention, $A_v \sim 0.1$, corresponds to small gas columns, 10^{20-21} cm^{-2}. No intrinsic X-ray absorption is seen in high luminosity AGN (with the exception of MR2251-179, see §II) but until recently the limits have been uninteresting. The SSS column measurements are sensitive mainly to oxygen absorption and give limits (expressed as an equivalent hydrogen column, N_H, for cosmic abundances) $N_H \simeq 2 \times 10^{21}$ atom cm^{-2} (Petre *et al.* 1984). Only IC4329A was seen to have a substantial column ($N_H \approx 5 \times 10^{21}$ cm^{-2}; this is consistent with the H I column expected from the observed optical reddening (Wilson and Penston 1979).

Since IC4329A is an edge-on spiral, we are almost certainly seeing absorption due to cool material somewhere in the plane of the parent galaxy. The IPC and EXOSAT CMA, with lower energy ranges, are sensitive to helium and hydrogen and can give limits of $N_H \simeq 3 \times 10^{20}$, similar to the line of sight through a typical spiral galaxy. Preliminary results from both instruments generally find columns in good agreement with the HI column through our own Galaxy (Elvis, Wilkes, and Tananbaum 1984; Pounds, McHardy, and Warwick 1984). We expect therefore that soon, useful upper limits on optical extinction can be placed from X-ray observations.

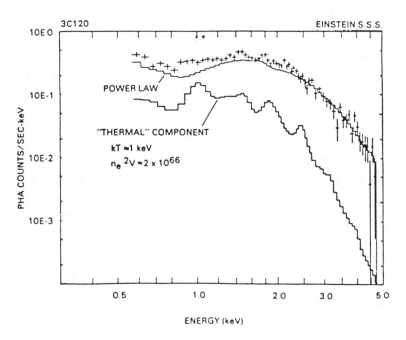

Figure 10: SSS spectrum of 3C120 showing probable 1 keV thermal emission at 15% of total luminosity (Petre *et al.* 1984; Mushotzky 1984a.)

X-ray absorption measurements are in principle particularly useful for measuring the column densities of relatively hot gases. An important example is the putative confining medium for the broad emission line clouds (see chapters by Shields and by Mathews). Because helium is fully ionized at $T \sim 10^5$ K the oxygen-derived limits are more restrictive on the allowed tempera-

tures of any such hot confining medium. The SSS limits require T
$>2.6 \times 10^7$ for the broad line region and $T > 2.2 \times 10^6$ K for the
narrow line region (Petre *et al.* 1984). Any further improvement
in these intrinsic X-ray column measurements will have to come
from the detection of absorption edges through improved spectral
resolution.

IV. CLASSES OF AGN WITH LITTLE
X-RAY SPECTRAL INFORMATION

a) Radio Galaxies

A few luminous broad-line, radio galaxies appeared in the
medium energy sky surveys (3C 382, 3C 390.3, 3C 111, 3C 120)
and are known to have X-ray spectra similar to Type 1 Seyferts
(Mushotsky 1984a) i.e., a power law of $\alpha \sim 0.7$. The low luminosity radio galaxy NGC 5128 (Cen A) also has a 0.7 power law
which is seen out to 1 MeV (Hall *et al.* 1976) with the addition of
a large absorbing column density.

Fabbiano *et al.* (1984) and Feigelson and Berg (1983)
have shown that soft X-ray emission is a common property of both
narrow-line and broad-line 3C radio galaxies. The good correlation
of X-ray and nuclear radio flux for both classes (Fabbiano *et al.*
1984) shows that their X-ray emission is predominantly of nuclear
origin. Surprisingly even 3C galaxies showing only normal stellar
spectra in the optical fit on this same correlation. This includes
3C 264 for which high angular resolution *Einstein* data confirms
a nuclear origin (Elvis *et al.* 1981). We have no idea of the form
of the X-ray spectra in the narrow-line and absorption-line radio
galaxies. We might expect from the similarity of their optical spectra (Costero and Osterbrock 1977) that narrow-line radio galaxies
would resemble Seyfert 2 galaxies. However a similar expectation
in the infrared was disappointed (Elvis *et al.* 1984). Absorption
line radio galaxies are even more mysterious with only the suggestion that they are low luminosity BL Lacs to go on (Elvis *et al.*
1981; Fabbiano *et al.* 1984).

b) Type 2 Seyferts

Objects that have been classified as "Type 2 Seyfert" are probably a mixed breed (Lawrence *et al.* 1985c). X-ray discovered narrow line Seyferts tend to have flat ($\alpha \sim 0.7$) power-law X-ray spectra, large X-ray columns, and large optical reddening, suggesting that they are obscured broad line objects (Veron *et al.* 1980; Lawrence and Elvis 1982; Maccacaro, Perola, and Elvis 1982; Mushotzky 1982). A continuity of X-ray, optical and infrared properties from Type 1 Seyferts, through "intermediate" Type 1, to Type 2 Seyferts suggests that at least some classical Type 2 Seyferts are also obscured broad line objects. If the absorbing material has a column density in excess of 10^{24} atoms cm^{-2}, it will be Compton thick, and could suppress both soft and hard X-rays, as well as the broad emission lines themselves (Kallman and Mushotzky 1985).

At least some "Type 2 Seyferts" are relatively normal starburst galaxies (e.g., NGC 6764; Osterbrock and Cohen 1982) and others may be metal rich starbursts with extremely hot (200,000 K) massive stars (so called "warmers"; Terlevich and Melnick 1985.) But many of the classical Type 2 Seyferts may be genuinely different. Since they have observed UV excesses and starlike nuclei they are presumably not heavily obscured. X-ray spectra could potentially distinguish these possibilities. None of the published IPC detections of Type 2 Seyferts (e.g., Kriss, Canizares, and Ricker 1980) had enough counts to fit an X-ray spectrum, and medium energy limits (e.g., Elvis *et al.* 1978) fall just short of being interesting. An EXOSAT observation of NGC 1068 also failed to detect 2-10 keV X-rays, but the measured soft X-ray fluxes through three filters roughly corresponding to .05, 0.1, and 1 keV (Lawrence *et al.* 1985b) are consistent with a power law of slope $\alpha \sim 1.5$, and may join up roughly with the observed IUE continuum. This is certainly different from the "Universal" Type 1 Seyfert spectrum (§IIa), but could be similar to the soft component that is occasionally seen (§IIb). A priority for the future must be medium energy detections or sensitive limits for Type 2 Seyferts, and high resolution soft X-ray spectroscopy.

c) LINERS and "Microquasars"

LINERS are very common in galaxy nuclei (see chapter by Keel). In his discovery paper Heckman (1980) estimated that about 1/3 of all bright galaxies had detectable LINER nuclei. 'LINER' is an acronym for 'Low Ionization Nuclear Emission-line Regions' which correctly implies that their spectra do not resemble Seyferts. Nor do they resemble H II regions. Several LINERS are known to be soft X-ray sources (Halpern and Steiner 1983) but no spectral information is available to distinguish competing theories. If they are "mini-quasars" then Seyfert-like spectra should be observed (Péquinot 1981; Ferland and Netzer 1983), possibly absorbed (Halpern and Steiner 1983). Alternatively, if they are "warmers" (Terlevich and Melnick 1985) or shock excited (Heckman 1980) a soft thermal spectrum should be observed.

The principal clue is afforded by NGC 2110. This active galaxy has an optical spectrum dominated by narrow lines of relatively low ionization (McClintock *et al.* 1979), but has faint broad wings on Hα (Shuder 1980). Halpern and Steiner describe it as a "transition case" between Type 1 Seyferts and LINERS. A medium energy X-ray spectrum is available (Mushotzky 1982). It has the usual power law $\alpha = 0.7$ form with a large low energy absorbing column. This is certainly strong supporting evidence for the "mini-quasar" theory of LINERS, but of course, as in the case of Type 2 Seyferts, LINERS may actually be a heterogeneous class.

Even weaker active nuclei than LINERS probably exist in virtually all bright spiral galaxies (see chapter by Keel and Keel 1983a,b). A very few of these 'microquasar' nuclei have been detected in X-rays (Elvis and van Speybroeck 1982). The best studied of these is M81 which is in fact bright enough to be a LINER and also to have detectable broad Hα wings. The uncertain IPC/MPC spectrum of M81 indicates a steep, unabsorbed continuum. If this result is verified it would suggest that the X-ray spectra of low luminosity AGN are as various as those of quasars (see §IIb).

d) Starburst Nuclei

Starburst nuclei are of course not "active" in the normally accepted sense, but they are important in the study of AGN for three reasons: (i) they can mimic AGN, as in the "warmers" theory of Terlevich and Melnick (1985), (ii) some nuclei may be mixed phenomena (see, e.g., Smith 1984), (iii) starbursts and nuclear activity may be causally related (Bailey 1982; Weedman 1983).

Nearby starburst nuclei are known to have complex extended X-ray emission roughly coincident with kpc scale H II region structure (e.g., M82, Watson, Stanger, and Griffiths 1984; NGC 253, Fabbiano and Trinchieri 1985; M83, Trinchieri, Fabbiano, and Palumbo 1985). NGC 1365 is also an extended soft X-ray source (Maccacaro, Perola, and Elvis 1982); however, one of the several optical knots is a weak Seyfert nucleus (Edmunds and Pagel 1982). The X-ray source is too faint to fit an IPC spectrum; consequently the contribution of the Seyfert nucleus to the X-ray source is unknown.

We may expect starburst nuclei in general to be strong, soft, thermal X-ray sources because of the rapid formation rate of supernova remnants (Weedman *et al.* 1981). Slightly older starbursts will produce substantial numbers of high mass X-ray binaries (like Cen X-3 or Cyg X-1), producing a hard X-ray spectrum not too dissimilar from Type 1 Seyferts. Thus the X-ray spectra may give us constraints on the initial mass function and age of a starburst. The X-ray map of NGC 253 (Fabbiano and Trinchieri 1984) suggests in addition that a small fraction of the starburst energy goes into the kinetic expansion of hot ($\sim 10^{5-6}$K) gas which is then collimated by the galaxy disk. Fabbiano (1985) points out that if this explanation is correct then collimated outflow of X-ray hot gas should be seen wherever substantial energy is deposited in a galaxy nucleus, i.e., in *all* spiral nuclei.

V. NEXT STEPS

Most of the newer data in this survey has come from two instruments on the *Einstein* satellite: the SSS and the IPC. When the reprocessing of the *Einstein* data base is completed the IPC will have yielded about 40 quasar spectra of reasonable quality. The *Einstein* instruments however had their designs frozen in the mid-1970s, nearly a decade ago. Current instrumentation can give qualitatively improved data of which we have only hints today. A flight opportunity for this new hardware will not occur until the launch of AXAF in 1991 or 1992.

a) Immediate Future

Until AXAF some smaller missions will send back data of similar quality to that in hand, but with the advantage that we now know which samples of objects to observe far better than when *Einstein* was launched.

EXOSAT is the only one of the two X-ray satellites operating in 1985 with the sensitivity to observe extragalactic sources (the other satellite is the Japanese TENMA). It is expected to operate until mid-1987. Problems with some of its imaging instruments have left it with a reduced sensitivity, similar to that of HEAO-A2 and the SSS. Its simultaneous 0.1 keV to 30 keV coverage will make it particularly valuable for the 'partial covering' type of observation discussed in §III.

Quasars, and the other classes of objects which currently have no X-ray spectra at all (§IV) will only become observable again in more than token quantities with the launch of the West German ROSAT (Röentgen Satellit) in 1987. The primary mission of ROSAT will be to make the first imaging X-ray survey of the sky. This (as well as considerations of cost) led to its wide field-of-view ($\sim 2°$) optics which thus do not reflect X-rays above about 2 keV. For soft sources and sources with small intrinsic column densities it will be able to provide useful IPC-like spectra with somewhat improved energy resolution ($E/\Delta E \sim 3$).

A third mission, which may fly a little later, is the X-ray Timing Explorer (XTE). This is a non-imaging satellite designed to study bright galactic sources. It therefore has limited sensitivity for extragalactic work. Its large area ($\sim 10^4$ cm^2) and high energy response (to above 100 keV) will make it valuable for determining the total luminosity of AGN and for detailed study of the rapid variables.

The X-ray Ultraviolet Explorer (XUVE) is due for launch in 1988. Its wavelength coverage of 1000 Å-100 Å means that few quasars will be detectable through the local interstellar medium. However, XUVE will have unexpected importance to quasar research in view of the detection of a large XUV excess in PG1211+143 (§IIb,d). In spite of the XUV bump, however, most of a quasar's luminosity could be emitted in the MeV γ-ray region (Bezler *et al.* 1984). For this reason GRO (Gamma-Ray Observatory, due for launch in 1988) will be important, although it may only detect a dozen or so active nuclei.

b) AXAF: High Resolution Spectra

All the 'spectra' discussed so far in this chapter have been the X-ray equivalent of multicolor UBVRI photometry. This is not surprising given that the effective area of the *Einstein* mirrors is that of a 6-inch telescope. This 'photometry' has been rich in results but is painfully limiting.

As an analogy see how the strong emission-line object 3C273 would appear in the optical at about the IPC spectral resolution ($E/\Delta E = 2.5$, Fig. 11a). A simple power law is a good fit apart from a feature in the red (this is Hα). The emission lines are invisible since they only make up a few percent of the flux in

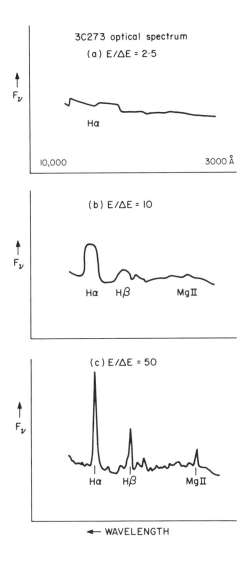

Figure 11: Optical spectrum of 3C273 (de Bruyn and Sargent 1978) convolved with a boxcar filter to (a) IPC resolution (E/ΔE ~ 2.5); (b) SSS or GSPC resolution (E/ΔE ~ 10); (c) AXAF grating resolution (E/ΔE ~ 50). The emission lines contain only a few percent of the optical luminosity and need high resolution to be seen clearly.

the optical band.

Deviations from a pure power law and the strongest emission lines become visible only at a resolution $E/\Delta E \sim 10$ similar to the SSS or to a Gas Scintillation Proportional Counter (GSPC, Fig. 11b). A true emission-line spectrum only appears at $E/\Delta E \sim 50$ (Fig. 11c), which will be attainable for the first time with significant area on AXAF using transmission or reflection gratings.

At this resolution we can study in excellent detail both the emission mechanisms and the environment of the quasar nucleus. Some early hints of this come from isolated *Einstein* results. As mentioned in §IIId 3C120 may have emission lines providing about 15% of its soft X-ray flux in the form of thermal plasma at $kT \sim 1$ keV (Fig. 10 Petre *et al.* 1984; Mushotzky 1984a). Such a plasma is rich in diagnostic lines Fig. 12).

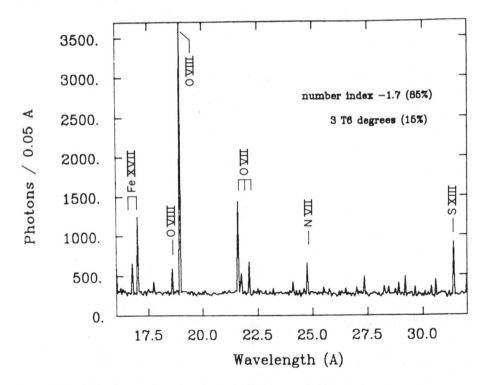

Figure 12: Theoretical 3×10^6 K plasma added to $\alpha = 0.7$ power law in the ratio 15:85. The strongest lines are identified.

This energy range is also rich in potential absorption features. §III discussed some of these. The most striking is the broad absorption feature discovered in PKS2155-305, a BL Lac object (Fig. 13, Canizares and Kruper 1984). This discovery was made with the high resolution ($E/\Delta E \sim 50$) Objective Grating Spectrometer (OGS) on *Einstein*. Because of its small effective area ($1/2$-2 cm^2, see lower panel of Fig. 13) this was the only extragalactic observation made with this instrument. The feature, probably O VIII Lyα, is clearly resolved with a width of $\geq 20{,}000$ km s^{-1}. It might be due to material in a relativistic jet that we are seeing end-on, or possibly to a hot Intergalactic Medium (Shapiro and Bahcall 1980). In either case it shows that high resolution X-ray spectra can have unexpected possibilities even in the most unpromising of objects, the 'featureless' BL Lacs objects.

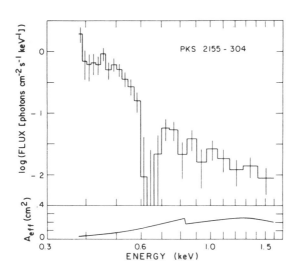

Figure 13: *Einstein* OGS spectrum of PKS2155-304 showing broad oxygen absorption feature (Canizares and Kruper 1984).

VI. CONCLUSIONS: OUTSTANDING PROBLEMS

We hope that this review had made it clear that X-ray astronomy, particularly X-ray spectra, can make important, and

specific, contributions to advancing quasar research. Already it is
clear that photoionization models for *individual* quasars need to be
constructed. Most of the conclusions concerning X-ray emitting
processes in quasars are based on small samples of objects with definite biases. The first priority for observation is larger complete
samples of quasar and Seyfert 1 spectra to allow a less partial
overview. Beyond this we must extend X-ray spectral observations to the other classes of active galaxies to see how emission
mechanisms vary over wide ranges of physical conditions, luminosity and radio power. In the longer term the ability to detect
emission lines and absorption features in large numbers of AGN
through grating spectroscopy will give us powerful new diagnostics
for understanding the structure and physics of quasars.

Any review such as this will be biased toward those results
that we are most familiar with, that is, our own. We apologize for
this bias and have done our best to overcome it. In this effort
we were helped greatly by challenging and stimulating discussions
with Gianni Zamorani, Richard Mushotzky, Julian Krolik, Gail
Reichert, Ken Pounds, and Claude Canizares. We are also grateful to Matt Malkan for producing the convolved 3C273 spectra
presented in Figure 11.

REFERENCES

Agrawal, P.C., Riegler, G.R., and Mushotzky, R.F. 1979, *Ap. J.*, **233**, L47.

Arnaud, K.A., Fabian, A.C., Hazard, C., Condon, J.J., and Sargent, W.L.W. 1984, M.N.R.A.S., submitted.

Avni, Y. 1978, *Astron. Ap.*, **63**, L13.

Avni, Y., and Tananbaum, H. 1982, *Ap. J.*, **262**, L17.

Bailey, M.E. 1982, *M.N.R.A.S.*, **200**, 247.

Barr, P., Ives, J.C., Sanford, P.W., and White, N.E. 1977, *M.N.R.A.S*, **181**, 43.

Bezler, M., Kendziora, E., Staubert, R., Hasinger, G., Pietsch, W., Reppin, C., Trumper, J., and Voges, W. 1984, *Astron. Ap.*, **136**, 351.

Bregman, J.M., *et al.* 1983, *Ap. J.*, **274**, 107.

Canizares, C.R. and Kruper, J. 1984, *Ap. J.*, **278**, L99.

Costero, R. and Osterbrock, D.E. 1977, *Ap. J.*, **211**, 675.

deBruyn, A.G. and Sargent, W.L.W. 1978, *Astron. J.*, **83**, 1257.

deZotti, G., Boldt, E.A., Cavaliere, A., Danese, L., Franceschini, A., Marshall, F.E., Swank, J.G., and Symkoviak, A.E. 1982, *Ap.J.*, **253**, 47.

Edmunds, M.G. and Pagel, B.E.J. 1982, *M.N.R.A.S.*, **198**, 1089.

Elvis, M., Maccacaro, T., Wilson, A., Ward, M., Penston, M., Fosbury, R.A.E., and Perola, G.C. 1978, *M.N.R.A.S.*, **183**, 129.

Elvis, M., Schreier, E.J., Davis, M., Tonry, J., and Huchra, J.P. 1981, *Ap.J.*, **246**, 20.

Elvis, M. and Van Speybroech, L. 1982, *Ap.J.*, **257**, L51.

Elvis, M., Briel, U., and Henry, J.P. 1983, *Ap. J.*, **268**, 105.

Elvis, M., Willner, S.P., Fabbiano, G., Carleton, N.P., Lawrence, A., and Ward, M. 1984, *Ap. J.*, **280**, 574.

Elvis, M., Soltan, A., and Keel, W.C. 1984, *Ap. J.*, **283**, 479.

Elvis, M., Wilkes, B., and Tananbaum, H. 1985, *Ap. J.*, **292**, (May 15), in press.

Elvis, M., Bechtold, J., Green, R., and Fabbiano, G. 1985. In preparation.

Fabbiano, G. 1985, Proceedings of the conference "X-ray Astronomy '84," Bologna, Italy.

Fabbiano, G., Miller, L., Trinchieri, G., Longair, M., and Elvis, M. 1984, *Ap.J.*, **277**, 115.

Fabbiano, G. and Trinchieri, G. 1985, *Ap.J.*, **286**, (Nov. 15).

Feigelson, E.D. and Berg, C.J. 1983, *Ap. J.*, **269**, 400.

Ferland, G.J. and Netzer, H., 1983, *Ap. J.*, **264**, 105.

Gioia, I.M., Maccacaro, T., Schild, R.E., Stocke, J.T., Liebert, J.W., Danziger, I.J., Kunth, D., and Lub, J. 1984, *Ap. J.*, **283**, 495.

Gorenstein, P., Harnden, F.R., and Fabricant, D.G. 1981, *IEEE Trans. Nucl. Sci.*, **NS-28**, 869.

Grandi, S.A. 1982, *Ap. J.*, **255**, 25.

Guilbert, P.W., Fabian, A.C., and McCray, R. 1983, *Ap. J.*, **266**, 466.

Guilbert, P.W., Fabian, A.C., and Rees, M.J. 1983, *M.N.R.A.S.*, **205**, 593.

Hall, R.D., Meegan, C.A., Walraven, G.D., Djuth, F.T., and Haynes, R.C. 1976, *Ap. J.*, **210**, 631.

Halpern, J.P. 1982, Ph.D. Thesis, Harvard University.

Halpern, J.P. and Steiner, J.E. 1983, *Ap. J.*, **269**, L37.

Halpern, J.P. 1984, *Ap. J.*, **281**, 90.

Harnden, F.R., Jr., Fabricant, D.G., Harris, D.E., and Schwarz, J. 1984, SAO Special Report No. 393.

Harnden, F.R., Jr., and Fabricant, D. G. 1985, in preparation.

Hayes, M.J.C., Culhane, J.L., Blisset, R.J., Barr, P., and Bell-Burnell, S.J. 1980, *M.N.R.A.S.*, **193**, 15p.

Heckman, T. 1980, *Astron. Ap.*, **87**, 152.

Holt, S.S., Mushotzky, R.F., Becker, R.H., Boldt, E.A., Serlemitsos, P.J., Symkoviak, A.E., and White, N.E. 1980, *Ap. J. (Letters)*, **241**, L13.

Ipser, J.R. and Price, R.H. 1983, *Ap. J.*, **267**, 371.

Joyce, R.M., Becker, R.H., Birsa, F.B., Holt, S.S., and Noordzy, M.P. 1978, *I.E.E.E. Trans. Nucl. Sci.*, **NS-25**, 453.

Kallman, T. and Mushotzky, R.F. 1985, *Ap.J*, **292**, (May 1) in press.

Kardashev, N.S. 1962, *Soviet Astr. A.J.*, **6**, 317.

Keel, W.C. 1983a, *Ap.J.*, **269**, 466.

_____. 1983b, *Ap. J. Suppl.*, **52**, 229.

Kriss, G.A., Canizares, C.R., and Ricker, G. 1980, *Ap.J.*, **242**, 492.

Kriss, G.A. and Canizares, C.R. 1982, *Ap. J.*, **261**, 51.

_____. 1985, *Ap. J.*, submitted.

Krolik, J.H., McKee, C.F., and Tarter, C.B. 1981, *Ap. J.*, **249**, 422.

Kwan, J.Y. and Krolik, J.H. 1981, *Ap. J.*, **250**, 478.

Lawrence, A. and Elvis, M. 1982, *Ap. J.*, **253**, 410.

Lawrence, A., Elvis, M., Pounds, K.A., and Watson, M.G. 1985a, in preparation (to be submitted to MNRAS).

Lawrence, A., *et al.* 1985b, in preparation.

Lawrence, A., Ward, M.J., Elvis, M., Fabbiano, G., Willner, S.P., Carleton, N.P., and Longmore, A. 1985c, *Ap. J.*, **290**, (March) in press.

Lightman, A.P., Giacconi, R., and Tananbaum, H. 1978, *Ap. J.*, **224**, 375.

Maccacaro, T., Perola, G.C., and Elvis, M. 1982, *Ap. J.*, **257**, 47.

Maccacaro, T., Gioia, I.M. and Stocke, J.T., 1984, *Ap. J.*, **283**, 486.

Malkan, M.A. and Sargent, W.L.W. 1982, *Ap. J.*, **254**, 22.

Malkan, M.A. 1983, *Ap. J.*, **268**, 582.

Maraschi, L. 1984, in *X-ray and UV Emission from Active Galactic Nuclei*, ed. Brinkmann, Max-Planck Institut.

Maraschi, L., Roasio, R., and Treves, A. 1982, *Ap. J.*, **253**, 312.

Margon, B., Chanan, G.A., and Downes, R.A. 1982, *Ap. J.*, **253**, L7.

Marshall, N., Warwick, R.S., and Pounds, K.A. 1981, *M.N.R.A.S.*, **194**, 987.

Marshall, F.E., Boldt, E.A., Holt, S.S., Miller, R.B., Mushotzky, R.F., Rose, L.A., Rothschild, R.E., and Serlemitsos, P.J. 1980, *Ap. J.*, **235**, 4.

Marshall, F.E., Holt, S.S., Mushotzky, R.F., and Becker, R. H. 1983, *Ap. J.*, **269**, L31.

Marshall, H., Avni, Y., Braccesi, A., Huchra, J.P., Tananbaum, H., Zamorani, G., and Zitelli, V. 1984, *Ap. J.*, **283**, 50.

Matteson, J.L. 1978, *Proc. AIAA*, 78-35.

McClintock, J.E., van Paradijs, J., Remilard, R.A., Canizares, C.R., Koski, A. T., and Veron, P. 1979, *Ap. J.*, **233**, 809.

Mezaros, P.. 1983, *Ap. J.*, **274**, L13.

Mushotzky, R.F., Holt, S.S., and Serlemitsos, P.J. 1978a, *Ap. J.*, **225**, L115.

Mushotzky,, R.F., Boldt, E.A., Holt, S.S., Pravdo, S.H., Serlemitsos, P.J., Swank, J.H. and Rothschild, R.E. 1978b, *Ap. J.*, **226**, L65.

Mushotzky, R.F., Serlemitsos, P.J., Becker, R.H., Boldt, E.A., and Holt, S.S. 1978c, *Ap. J.*, **220**, 790.

Mushotzky, R.F. and Marshall, F.E. 1980, *Ap. J.*, **239**, L5.

Mushotzky, R.F., Marshall, F.E., Boldt, E.A., Holt, S.S., and Serlemitsos, P. J. 1980, *Ap. J.*, **235**, 377.

Mushotzky, R.F. 1982, *Ap. J.*, **256**, 92.

_____. 1984a, *Advances in Space Research*, 3, no. 10-12, 157.

_____. 1984b, Proceedings of "X-ray and UV Emission from Active Galactic Nuclei," ed. Brinkmann, Max Planck Institut.

Nousek, J.A., Fried, P.M., Sanders, W.T., and Kraushaar, W.L. 1982, *Ap. J.*, **258**, 83.

Osterbrock, D.E. and Cohen, R.D. 1982, *Ap. J.*, **261**, 64.

Osterbrock, D.E. 1979, *Astron. J.*, **84**, 901.

Péquinot, D. 1981, Ph.D. Thesis, Observatoire de Meudon.

Petre, R., Mushotzky, R.F., Kroloik, J.H., and Holt, S.S. 1984, *Ap. J.*, **280**, 499

Piccinotti, G., Mushotzky, R.F., Boldt, E.A., Holt, S.S., Marshall, F.E., Serlemitsos, P.J., and Shafer, R.A. 1982, *Ap. J.*, **253**, 485.

Pounds, K.A., McHardy, I.M., and Warwick, R.S. 1984, Proceedings of the conference "X-ray Astronomy '84," Bologna, Italy.

Pravdo, S.H., Nugent, J.J., Nousek, J.A., Jensen, K., Wilson, A.S., and Becker, R.H. 1981, *Ap. J.*, **251**, 501.

Pravdo, S.H. and Marshall, F.E. 1984, *Ap. J.*, **281**, 570.

Reichert, G.A., Mason, K.O., Thorstensen, J.R., and Bowyer, S. 1982, *Ap. J.*, **260**, 437.

Reichert, G.A., Mushotzky, R.F., Petre, R., and Holt, S.S. 1985, Ap. J., in press.

Rothschild, R., Boldt, E., Holt, S., Serlemitsos, P., Garmire, G., Agrawal, P., Riegler, G., Bowyer, S., and Lampton, S. 1979, *Space Sci. Instr.*, **4**, 269.

Rothschild, R.E., Mushotzky, R.F., Baity, W.A., Gruber, D.E., Matteson, J.L., and Primini, F.A. 1983, *Ap. J.*, **269**, 423.

Schmidt, M. 1968, *Ap. J.*, **151**, 393.

Schmidt, M. and Green, R.F. 1983, *Ap. J.*, **269**, 352.

Setti, G. and Woltjer, L. 1973, in *X- and Gamma-Ray Astronomy*, eds., Giacconi, R. and Bradt, H.V., pp. 208-211.

Shapiro, P.R. and Bahcall, J.N. 1980, *Ap. J.*, **241**, 1.

Shields, G.A. 1978, *Nature*, **272**, 706.

Shuder, J.M. 1980, *Ap. J.*, **240**, 32.

Smith, M.G. 1984, Proceedings of "Active Galactic Nuclei," Manchester, April 1984, Manchester University Press.

Tananbaum, H., *et al.* 1979, *Ap. J. (Letters)*, **234**, L9.

Tennant, A.H. 1984, Ph.D. thesis, University of Maryland, also published as NASA Technical Memorandum 85101.

Terlevich, R. and Melnick, J. 1985, M.N.R.A.S., submitted.

Trinchieri, G., Fabbiano, G., and Palumbo, G. 1985, *Ap. J.*, **289**, (Feb. 15).

Urry, M. and Mushotzky, R.F. 1982, *Ap. J.*, **253**, 38.

Urry, M. 1984, Ph.D. Thesis, Johns Hopkins University, also published as NASA Technical Memorandum 86103.

Veron, P., Lindblad, P.O., Zuiderwiyk, E. J., Veron, M.P., and Adam, G. 1980, *Astron. Astrophys.*, **87**, 245.

Watson, M.G., Stanger, V., and Griffiths, R.E. 1984, *Ap. J.*, **286**, 144.

Weedman, D.W., Feldman, F.R., Balzano, V.A., Ramsey, L.W., Sramek, R.A., and Wu, C.-C 1981, *Ap. J.*, **248**, 105.

Weedman, D.W. 1983, *Ap. J.*, **266**, 479.

White, N.E., Fabian, A.C., and Mushotzky, R.F., 1984, *Astron. and Astrophys.*, **133**, L9.

Wills, B.J., Netzer, H., and Wills, D. 1985, *Ap. J.*, **288**, 94.

Wilson, A.S. and Penston, M.V. 1979, *Ap. J.*, **232**, 389.

Worrall, D.M., Mushotzky, R.F., Boldt, E.A., Holt, S.S., and Serlemitsos, P.J. 1979, *Ap. J.*, **240**, 421.

Zamorani, G., et al. 1981, *Ap. J.*, **245**, 357.

Zamorani, G., 1982, *Ap. J.*, **260**, L31.

BROAD ABSORPTION LINE QUASARS ("BALQSOs")

Ray J. Weymann

Steward Observatory, University of Arizona
Tucson, AZ

David A. Turnshek
Space Telescope Science Institute
Baltimore, MD
and
Wayne A. Christiansen
Department of Physics and Astronomy,
University of North Carolina
Chapel Hill, NC

ABSTRACT

We review several observational and theoretical problems encountered in the interpretation of the spectra of Quasars which have broad absorption lines in their spectra ("BALQSOs"). The distribution of the parameters characterizing the Mg II and C III] emission line profiles is not significantly different in the BALQSOs compared to normal QSOs, suggesting that there are no gross differences in the broad emission line regions between normal and BAL QSOs. No satisfactory models to explain the observed levels of ionization have been proposed as yet, the photoionization models coming the closest yielding some column densities off by an order of magnitude from those observed.

Two kinematic and geometrical models for the absorption – the "cloudy filament" model and the "P-Cygni" model – are described. The cloudy filament model leads to extremely small cloudlets. The P-Cygni model seems to be in conflict with the Mg II and C III] observations.

Acceleration mechanisms are reviewed in the context of the cloudy filament model. We conclude that winds or blast waves rather than photons are involved, however, the origin and survival of the clouds pose problems: If the clouds are pre-existing the wind may shred them via Rayleigh-Taylor instabilities, whereas if they cool and form following a blast wave via thermal instabilities there may not be time for the clouds to cool.

I. INTRODUCTION

Quasars which show broad absorption lines in their spectra (BALQSOs) offer a unique set of challenges and opportunities for understanding some of the physical processes at work in AGNs and QSOs. In our opinion, BALQSOs have not received the attention they warrant on the part of either observers or theorists.

For one thing, in contrast to the controversy still associated with the interpretation of the broad *emission* lines we are looking at material which certainly has been accelerated radially outwards at speeds of up to 0.1-0.2 c. In addition, direct estimates are available for the column densities of the BALQSO clouds; column densities can only be indirectly inferred for the BELR clouds and are very uncertain.

Since two reviews on the subject of BALQSOs have appeared fairly recently (Weymann and Foltz 1983, hereafter WF83; Turnshek 1984b, hereafter T84) we concentrate in the present review on those developments which have taken place since WF83 and T84, especially those results presented at the 1984 Santa Cruz Workshop. Before taking up some of these detailed topics, however, we give a brief overview of the subject, referring the reader to WF83 and T84 for further details and illustrations of many of the spectra.

The BALQSO class of QSOs are characterized by strong broad absorption whose extent represents outflow velocities with respect to the emission line centroids from about 0 to as high as about 0.2 c. The absorption troughs themselves vary considerably in shape and extent, but a typical width is 10,000 km s^{-1}. Some show no structure at the highest resolutions used so far while others show very complex structure, with numerous sharp lines superposed on relatively featureless absorption (cf. RS23 and 1303+308 in WF83). All known BALQSOs exhibit strong C IV and strong to moderate Si IV absorption. All, or very nearly all, exhibit strong N V and O VI when the redshifts are high enough for these lines to be studied. On the other hand, Lyα is frequently much weaker than N V and is sometimes not visible at all. With two interesting exceptions, one of which is discussed in §V, Mg II is also very much weaker than C IV. (New data on Mg II strengths were presented at the workshop and are discussed below.)

There is a rather strong suspicion that the character of the absorption profiles is correlated with the character of the emission line profiles in the sense that the stronger, narrower C IV emission profiles having large emission line peak-to-continuum ratios tend to be associated with smooth relatively featureless absorption contiguous to the emission (cf. PHL5200, RS23, and H1413+113 in WF83). Conversely, complex absorption profiles, often detached in velocity space from the emission, seem to be associated with broader, weaker, and more rounded C IV emission profiles having smaller emission line peak-to-continuum ratios (cf. 1303+308, H1414+087, 1309-086, 0932+501 in WF83).

In addition, Hazard (1985) has called attention to what appears to be a more detailed correlation. The C IV absorption troughs frequently consist of a deep relatively narrow steep-sided portion with a more gentle slope to the blue gradually recovering to the continuum (1413+113, WF83 provides a good example). Hazard notes that the width and depth of the deep portion of the trough is about the same as the width and height of the emission line. It is difficult to quantify these suspicions at present, partly because homogeneous sets of spectra of adequate S/N still involve a rather limited number of objects and also because it is still possible that selection effects connected with the discovery of BALQSOs might affect such a correlation.

The fraction of QSOs which are BALQSOs is still poorly known, and the possible dependence of this fraction on redshift, luminosity, and ratio of optical to radio flux is more poorly determined still. As noted frequently, the *intrinsic* fraction of QSOs which are undergoing the BALQSO phenomenon is equal to the *observed* fraction divided by the covering fraction of the clouds to the central source. In addition, BALQSOs may be rarer among QSOs which are strong radio sources than among optically selected QSOs in general, and may have weaker radio emission than the average optically selected QSO (Stocke *et al.* 1984). The most recent estimate for the incidence of BALQSOs among all QSOs with redshift greater than 2.0 is about 3 to 10% (Hazard *et al.* 1984). There is also a suspicion (Hazard 1985) that the fraction may be higher at higher redshifts (but see §V). In some other samples however, other observers have found a somewhat lower fraction.

All this observational material raises many questions for both observers and theoreticians, a number of which were listed by Dr. Burbidge in her introductory comments:

Are BALQSOs a rather special subset of all QSOs? Are they found, for example, only in the more luminous objects? The known BALQSOs cover a range of ~40 in luminosity, but whether any examples exist at luminosities characteristic of bright Seyfert nuclei is not known yet.

Do BALQSOs represent a particular evolutionary phase which all luminous QSOs undergo?

Does the nature of the QSO host galaxy play a critical role in selecting which QSOs will develop the BAL phenomenon?

Is geometry (e.g. viewing angle with respect to an accretion disk or the plane of the host galaxy) a critical factor?

What is the dominant ionization mechanism in the clouds?

What is the acceleration mechanism?

How do the troughs develop with time? Do they break up into finer and finer filaments?

At present, we do not know the answer to any of these

questions.

In the next section (II), we summarize recent observational work on the emission and absorption line properties of BALQSOs and a comparison of these properties with "normal" QSOs. This is an essential first step in answering the first of the questions above. In §III we discuss in some detail the attempts to understand the ionization mechanism, since the constraints set by the level of ionization can be used to constrain the acceleration mechanism. In §IV we discuss possible mechanisms for accelerating the BAL clouds. Finally, in the last section, (V), we discuss the recently-discovered low-redshift BALQSO, compare two possible models for BALQSOs, and summarize what we feel are the most important problems for further investigation.

II. RECENT OBSERVATIONS OF EMISSION AND ABSORPTION LINES

a) Observations of Mg II and C III]

Both Junkkarinen and Baldwin (Hartwig and Baldwin; hereafter HB85) presented new data at the Santa Cruz Workshop obtained with CCD detectors on the C III] emission and the Mg II emission and absorption features in BALQSOs. These results confirm previous work in demonstrating that in the great majority of cases the Mg II absorption is very much weaker than the C IV absorption. When the Mg II is detected it is generally less extensive in velocity space than the C IV. These observations strengthen the conclusion that the BAL clouds are optically thin in the Lyman continuum [a result also established directly by Turnshek, Turnshek, and Briggs (1985) in the case of IUE observations of 0932+51]. This in turn again argues for the view that the BAL clouds are physically distinct from the BEL clouds – or at least those giving rise to the Balmer and Mg II emission in the BEL region.

These same sets of observations, especially the extensive set by HB85, also strongly suggest that – with the one exception noted below pertaining to C IV – there are no striking systematic differences between the Mg II and C III] emission line properties of normal and BALQSOs. HB85 conclude that with the possible case of three BALQSOs having strong Al III/C III] ratios, there are not significant differences in the Mg II/C III] properties.

This is of interest for two reasons: First, the weakness of Lyα emission in many BALQSOs might have been attributed to some gross abnormality in the emission line region. Instead, it appears that its weakness or absence is usually due to overlying N V absorption. [In some instances (e.g. 1309-056) the absence of a strong Lyα emission peak cannot plausibly be ascribed to overlying N V absorption, but may simply be a property of that particular BELR. Compare, for example, the profiles of 1309-056 with the luminous non-BALQSO B2-1225+31 in Young *et al.* (1982).] In the case where there is absorption of Lyα the conclusion that the BAL clouds lie outside of the BEL region is reinforced. Second, the very fact that there are in general no gross differences in the statistical distribution of Mg II and C III]+Al III emission line properties between normal and BALQSOs suggests that models to produce the BAL clouds involving explosive events which would destroy the Mg II and C III]-producing BELR clouds must recur over sufficiently long intervals of time to allow the BELR to recover.

b) The C IV and N V Emission Line Properties

It has been noted in T84 that the N V/C IV ratio seems anomalously large in BALQSOs, a result confirmed in HB85. All these authors also agree that the C IV emission line strengths are anomalously low in BALQSOs. However, there is still some disagreement as to whether the enhanced N V/C IV ratio in BALQSOs is due mostly to enhanced N V or reduced C IV. HB85 favor weakened C IV, while T84 concluded that the N V was enhanced and proposed (Turnshek 1984a) that the enhancement was partly due to scattering of Lyman α emission by the outflowing N V ions. One ought to see similar enhancement in "intrinsic" BALQ-

SOs which show no observable absorption because no clouds are in the line of sight. (However, the profile may well be different due to orientation effects.) If the observed incidence of BALQSOs is taken as 3% and the covering factor is 20%, for example, then 15% of all QSOs should show N V comparable in strength with the BALQSO N V strengths. In the "intrinsic" but not "observed" objects, however, the Lyα emission would probably be normal and must be carefully removed before the N V strength can be accurately measured.

HB85 also find that in a subset of the BALQSOs with detached absorption troughs, the profile of the C IV emission differs from normal QSOs in that the redward wing of the C IV appears either cut off or far less extended than C III]. The interpretation of this is not at all clear. Inspecting the data presented by HB85 as best illustrating this effect, it is our impression that the C IV emission line profiles are rather similar to the core of the Mg II profiles but lack the broad underlying base (Fe II ?) on which the core sits.

III. IONIZATION MECHANISMS AND MODELS

As discussed in §IV, arguments based upon the ionization parameter in the BAL clouds play an important role in discussions of the physical conditions in the clouds and the mechanism responsible for their acceleration. It is therefore important to establish limits on this parameter, and more fundamentally to attempt to establish whether photoionization is really the dominant ionization mechanism.

The models may be divided into two different classes, giving quite different results. In one class, the "cloudy filament" models, the absorption is assumed to arise in a large number of discrete clouds whose volume filling factor is quite small and in which the total solid angle subtended by the clouds as seen from the continuum source is fairly small (e.g. $\sim$0.1, cf. Junkkarinen 1983). In the other class of models, the "P-Cygni" model (cf. Drew and Boksenberg 1985, hereafter DB85, and references therein), the absorption is produced by a smooth flow (in which denser condensations might be embedded) having roughly spherical symmetry. We now describe some of the characteristics of these models.

a) Cloudy Filament Models

In comparing these models with the observations, it is necessary to have estimates of the column densities of the various ions giving rise to the absorption troughs. These are difficult to obtain because it is not easy to establish the level of the effective continuum and also because in some cases there may be significant saturation.

From T84 we adopt, for the various ions given in column 1 of Table 1, the column densities shown in column 2, which are the mean for several BALQSOs.

TABLE 1

Ion	Log N (obs)	Power Law (−1.1)	Double Component
		8.25/8.5	8.0/8.25
C IV	16.2	16.2/16.2	16.2/16.2
C III	16.0 ::	15.7/16.2	15.9/16.2
Si IV	15.4	13.7/14.3	14.2/14.7
N V	16.4	15.6/14.7	15.5/15.2
O VI	16.3 :	16.2/15.8	16.1/15.6
H I	15.5	16.9/17.0	15.8/16.0

The value for O VI is based upon only one object, while the value for C III is even more uncertain, being based upon rough estimates in another single object. The range of column densities is typically about a factor 2-3 from the mean. Additionally, it should be noted that these means are for the *total* column density integrated over all velocity space. There are sometimes large changes in the level of ionization as a function of velocity.

It is clear from Table 1 that the clouds are normally optically thin to hydrogen Lyman continuum radiation, though models suggest that the He^+ Lyman continuum optical depth may be of order unity.

As noted previously (Turnshek 1981), upon attempting to reproduce these column densities with photoionization models with, for example, solar abundances and a simple power law with spectral index -1, one finds that very high ionization parameters are required to explain the small ratio of H I to C IV and especially N V and O VI. However, such a high ionization state also drives the silicon to higher states than Si IV and produces Si IV column densities lower than those of Table 1 by factors of about 50-250.

Conversely, if the ionization parameter is lowered to the point where the Si IV/C IV ratio is in the observed range, then the H I column density is too high by several hundred.

One can attempt to overcome this problem by modifying the shape of the continuum in such a way that there is a large flux at energies slightly greater than one Rydberg, followed by a steep decline to about 3.3 Rydbergs (the Si IV-Si V ionization potential). In this way a larger Si IV/H I ratio is obtained while still producing significant amounts of O VI. Qualitatively, such a radiation field is not completely *ad hoc*, because it is known from IUE and X-ray spectra that the slope of the continuum must be much steeper in the extreme UV (1-20 Rydbergs) than it is in the range 0.25-1 Rydberg (see for example Kinney *et al.* 1985). One could speculate that this drop may be associated with the exponential falloff of a fairly cool thermal component.

We have explored the effect of further modifying the continuum shape by putting in a small second component between 3-12 Rydbergs. This second (and totally *ad hoc*) component was put in to continue to minimize the production of Si VI (thus enhancing further the Si IV) while still producing significant C IV,

N V, and O VI. This continuum, along with a simple power law
with index −1.1 [which according to Malkan (1984) is a good fit
for most AGNs between the near IR and the X-ray] is shown in
Figure 1. This double component continuum improves the situation substantially, but it is still not possible to bring both the
Si IV and N V column densities into good agreement with the
observations.

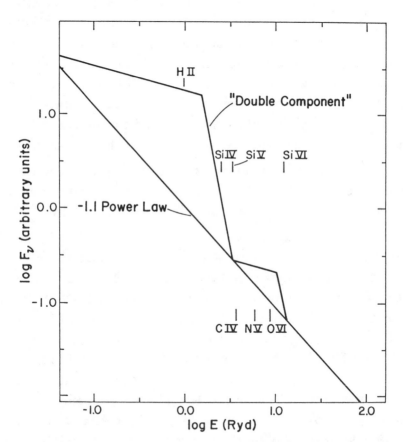

Figure 1: Two flux distributions assumed in calculating the ionization equilibria for the ions shown in Table 1. The power law with spectral index −1.1
produces far too much neutral hydrogen for acceptable ratios of the metal ions.
The situation is improved somewhat with the rather *ad hoc* double component
flux distribution shown which yields much stronger hydrogen ionization. The
ionization edges for producing the ions indicated are shown. See the text for
further discussion.

In any case, to a very good approximation the cloudy filament models are described by a single ionization parameter, ξ,

$$\xi = \frac{L}{n_e D^2}, \tag{1}$$

where L is the total luminosity shortward of the Lyman continuum, D is the distance of the cloud ensemble from the continuum source and n_e is the electron density. For illustrative purposes, in Table 1 we have assumed that $L = 10^{46}$ ergs/sec and D = 3 pc. The log of the electron density for the two best fits for the double component continuum, along with those for the two best fits for the simple power law are given in the top row of the last four columns of Table 1. For other luminosities and distances they can be scaled according to equation (1). Note that the models are for a fixed column density of C IV, not a fixed total column density.

Unless the empirical determinations of the ratio of the Si IV and N V column densities are seriously in error (which we doubt, despite the uncertainties described above), the discrepancies between the observed and model column densities imply that either: i) there are significant departures from solar abundances, ii) the continuum radiation field seen by the clouds departs even more radically from a simple power law then the double component continuum, iii) the cloudy filiment model is completely wrong, or iv) some other ionization mechanism plays an important role in the clouds.

It is clear that no single temperature can explain (via collisional processes) the wide range of ionization encountered in the BALQSOs. However it is not clear whether or not a suitable and physically plausible run of temperature and density vs. distance can explain the observed column densities. Such variations might result from the passage of shocks of moderate strength through the clouds and might also involve conduction or super-thermal particles associated with a surrounding much hotter gas. Even if such a model can be plausibly constructed, then for collisional ionization to dominate over photoionization we must require (for the fixed L and D of Table 1) that log n ≳ 8. This in itself creates a problem, since, for given L, the total emissivity of the gas can be written in terms of the column density, ionization parameter, ξ, and the covering factor $(\Omega/4\pi)$. If the ionization parameter is made so low (e.g. by raising the electron density) that collisional ionization dominates over photoionization, then too much emission is produced by the BALR clouds themselves unless covering factors smaller than those which seem permitted by the observed incidence of BALQSO, are invoked. Quite aside from the filling in of the troughs by this emission, the associated energy losses become a problem for whatever mechanism is postulated to maintain the ionization, as emphasized by Junkkarinen (1985).

All of these calculations have assumed solar composition and the possibility certainly exists that the composition in the BAL clouds is markedly non-solar. Some support for this possibility comes from the observation by Turnshek and Briggs (1985) that in 0932+51 there is a high-velocity clump of material in which the ionization is rather low (probably because the clump has a higher than average density, since this clump was observed with IUE not to be optically thick at the Lyman limit). In particular, a narrow trough arising from 1334 C II appears to have a strength comparable to the corresponding Lyα line. Because the continuum level is extremely hard to ascertain and because there may well be saturation effects, the column densities may not really be comparable, but assuming they are it becomes still more difficult to explain this near equality using photoionization because the C II-C III ionization potential is only 1.8 Rydbergs. We find that a clump with density somewhat higher than the mean of Table 1 can account for the H I, C II and C IV strengths of this clump only if the carbon is enhanced by at least 10 over its solar value.

Before leaving the subject of the ionization mechanism in the cloudy filament models we make one last caveat: There are almost certainly a large number of strong resonance lines from abundant ions distributed from 1 to 4 Rydbergs and possibly beyond. The absorption troughs associated with these transitions will themselves severely modify the continuum radiation as is obvious from inspection of the region of the continuum between the C IV and O VI lines that we can directly observe. Therefore, before concluding that the cloudy filament photoionization models are not adequate it would probably be worth carrying out some self-consistent calculations in which the effects of the troughs appearing in the extreme UV on the continuum are taken into account.

b) The P-Cygni Models

The P-Cygni models have been most recently described in DB85. As this work has appeared just as this review was nearly completed, our description is necessarily brief.

In DB85, it is assumed that there is a fairly smooth, roughly spherically symmetric flow commencing at extremely small distances from the continuum source–typically 0.01 or 0.003 pc. The column densities are so high that continuum X-ray absorption very strongly modifies the radiation field, and in fact in these flows the optical depth to electron scattering becomes quite large. Because the flows occur so near the opaque continuum source, a large part of the emission associated with the flow is occulted just as in P-Cygni stars, and the considerations leading to the covering factors described above for the cloudy filament models are modified. DB85 avoid the necessity of determining column densities by using a moment method in which the product of the mean appropriately weighted ionization fraction of the ion in question times the mass ejection rate is empirically determined.

Arbitrary velocity vs. distance laws are adopted, together with the equation of continuity, to yield the run of density with radial distance. One then adopts a mass loss rate and a radiation field, computes the degree of ionization in the flow and in this way attempts to match the observed ion abundance-mass loss rate product determined empirically. DB85 find that the Si IV trough can be produced in observable strength only if the X-ray lumi-

nosity is rather low and only if the mass loss rate is of order 40
solar masses/year or higher. DB85 do not attempt to match the
strengths of ions other than Si IV because of concerns over saturation, so that it is not possible to make the detailed comparison
we made above for the cloudy filament models.

In §V we will summarize our impression of the various
advantages and disadvantages of these two models. In the next
section, however, we will assume the validity of the constraints
imposed by the cloudy filament models and discuss the implication
of these constraints for acceleration mechanisms.

IV. CLOUD ACCELERATION MECHANISMS

The very high velocities attained by the BAL clouds, the
wide variety of absorption line profiles encountered and the possible correlation between emission line and absorption line profile
characteristics all pose challenging problems for attempts to devise
consistent and comprehensive models for BALQSOs.

In this section we consider the following related questions:

What forces accelerate the BAL material?

What are the typical distances of the BAL clouds from
the continuum source?

How filamentary is the material in the clouds (i.e., what
is the volume filling factor?)

What explains the wide variety of profile shapes, from
the smooth P-Cygni type profiles of PHL5200 and H1413 (WF83)
to the highly complex, many-component absorption of 1303+308
(WF83)?

a) Constraints Imposed by Ionization Models

As was clear from the preceding section, our understanding of the mechanism(s) governing the ionization level in the BAL
clouds is poor. Nevertheless, we will adopt the cloudy filament
model discussed in §III. Then, unless the ionization parameter is

very different from that deduced in §III, there are important and interesting constraints which follow. Let us therefore adopt the following condition which follows from the best fits of Table 1:

$$\frac{n_e(D_{pc})^2}{L_{46}} \gtrsim 10^9. \tag{2}$$

This level of ionization is not very different from the ionization parameter characterizing the BELR region of typical QSOs. In equation (2) above, we use the inequality to indicate the possibility that collisional ionization could be dominant over photoionization.

We further take the total column densities to be typically 1×10^{20} cm^{-2} based upon normal abundances, the typical C IV column densities and the ionization equilibrium inferred above. We may then write

$$n_\epsilon \Delta S \sim 10^{20} \tag{3}$$

In this relation, ϵ is the volume filling factor of the material giving rise to the absorption trough and ΔS is the total thickness of the region containing the material.

In many BALQSOs – namely those with observable structure – it seems fairly clear that we are dealing with a few large clouds, with moderate optical depths in the C IV lines, and many smaller clouds with optical depth of order unity or less. These latter clouds are sometimes not visible in the Si IV troughs, leading to an appearance of more isolated structure. In other objects on the other hand (e.g. RS23), no structure has been detected at resolutions down to 60 km s^{-1}.

The *intrinsic* line widths associated with these clouds are uncertain–they probably lie between about 10 km s^{-1} to 50 km s^{-1}. A typical total width for a BAL trough is about 10,000 km s^{-1}. Thus, even if none of the clouds overlapped in velocity space, the number of individual clouds in the line of sight probably exceeds 200 and, allowing for some overlap and the possibility of smaller intrinsic widths than 50 km s^{-1}, could range as high as 1000 see also Junkkarinen *et al.*, 1983).

The number of clouds in the line of sight, η, and the volume filling factor, ϵ, are related to the ensemble thickness ΔS and the cloudlet size r by:

$$\eta \approx \epsilon(\Delta S)/r \qquad (4)$$

Then equation (3) can be written as

$$\eta r n \sim 10^{20} \qquad (5)$$

From these relations we may estimate (using an assumed value of 300 for η, the number of cloudlets in the line of sight) the sizes of the individual cloudlets and the electron density as a function of the distance from the continuum source (Table 2). In Table 2 we also show the corresponding filling factor as a function of the distance for two different assumptions about the ratio $(D/\Delta S)$:

i) ΔS is independent of D and the cloud ensemble has a radial extent comparable to its lateral extent. This assumption is to be expected in the ram-pressure acceleration model described below. For ΔS we adopt a value of 1 pc. This value comes from the observation that the N V absorption trough appears to occult the Lyα emission line frequently, implying that the ensemble of BAL clouds responsible for the N V absorption covers all of most of the Lyα emission line region (see Turnshek and Weymann 1985).

ii) ΔS is comparable to D. One would expect such a dependence in an "impulsive" or "ballistic" acceleration model, since the width of the entire absorption trough is generally comparable to the mean velocity displacement of the trough as a whole, and we expect the distances to be more or less proportional to the velocities under this circumstance.

Except for the two assumptions i) and ii) above, it appears to us that the content of Table 2 is fairly independent of whatever acceleration mechanism is at work.

TABLE 2

D	log n_e	log r (cm)	log	ϵ
1 pc	9.0	8.5	-7.5	-7.5
3 pc	8.0	9.5	-6.5	-7.0
10 pc	7.0	10.5	-5.5	-6.5
30 pc	6.0	11.5	-4.5	-6.0
100 pc	5.0	12.5	-3.5	-5.5
300 pc	4.0	13.5	-2.5	-5.0
1 kpc	3.0	14.5	-1.5	-4.5

On the basis of the absorption troughs alone, there is really no way of determining which of the rows in Table 2 involving various distances, densities and filling factors is to be preferred. Very recently however, as discussed in §V, the failure to detect broad [O III] emission in the low redshift BALQSO PG1700 strongly suggests that the gas responsible for the absorption troughs is within about 30 pc of the continuum source.

With these constraints in mind we now consider possible acceleration mechanisms.

A number of authors have discussed various cloud acceleration and cloud confinement mechanisms, primarily in the context of the BEL region. Recently, A. J. Allen (1984) has reexamined acceleration mechanisms in the context of the BELR clouds, and the general framework of this discussion can be applied to the case of the BAL clouds as well. Allen considers the following mechanisms:

a) Radiative acceleration of pre-existing clouds.

b) Impulsive acceleration of pre-existing clouds following the passage of a strong shock or a series of shocks.

c) Acceleration of pre-existing clouds by a wind via ram-pressure.

d) Acceleration of hot material (e.g. behind a blast wave or in a wind), followed by condensation of some of the hot material into clouds via radiative cooling.

Allen rejects radiative acceleration as a viable acceleration mechanism, citing work by Mathews and Blumenthal (1977) and subsequent work by Krolik (1979) on Rayleigh-Taylor (R-T) instability, concluding that 'optically thin clouds ... are unable to be efficiently accelerated by radiation pressure.' We think there are several significant uncertainties in this conclusion. First, most analyses have assumed that the local radiative acceleration is proportional to the density (with the consequent problem of growing sound waves) and/or that the Lyman continuum and Lyman α opacity are dominant. The ionization is sufficiently high in the BAL clouds that the first statement may not be true and the second statement is certainly not. Second, the instabilities in the theoretical models of clouds with small to moderate Lyman continuum optical depth clouds arise, in part, because of radiative trapping of Lyα. If, as indicated above, the BALs are formed by individual clouds each much smaller than the whole ensemble and moving at highly supersonic speeds with respect to each other then the line photons will not be trapped at all. The clouds are thus likely to be either R-T stable or to have such small growth rates that R-T disruption may not be an important factor in considering radiative acceleration. For this reason, we examine radiative acceleration further in the BAL clouds.

Because of the moderately low column density and high levels of ionization, the contribution to the radiative acceleration of the BAL clouds is almost certainly due primarily to the resonance lines of the lithium-like iso-electronic sequence which dominate the spectrum: C IV, N V and O VI, with smaller contributions from Lyα and Si IV. For illustrative purposes we will assume that each gram of material is exposed to the full unattenuated continuum. This assumption thus overestimates the radiative acceleration. We assume that the relative abundances of these ions are proportional to the *observed* ion abundances. However, we still need to rely on the ionization models to give the number of ions of a particular species (we choose C IV) per gram of material. We use the log n=8 double component model in Table 1. The terminal velocity of the material is then related to the distance at which the acceleration commenced by

$$(D)_{pc} \approx \frac{2L_\nu(1550)}{4\pi} \frac{1}{V_\infty^2} \frac{1}{c} \left(\frac{\pi e^2}{mc}\right) \sum f_i \left(\frac{n_i}{\rho}\right) \approx \left(\frac{10L_{46}}{V_{10000}^2}\right)_{pc}.$$

(6)

In equation (6), the sum is over the 5 lines listed above, f_i being the f-value and (n_i/ρ) the number of ions of that species per gram of material.

Thus, for intermediate velocities the material must start at about 10 pc and for the high-velocity material, possibly as close as 1 pc. Referring to Table 2, clouds at these distances have sizes in the range 3×10^8 to 3×10^{10} cm and crossing times of order 10^9 to 10^{10} sec. The sound crossing time for a cloud is so many orders of magnitude shorter (10^2–10^4 sec) than the acceleration times of the clouds themselves that we are led to conclude that if radiative acceleration is the dominant acceleration mechanism, then the clouds must be confined – presumably by a much hotter, rarified medium. Moreoever, as shown by Krolik, McKee, and Tarter (1981) (hereafter KMT), there are theoretical arguments for supposing that even if the clouds were not initially confined by a hot gas, their expansion would automatically generate such a hot confining medium.

Consider first that this confining medium is static. In order that the drag not seriously lower the terminal velocity, the column density of the confining medium over the characteristic acceleration distance must not exceed the column density of the cloud itself. Reference to Table 2 shows that even for the D=10 pc case, this requires confining medium densities so low that the confining particles would have to be relativistic. Under these conditions it is then hard to imagine that the confining medium could be static.

Consider the alternative then that the medium is either flowing outward at the same velocity as the cloud or is actually flowing outward more rapidly than the clouds at, for example, the highest observed velocities in the BALQSO troughs.

The latter alternative then leads, as shown below, directly to the conclusion that ram-pressure acceleration associated with this outflowing material is more important than radiative acceleration, while the former alternative leads to the picture described in mechanism c) i.e., a strong shock passes through a region and heats and accelerates it. Subsequent cooling may produce clouds moving at the wind speed.

There is, in principle, the alternative possibility that the acceleration mechanism is so efficient that the clouds are able to drag the medium with them. If the confining medium is a hot gas heated only by radiation, rather than shocked, then it is likely, as discussed below, that it is not hotter than about 10^8 degrees, and for a temperature of 20000 in the clouds which are in pressure equilibrium with the hot gas, a density ratio of 5000 or less between the cold and hot gas is inferred. Reference to the filling factors of Table 2 suggest that if the clouds are at distances of 10 parsecs or less from the source, (which seems required for radiative acceleration to operate on the clouds alone) then the mass of gas in the hot phase is perhaps two orders of magnitude or greater than the mass of gas in the cold phase and radiative acceleration of both components thus seems very unlikely.

Our conclusion, then, is *that the assumption of radiative acceleration leads to a situation in which other processes in fact dominate the acceleration.*

b) Ram-Pressure Acceleration of Pre-Existing Clouds

We next consider the ram-pressure acceleration of pre-existing clouds, possibly by a blast wave or by a steady wind.

This is the same mechanism studied in the context of supernovae remnants by Cowie *et al.* (1981). The expression for the terminal velocity of the clouds embedded in a wind can be written

$$D_{pc} \approx \frac{4L_W}{4\pi} \frac{1}{V_\infty^2} \left(\frac{c}{V_{wind}}\right) / N m_H c \approx \left(\frac{700 L_{46}}{V_{10000}^2}\right) \quad (7)$$

In equation (7), L_W is the power in the wind, V_∞ is the terminal velocity of the cloud and N is its column density. In this simple expression we have assumed that the cloud velocity is much less than the wind velocity and have neglected the cloud's expansion. Comparing this expression to equation (6) for the radiative acceleration leads to the conclusion that the clouds are more effectively accelerated by the winds and can therefore have originated at larger distances, provided that the power in the thermal wind is comparable to the power in the "photon wind." The photoionization condition, together with estimates for the cloud temperature, the assumption of ram-pressure confinement and the assumption $V_w \sim 0.1$ c suggest this must be approximately the case. This increased efficiency arises mainly from two factors: first, for fixed power in both photon and particle winds there is more available momentum by a factor (c/V) in the particle wind. Second, a large fraction of the wind momentum is actually communicated to the cloud, while a substantial portion of the photons pass through these optically thin clouds.

There are three objections that come to mind in connection with this mechanism. First, while it is obvious that there is a strong photon source, the existance of a wind is only inferred. Second, it is not clear that the clouds can survive the passage of an initial shock or the subsequent Rayleigh-Taylor and Kelvin-Helmholtz instabilities. Third, if the gas in which the clouds are embedded is too hot, then the clouds may not be able to survive against evaporation by the surrounding hot gas. The second point – in particular the Rayleigh-Taylor instability – was the reason why this mechanism was rejected by Allen, who pointed out that over a few e-folding times of the largest unstable modes, the clouds are only accelerated to velocities of the order of their internal sound speed which is three orders of magnitude less than those observed.

We should stress [as have both Allen (1985) and McKee (1985)] that disruption of the clouds by either K-H or R-T instabilities is not the issue *per se*. The material will still be accelerated whether or not it is finely shredded by the instability. However, if it is finely shredded then it is hard to imagine that it can survive for long against evaporation by surrounding hot gas. However, assuming smaller clouds could survive, from the observational point of view, there will be a difference in the observed profile between a relatively small number of large clouds and a large number of small clouds in terms of the amount of structure seen, so that it is of interest to clarify this point.

While Allen's conclusions would certainly be correct if the linear perturbations continued to grow to the point that they led to complete shredding of the cloud into small filaments, it is not clear that this is the case. A number of studies of RT or KH growth point towards the stabilizing effects of evaporative processes on small scale modes (Manheimer and Colombant 1984; Nulsen 1982; Königl 1984). There are also models for RT development (Sharp 1983) which lead to the conclusion that even in the case of one dimensional slabs without shear flow, acceleration before disruption to velocities about an order of magnitude higher than inferred from the linear analysis will occur. Christiansen *et al.* (1977) speculate that a strong flow of gas around the cloud may continuously ablate material from the surface of the cloud and lead to slow, rather than catastrophic disruption.

There have also been some numerical studies (mostly in the context of shock-induced star formation) of the fate of shocked pre-existing clouds. They consistently show the emergence of a high density core immediately after shock passage but they have not been carried forward for long enough times to establish whether or not the speculations above are or are not correct.

A detailed numerical study (which does not artificially damp growth rates at wave numbers which are physically important) of the flow in and around the cloud which is carried forward to times well beyond that required for the initial shock to pass is required to see what velocities can realistically be expected from ram-pressure and shock mechanisms before disruption, but this a formidable undertaking.

As noted in the introduction, one sometimes sees BAL profiles in which a rather sharp red (low-velocity) edge is followed by extensive absorption with a more gently sloping blue (high-velocity) component, (e.g. UM275 and Q0932+501; WF 83). In the ram pressure acceleration model we interpret such profiles as arising from the line of sight passing through both the main cloud and smaller ablated 'cloudlets' which have been torn off the main cloud and accelerated to higher speed. In fact, a semi-quantitative model to explain the wide variety of BAL profile shapes in terms of where the line-of-sight intersects the ablated cloud has been developed (Christiansen and Weymann 1985). In addition, in this model there is no connection between the size of the cloud ensemble and its distance from the central source. According to equation (7) we could consider the material to be located anywhere from about a hundred to several thousand parsecs from the central source. From Table 2 we would then infer much lower filling factors and particle densities than if the BAL material were closely associated with the BEL region. As noted in § V however, there appears to be an observational constraint of about 30 pc on the distance of the clouds from the source.

c) Blast Wave Acceleration Followed by Radiative Condensation

We see one clear advantage and two possible difficulties associated with this mechanism in the context of the BALQSOs.

The advantage, stressed by Allen, is that the acceleration takes place before the cloud condenses so that R-T instability is not a problem.

The first difficulty arises from the numerous examples of clouds at quite low velocities (e.g. 5000 km s^{-1}) embedded in flows which certainly extend to 30,000 km s^{-1} or more (1303+308 is a good example – see WF83). One could argue that this is empirical evidence that ram-pressure accelerated clouds do actually survive. Alternatively, we may suppose that the low velocity cloud actually condensed out of a low-velocity portion of the flow. The most plausible circumstance under which this should occur seems to us to involve a rapidly accelerating shock advancing into an ambient medium with a strongly decreasing density gradient. If condensations subsequently form out of the shocked gas at approximately constant pressure then the low velocity clouds will be at much higher densities than the higher velocity clouds. This in turn implies that there should be systematically higher ionization in the high-velocity clouds compared to the low-velocity clouds since the density decrease must be substantially faster than $1/D^2$ (where D is the distance from the continuum source) to produce such a rapidly accelerating shock. As far as we know, there is no evidence for (or against) such a trend.

The second possible difficulty has to do with whether the shocked gas is thermally unstable at all, and if it is, whether or not there is time for the gas to cool in a crossing time. As noted above, the ionization parameter characterizing the BAL clouds does not seem very different from that of the BELR clouds. At first sight this seems very suggestive, since the analysis of KMT demonstrated that the ionization parameter characterizing the BELR lay in a domain which implied that a small amount of cold gas could coexist with a larger amount of hot gas at about 10^8 K, this temperature being set by the Compton interaction. Under these circumstances there are, crudely speaking, three possible thermal equilibria: the hot, stable Compton-dominated phase, a warm unstable bremsstrahlung-dominated phase, and a cool stable line-dominated phase. In the KMT scenario, cool clouds (of undiscussed and unknown origin!) are continually injected, become destroyed, and act as a supply for the hot gas which KMT show must inevitably come into existence.

In the context of the mechanism under discussion for acceleration of the BAL clouds, however, the existence of a hot stable phase is just what we need to avoid since gas which has been shock heated to a temperature higher than the hot stable phase is unable to cool down any further. That is, if there is a hot stable phase, at, say 10^8 K, then following passage of a blast wave over the ambient material which is strong enough to accelerate it to the observed velocities, the gas must become heated to several billion degrees or higher. The electrons may initially be mildly relativistic and cooling processes involving electron-positron pairs may initially dominate. Thereafter, Compton cooling will lower the temperature to the Compton equilibrium temperature. Only if pockets of gas were to somehow find themselves below the unstable *warm* equilibrium temperature would cooling proceed to the cold phase. In fact, however, the simple statement that the ionization parameter of the BAL material is not very different from the BELR material is also equivalent to the statement that the characteristic bremsstrahlung cooling time (evaluated at the Compton temperature) is not very much longer than the Compton cooling time–which is tantamount to saying that a hot stable phase *may not* exist. The ionization parameter in the BAL clouds is certainly uncertain enough that this may be the case.

Let us now assume that no hot stable phase exists and check whether the clouds have time to condense. The cooling time is given approximately by the Compton cooling time. If the material is ever to condense, the cooling time cannot be long compared to the crossing time. The ratio of the Compton cooling time to the crossing time is (KMT)

$$\frac{t_{cool}}{t_{cross}} \approx \frac{3 D_{pc} V_{10,000}}{L_{46}} \tag{8}$$

For $V_{10,000} \approx 3$, this ratio is less than one only if the QSO is extremely luminous *and only if the BAL clouds are very close to the source* – less than the BELR size, in fact. As we have mentioned, and as we discuss further in §V, there are reasons for thinking that the BAL clouds are beyond the BELR and cover it. The condensation mechanism would then seem to require explosive events initiated inside the BELR, following which a normal BELR is somehow restored.

d) Thermal Evaporation

In either the shock/wind acceleration model of preexisting clouds or the shock/condensation model, the cloud finds itself immersed in exceedingly hot gas. The cloudlets are so small and have such small column densities and the gas is so hot that the mean free path of the hot electrons for coulomb interactions is very much larger than the cloud size. Under this circumstance one wonders whether such small clouds could ever arise in the condensation model and whether they could ever be accelerated and/or confined in the ram-pressure model.

The existence of even a weak magnetic field may drastically alter the picture however, since the proton gyro-radius for a gas of several billion degrees in a field as weak as 10^{-6} gauss is of order 10^{11} cm. The mildly-relativistic electron gyro-radius is somewhat over two orders of magnitude smaller, so that the effective plasma mean free path – the geometric mean of the electron and proton gyro-radii – is about 10^{10} cm/B_{-6}. It seems very likely, therefore, that momentum coupling between the cloud and the shocked gas is ensured except possibly for the very smallest distances of Table 2 and extraordinarily weak fields.

This still leaves open the question of the evaporation of the cool cloud. According to McKee (1985) under most circumstances, magnetic fields will not significantly alter the evaporation rate.

It appears, however, that a ram-accelerated pre-existing

cloud may be one circumstance under which the magnetic field does greatly reduce the evaporation rate. This may come about because the field lines embedded in the flow around the cloud, and in the material evaporated or ablated off the cloud, would be drawn into tangential ribbons parallel to the wind-cloud interface, thus inhibiting the penetration of the hot particles into the cloud. This possibility again emphasizes the importance of establishing how catastrophic the R-T and K-H surface instabilities are. If they are not catastrophic, heating and mixing probably takes place at the wind-cloud interface but may be confined to the R-T ablation layer speculated upon above.

We end this section with the reminder that this entire discussion has been predicated on the assumption that the cloudy filament model of §III is essentially correct. The implications for acceleration mechanisms if the P-Cygni models are more nearly correct still need to be explored.

V. DISCUSSION AND SUMMARY

In this section we will briefly discuss the implications of the newly discovered low redshift BALQSO, give our assessment of the relative advantages and disadvantages of the two classes of models described in §III, and conclude with a summary of several of the unsolved problems connected with the BALQSOs.

a) Implications of the Discovery and Properties of PG1700+518

Just prior to the Santa Cruz workshop, it was discovered that the bright, low redshift (0.29) QSO PG1700+518 had a strong, broad absorption trough in Mg II (Pettini and Boksenberg 1984). Subsequent IUE observations and optical observations (Turnshek *et al.* 1985) establish that this object indeed has the strong broad C IV and Si IV troughs characteristic of the high redshift BALQSOs, though the strength of the Mg II is itself rare among BALQSOs as discussed in §II. The optical observations also show strong Fe II emission and no evidence of either sharp or broad [0 III]. The latter is expected to be present in observable strength unless the covering factor is extremely small, or unless the density in the BAL clouds is high enough to suppress [O III]. The former possibility seems unlikely simply on the basis of the observed incidence of BALQSOs. Thus, unless there is something quite anomalous about this particular object (which is conceivable because of the very strong Mg II), the failure to find [0 III] suggests that the BAL clouds are no further than 10-30 pc from the continuum source.

Turnshek *et al.* also show that the existence of this object is compatible with the hypothesis that the fraction of QSOs which are BALQSOs is independent of redshift, though of course statistical arguments based upon one object are hardly conclusive.

Scales for the BAL region of 10-30 pc or less also imply that the BALQSO phenomenon is a steady or quasi-steady phenomenon rather than a one-time event in the life of the QSO, since the crossing times are of order a few hundred or thousand years and this is surely smaller than the life time of a QSO.

b) Advantages and Disadvantages of the P-Cygni and Cloudy Filament Models

We see the following problems with the Cloudy Filament models: 1) The discrepancy between observation and models for the relative strengths of the troughs in the observed ions is uncomfortably (though not fatally) large. 2) The cloudlet sizes deduced in Table 2 are extremely small—especially if one restricts the distances to 30 pc or less—and it is not clear if such cloudlets can survive against evaporation associated with the confining hot gas which we have argued must be present to confine them.

On the other hand, the presence of substantial structure in the profiles of many—but not all—BALQSOs is certainly what one might expect from the cloudy filament model.

The P-Cygni models are characterized by extremely high ionization parameters—about four orders of magnitude higher than those characterizing the cloudy filament models. Consequently, very much larger total column densities–about 6 orders of magnitude larger–are required to produce observable Si IV. This in turn implies that continuous absorption of the hard photons is very important. As noted in §III, a comparison of the relative strengths of all the ions has not been given in detail, but a crucial additional constraint is that ratios like C III/C IV not be very small. The smooth flows certainly cannot give rise to the highly structured profiles sometimes seen, but there is no reason why denser condensations embedded in them could not give rise to structure. Indeed, such condensations are expected in the thermally unstable regimes of the flow. Whether such models can give rise to the completely detached troughs is more doubtful. In DB85 the problems associated with computing line profiles are noted but it would nonetheless be very instructive to see how close one can come to reproducing the observed profiles.

The two models also predict very different time scales for variability in the troughs. We presume that the very high ionization present in the P-Cygni models would also lead to very different predictions from the cloudy filament models for ions higher than O VI – e.g. Ne VIII and Mg X.

The biggest problem we see in connection with the P-Cygni models has to do with the fact – noted explicitly by DB85 – that the flows do not give rise to normal low ionization emission lines, though DB85 suggest that condensations in the flow could produce some emission. The result discussed earlier that the C III] emission lines do not seem strikingly abnormal suggests to us that the emission lines in these objects are produced in regions in which the constraints of density and ionization parameter imply distances from the source of the emission clouds of a few parsecs rather than 0.003-0.01 pc. Such a region will inevitably produce strong Lyα emission as well, but the numerous examples of Lyα apparently occulted by the N V absorption argues strongly for the BAL clouds to be at distances of a few pc or greater (Turnshek and

Weymann 1985) and for this reason we did not consider distances less than 1 pc in our Table 2. The object 0302+17 (Foltz *et al.* 1985) provides a beautiful example of a strong Lyα emission line when the N V trough does not extend to high enough velocities to absorb it.

c) Problems for the Future

We conclude with a list of some future programs which are just a small fraction of those which need to be carried out to yield a better understanding of these objects.

We need a much larger sample of BALQSOs to study. Although the sample has grown enormously over the past few years it is still so small that questions involving systematic trends with redshift, luminosity, X-ray and radio flux, and emission and absorption characteristics are still entirely unclear. We think that this will require a machine-selection procedure, partly to ensure some objective and quantifiable set of selection criteria, but also just because of the sheer amount of plate material that must be examined. A study over a large area of the sky yielding objects bright enough (e.g. < 18.0-18.5) to be studied with good signal to noise without huge investments of telescope time is strongly to be preferred over studies going much fainter over smaller areas of sky.

Better determinations of the column densities in individual clouds in the troughs need to be obtained and more sophisticated attempts to understand the ionization equilibrium and investigate possible abundance abnormalities need to be carried out. These models will become more meaningfully constrained as and when far UV and X-ray spectra of these objects become available.

Monitoring of the highly structured BALQSOs should be carried out to see if any changes in the strength or velocity of the clouds occur over timescales of a few years. Over the nearly two decades since PHL 5200 was discovered, no changes have been seen (Junkkarinen *et al.* 1983) but objects with more structure might reveal changes more readily.

Finally, detailed theoretical consideration of the acceleration, confinement, and evaporation of the clouds under the possible modes of acceleration discussed above are required.

We have received numerous helpful comments and material from many colleaques during the preparation of this review. We especially wish to thank: A. J. Allen, J. Baldwin, E. M. Burbidge, R. F. Carswell, C. Foltz, G. Hartwig, R. Jokipii, V. Junkkarinen, J. Krolik, W. Mathews, C. McKee, and H. Netzer.

The illustrative ionization calculations were carried out with a version of G. Ferland's "Cloudy" code, the use of which is gratefully acknowledged. Support from the National Science Foundation is also gratefully acknowledged. Last and by no means least we express our appreciation to Dr. J. Miller and his associates at Lick Observatory for organizing and convening the workshop.

REFERENCES

Allen, A. J. 1984. *M.N.R.A.S.*, **210**, 147.

————. 1985, personal communication.

Christiansen, W.A., Pacholczyk, A.G., and Scott, J.S. 1977. *Nature*, **266**, 593.

Christiansen, W.A., and Weymann, R. J. 1985, in preparation.

Cowie, L.L., McKee, C.F., and Ostriker, J.P. 1981. *Ap. J.*, **247**, 908.

Drew, J.E., and Boksenberg, A. 1984. *M.N.R.A.S.*, **211**, 813.

Foltz, C.B., Weymann, R.J., Boroson, T.A., Price, C., Shechtan, S., and Hazard, C. 1985, in preparation.

Hartig, G.F., and Baldwin, J.A. 1985, preprint (HB 85).

Hazard, C., Morton, D.C., Terlevich, R., and McMahon, R. 1984. *Ap. J.*, **282**, 33.

Hazard, C. 1985, personal communication.

Junkkarinen, V.T. 1983. *Ap. J.*, **265**, 73.

_____. 1985, personal communication.

Junkkarinen, V.T., Burbidge, E.M., and Smith, H.E. 1983. *Ap. J.*, **265**, 51.

Kinney, A.L., Huggins, P.J., Bregman, J.N., and Glassgold, A.E. 1985, preprint.

Königl, A. 1984. *Ap. J.*, **284**, 303.

Krolik, J.H. 1979. *Ap. J.*, **228**, 13.

Krolik, J.H., McKee, C.F., and Tarter, C.B. 1981. *Ap. J.*, **249**, 422.

Malkan, M. 1984, talk presented at Santa Cruz Summer Workshop, July 1984.

Manheimer, W.M. and Colombant, D.G. 1984. *Phys. Fluids*, **27**, 983.

Mathews, W.G., and Blumenthal, G.R. 1977. *Ap. J.*, **214**, 10.

McKee, C.F. 1985, personal communication.

Nulsen, P.E.J. 1982. *M.N.R.A.S.*, **198**, 1007.

Pettini, M., and Boksenberg, A. 1984, *Gemini* (RGO Newsletter).

Sharp, D.H. 1983, Proc. Int. Conf. on Fronts and Patterns, Los Alamos Scientific Labs (LA-UR83-2130).

Stocke, J.S., Foltz, C.B., Weymann, R.J., and Christiansen, W.A. 1984. *Ap. J.*, **280**, 476.

Turnshek, D.A. 1981, Ph.D. Thesis, University of Arizona (University Microfilms Inc., Ann Arbor, MI)

_____. 1984a, *Ap. J. (Letters)*, **278** L87.

_____. 1984b, *Ap. J.*, **280**, 51 (T84).

Turnshek, D.A., and Weymann, R.J. 1985, preprint.

Turnshek, D.A., Turnshek, D., and Briggs, F. 1985, in preparation.

Turnshek, D.A., Foltz, C.B., Weymann, F.J., Lupie, O.L., McMahan, R.G., and Peterson, B.M. 1985, submitted to Ap. J. (Letters).

Weymann, R.J. and Foltz, C.B. 1983, in *Quasars and Gravitational Lenses*, Proc. 24th Liége Int. Astrophys. Colloq. June 1983), p. 538 (WF83).

Young, P., Sargent, W.L.W., and Boksenberg, A. 1982. *Ap. J. Suppl.*, **48**, 455.

THE GALAXIES ASSOCIATED WITH QUASI-STELLAR OBJECTS AND ACTIVE GALACTIC NUCLEI

Joseph S. Miller

Lick Observatory
Board of Studies in Astronomy and Astrophysics
University of California, Santa Cruz

ABSTRACT

Since the discovery of quasi-stellar objects there has been considerable interest in their relationship to galaxies. In spite of a large amount of work on this problem, our knowledge of the nature of the host galaxies of QSOs is very limited. Moreover, in the literature there is still considerable variability in the way names for different types of active galaxies and QSOs are used, which has added to the confusion about the underlying galaxies of active systems. Imaging studies have shown that virtually all QSOs and active galaxies with redshifts less than 0.5 have extended nebulosities, but these studies are unable to determine the nature of the nebulosities. Spectroscopic studies in principle will allow definite interpretations of the nebular light, but the results to date are rather limited because of the difficulty of the observations. It appears that the host galaxies of the radio-loud luminous QSOs are peculiar, there being no clear evidence that they are situated in normal giant ellipticals as might be expected. The situation is also unclear for the radio-quiet QSOs and most classes of active galaxies. There is considerable evidence that the presence of an active galactic nucleus is often correlated with abnormal activity throughout the host galaxy.

I. INTRODUCTION

There has been considerable interest in the relationship of quasi-stellar objects to active galaxies and normal galaxies since their discovery more than twenty years ago. Initially this interest was stimulated by the so-called redshift controversy, as it was generally felt that demonstrating QSOs were in galaxies of stars having the same redshift as the nuclear emission would give strong support to the cosmological redshift hypothesis. As evidence has accumulated that at least some QSOs or QSO-like objects (e.g., BL Lacertae objects) are in galaxies of stars with the same redshifts as their nuclei, attention has increasingly focused on the nature of the host galaxies themselves and the relationship of QSOs to other kinds of extragalactic objects. In spite of all the considerable effort expended in these areas, our knowledge about the nature of the host galaxies remains extremely limited and in some ways rather puzzling. Similarly, our knowledge of the relationships which exist among the various kinds of active extragalactic objects is also quite limited. Are these different objects all basically the same, with minor differences in physical conditions or structure, or are there substantial physical differences among the various types of active systems? Clearly related to these questions is the problem of what constitutes the defining characteristics for membership in the various categories, e.g., radio-loud and radio-quiet QSO, Seyfert galaxy, radio galaxy, etc. Some objects are classified on the basis of morphology, others on the basis of specific physical activity, and others still on the basis of how they were classified many years ago.

It should be stressed that the above issues, which will be the primary issues of discussion in this chapter, are all in a rapid state of change at present. Modern instruments, especially those using CCDs as detectors, that have recently come into routine use on large telescopes, are providing a considerable amount of new information on the nature of galaxies that have active nuclei. I feel that the subject is in a state of transition, thus I will be more concerned with general ideas and overviews rather than a detailed treatment of the published literature and material that was presented at the Workshop.

II. CLASSIFICATION OF
ACTIVE EXTRAGALACTIC OBJECTS

There is considerable variety in the way workers in the field use the various names for types of active objects. For example, 3C 120 has been called a Seyfert galaxy, a radio galaxy, an N galaxy, and a quasar. To some extent this confusion results from a lack of clear-cut criteria for assigning objects to categories. I feel the lack of such criteria derives from our relatively poor understanding of the nature of active objects. The defining characteristic of these types, such as they are, arose over many years and are based on a variety of considerations. It could well be that distinctions between the various types are artificial and physically they are all the same kind of thing; a number of workers in the field make this assumption either implicitly or explicitly. On the other hand there is spectroscopic evidence for real differences between various objects called broad-lined radio galaxies, quasars, and Seyfert galaxies, for example, and it is not clear how fundamental the differences are in a physical sense. To make an analogy, do the various types differ in a sense similar to the differences between main sequence stars of different mass or more like the difference between dwarf and giant stars? There could even be differences as fundamental as the difference between planetary nebulae and H II regions. I don't know the answer to these questions. I suspect, since many of the observed phenomena appear to be very similar across all classes of classification, that basically the same kind of object is involved. But I feel it is still premature to lump all objects together for fear of the possibility that there may be important physical distinctions to be made and we will confuse the issue by doing this. At the least, there are some rather fundamental differences in host galaxies among the various types, as we shall see in § III.

This confusion results in part from the lack of agreement as to what constitutes a QSO. For example, leaving aside historical considerations, it is rather unsatisfactory to call an active galaxy a QSO simply because it looks stellar on the Palomar Sky Atlas plates. A nearby Seyfert galaxy moved to a distance corresponding to a redshift of 0.1 to 0.2 would look stellar on these plates. To take higher resolution plates of such an object and discover that it is indeed in a galaxy does not prove QSOs are in galaxies, but that Seyfert galaxies are in galaxies. This may all seem rather obvious, but there are a number of papers in the literature which give it little attention.

I do not wish to attempt in this chapter to give a detailed treatment on the classification of various kinds of active extragalactic objects. For the sake of the discussion I will adopt the following terminology, which I feel is reasonably consistent with what most workers use. In all cases, except the two noted, exhibiting prominent emission lines in the spectrum is a required property. An object will be called a QSO if it is a stellar-appearing object optically more luminous than a first-ranked cluster elliptical. A quasar is a QSO that produces radio emission that is significant in comparison to its optical emission. Most quasars were discovered as a result of radio observations. A Seyfert galaxy is an active galaxy with relatively weak radio emission and a nucleus with optical luminosity approximately equal to or less than a first-ranked cluster elliptical. A radio galaxy is an active galaxy with radio emission comparable to or greater than its optical emission, and nearly all radio galaxies were discovered because of their radio emission. N galaxies are so-called on the basis of having a stellar-appearing nucleus which dominates a faint nebulous envelope. Virtually all of the classical N galaxies are elliptical galaxies with strong radio sources. Blazars come in two varieties: BL Lacertae objects and optically violently variable quasars. Both varieties exhibit high polarization and high variability in polarization and light output. The BL Lac objects tend to be less luminous than the OVV quasars and have weak or no detectable emission lines. The OVV quasars can be among the very brightest objects at their redshifts, but there is a definite possibility that the radiation we see is beamed and hence not a simple measure of the luminosity. OVV quasars show strong emission lines when their continua are faint, but the emission lines can be difficult to detect when they are bright. Essentially all known blazars are radio sources, and it could well be that the distinction between BL Lac objects and OVV quasars is artificial, with them being the low and high luminosity examples of the same kind of object. Starburst galaxies are galaxies in which a recent burst of star formation results in an energy output rather large in comparison to that of the rest of the galaxy. LINERs are low ionization emission regions in the nuclei of some galaxies and represent relatively low luminosity active objects.

All of the above definitions are rather qualitative and somewhat vague. There are many objects that clearly would fall in the poorly defined regions that separates some classes (e.g., how does one distinguish between a highly luminous Seyfert galaxy and a low luminosity QSO?). Perhaps the vagueness of the boundaries is a direct result of the actual continuity in physical properties between various types. Alternatively, as I have said above, the various types could actually be physically rather different and the above definitions are inadequate for clearly typing some objects. We just don't know, and for the present it is best to distinguish between the various types lest we miss something important.

III. THE GALAXY COMPONENT OF ACTIVE SYSTEMS

For many years it has been known that the majority of Seyfert galaxies are spirals, that radio galaxies are universally giant ellipticals, and that N galaxies are also ellipticals, but the types of galaxies associated with quasars and radio quiet QSOs have been unknown. In fact until recently, convincing proof that QSOs are in galaxies at all has been lacking. As we shall see, what we have been able to learn about the galaxy components of true QSOs has made the subject more complex rather than clearer.

Studies of the galaxy components of QSOs divide into two types by the observational approach: direct imaging and spectroscopy. The former has the advantage of high observational efficiency and the ability to provide morphological information, but has the strong disadvantage that very little can be learned about the mechanism producing the light. Spectroscopy suffers from the relatively low efficiency of spectrographs but is the only way that convincing information about the nature of the material producing the light can be learned. An overview of results from these approaches follows.

a) Imaging Studies

Since the pioneering work by Kristian (1973), there have been a number of searches for studies done of nebulosity associated with QSOs. The earlier work was done largely with photographic plates, but more recently studies using linear detectors with high dynamic range such as electronographic tubes and CCDs have produced more detailed and quantitative data. At their best, imaging studies can provide quantitative data on the surface brightness and color morphology of the nebulosities, but analysis of the observations is complicated by the presence of the bright nuclear object.

Two papers have appeared recently that represent fairly comprehensive statements of work by groups that have been deeply involved in imaging studies for years. These are by Behren, Fried, Wehinger, and Wyckoff (1984) and Hutchings, Crampton, and Campbell (1984); workers from each of these groups were at the Workshop and discussed the results in these and the earlier papers referenced in them. In a study of 17 objects, Gehren *et al.* report that virtually all QSOs with z $\lesssim$ 0.5 are resolved, showing the structure of an extended nebulosity. On the assumption that this nebulosity is a galaxy, they conclude that the underlying galaxies of QSOs are quite luminous and the evidence suggests that galaxies associated with radio-loud objects are on average about 2 mag brighter than those associated with radio quiet objects. While many of these objects have active nuclei of too low a luminosity to be considered true QSOs as discussed in § II, a significant fraction would be called QSOs or quasars. They also find that these objects are usually situated in groups or clusters of galaxies, and that the galaxies with the active nuclei tend to be the most luminous in the group. There is some evidence that radio-loud objects are associated with giant ellipticals in which a significant amount of hot gas and young stars may be present, perhaps as a result of some interaction with another galaxy. Hutchings *et al.* report the study of a much larger sample, 78 objects, but the majority of these objects would not be classified as QSOs as discussed in § III. All but seven objects are clearly resolved. As in the Gehren *et al.* study, they find the galaxies associated with radio-loud objects (assuming that the nebulosities are galaxies) are more luminous than the radio quiet galaxies, about one-third of the objects appear to be interacting with another galaxy, and about one-fourth lie in small groups or clusters of galaxies. Over 40% of the nebulosities show some indications of spiral structure, and there is no positive evidence that associated galaxies are ellipticals. It is not possible to say with certainty from the data presented, but I suspect the many, perhaps the majority of the objects in their study, would have been called Seyfert galaxies from the outset if they were relatively close. In a similar imaging study of 24 X-ray selected objects which the authors call quasars, Malkan, Margon, and Chanan (1984) report that certainly 15 and possibly 17 are resolved, but they admit that it isn't possible to distinguish these objects from very high luminosity Seyfert galaxies. They conclude that the evidence available is consistent with the view that the nebulosity of a typical object in their sample is the light of a spiral galaxy.

At the Workshop, Stockton presented results of a study of 74 QSOs based on images of [O III] taken through 30Å interference filters. Many of the objects in the sample show very extended emission, sometimes as far as many tens of kiloparsecs from the active object. Some of this emission had the appearance of long tails that clearly look like the results of interactions, while others are more ill-defined and difficult to categorize. Stockton concluded that the existence of this extended emission was correlated with the presence of an active nucleus, was probably low density gas, but was not gas in the spiral arms of a galaxy. A tentative conclusion one can draw from this study is that the presence of an active nucleus can be correlated with phenomena extending over at least the dimensions of a galaxy.

Of considerable interest is the careful imaging study of 3C 273 by Tyson, Baum, and Kreidl (1982). Nobody disputes that 3C 273 is a quasar under any definition. They found that the extended light around the quasar could be well represented morphologically by a first-ranked giant elliptical very similar to NGC 4889 in the Coma cluster. However, the quasar itself is not centered in the elliptical nebulosity, but appears to have a displacement that corresponds to a few kiloparsecs at the redshift distance of 3C 273. These data imply that if indeed 3C 273 is associated with a normal giant elliptical galaxy, it is not at the nucleus of the galaxy. Alternatively, it could be the nucleus of an elliptical galaxy that has a distorted light distribution, or it could be that 3C 273 is merely projected on a galaxy that is part of the small group near 3C 273 (Stockton 1979). The situation is unclear.

The principal conclusion one can draw from the various imaging studies of active objects is that with good resolution one can detect extended emission around virtually all of the ones with redshifts $\lesssim 0.5$. The objects in the studies are unquestionably mixed, ranging from rather typical Seyfert and radio galaxies to true QSOs. In particular, selection by X-ray emission appears to be an excellent way of finding more distant Seyfert galaxies. There is little or no proof that the extended light associated with the active objects detected in these imaging studies comes from stars; if that is assumed to be the case, the galaxies show a large range of luminosity. Also, the morphological information suggests that spiral galaxies are more likely to be involved than ellipticals. However, as we shall see below, there is considerable evidence that the nebulosities around many of the active objects, particularly the true QSOs, are *not* normal galaxies of stars, and I believe more secure interpretations of the nature of the extended light awaits higher resolution spectroscopic and imaging studies with the space telescope.

b) Spectroscopic Studies

Spectroscopic investigations of the nebulosity surrounding active objects can provide definitive information on the nature of the material producing the emission, but the observations are considerably more difficult than those involved in imaging studies. Until recently, spectroscopic data on the nature of the nebulosities has been very limited and has led to no straightforward interpretations. Early studies such as those by Wampler *et al.* (1975), Richstone and Oke (1977), Stockton (1976), Morton *et al.* (1978), and Wyckoff *et al.* (1980) showed the nebular light to be dominated by emission lines or have a spectrum not easily interpretable. My spectroscopic study (Miller 1981) was directed principally at detecting the presence of elliptical galaxies associated with BL Lacertae objects, N galaxies, and QSOs. I found that BL Lacertae objects were associated with very luminous giant elliptical galaxies, while N galaxies were ellipticals typically a few magnitudes fainter than a first-ranked cluster elliptical. No definitive evidence was found for galaxies with late-type stars for any of the nine QSOs and quasars studied, and I concluded that any elliptical galaxies associated with these objects were typically at least 2 mag fainter than a first-ranked cluster elliptical. It was found that, in nearly all the cases, N galaxies could be clearly distinguished from QSOs by the spectra of the central objects.

Many of the subsequent spectroscopic studies have been of objects of relatively low luminosity that would not be classified as true QSOs (see for example Boroson, Oke, and Green 1982, and Balick and Heckman 1983). These studies are in agreement with the imaging studies that the underlying galaxies are likely to be fainter than first-ranked cluster galaxies and are probably spirals. The paper on Markarian 1014 by Mackenty and Stockton (1984) is especially interesting. As the authors point out, this object has a nuclear luminosity that clearly puts it on the borderline between the most luminous Seyfert galaxies and QSOs. The imaging and spectroscopic data indicate that the large, asymmetric nebulosity surrounding the nucleus contains both hot and cool stars as well as ionized gas; the authors conclude it is probably a luminous spiral galaxy, but a definitive classification is not possible. They point out that other, similar studies also had great difficulty in classifying the underlying galaxies of active nuclei as either spirals or ellipticals and suggest that the problem is more likely with the underlying galaxies than with the data. Similarly, Romanishin *et al.* (1984) felt they could rule out that the low redshift object 0241+622 is in an elliptical galaxy from morphological data and suggested it is in a spiral; the spectroscopic data are not of sufficient quality to add much to this picture.

Of considerable importance is the recent work of Boroson and Oke (1984) and Boroson, Persson, and Oke (preprint, presented by Boroson at the Workshop). In the first of these two papers, Boroson and Oke discussed their work on eight high luminosity quasars. Unlike their earlier work with Green (Boroson *et al.* 1982) which treated low luminosity active objects whose classification as true QSOs is doubtful, the eight objects in this study would unquestionably be called QSOs. They obtained spectroscopic data for both the active nucleus and the surrounding nebulosity. They found that with only one exception, 3C 48, the objects could be clearly divided into two groups. One group shared the following characteristics: a nebular spectrum with a flat continuum and strong emission lines, an extended, steep-spectrum radio source, and nuclear emission that showed relatively broad permitted lines and either weak or absent Fe II emission. The other group had compact, flat-spectrum radio sources, a nebular spectrum with a red continuum and weak or no emission lines, and narrower permitted nuclear emission lines with prominent Fe II emission. 3C 48 did not fit this scheme, since though it has a compact radio source, its nebular spectrum shows strong emission lines on a flat continuum displaying strong Balmer absorption lines. In fact, 3C 48 was the only object in the study whose nebular spectrum definitely showed the presence of stellar absorption lines. Moreover, these lines were characteristic of hot stars, not late-type ones.

This paper of Boroson and Oke demonstrated clearly that quasar activity cannot be considered a phenomenon confined solely to the nucleus of an otherwise normal galaxy. In fact, based on what we would have expected, the results are surprising. By analogy with radio galaxies, one would have expected these radio-loud quasars to be located in luminous giant elliptical galaxies. But they found no clearcut spectroscopic evidence for an elliptical galaxy component in any of the objects. The nebula of 3C 48 where they observed was dominated by hot stars. The luminosity implied by the brightness of these stars is very high, so that if the quasar were removed, the remaining galaxy would be extremely peculiar, if not unique. Among the remaining seven objects they studied, three had nebular spectra which were *consistent* with the presence of a normal giant elliptical. For the rest, nebular spectra appeared inconsistent with that of a pure elliptical galaxy, and for two, 3C 48 and 4C 37.43, at most only a fraction of the visual light could be coming from late-type stars. If anything, we might have expected the extended, steep-spectrum classical double radio sources to be in giant ellipticals, but these are the ones in their sample with blue continua. If one wishes to maintain the position that radio-loud objects are all situated giant ellipticals, perhaps these results could be understood if many of these objects have had recent bursts of star formation; clearly they are not normal ellipticals.

The results discussed above were extended by a second paper by Boroson, Persson, and Oke (preprint, discussed by Boroson at the Workshop), in which a number of additional objects were added. They confirmed the various relationships among the nuclear spectrum, the spectrum of the nebulosity, and the radio properties for the objects. They found that strong nuclear [O III] emission was correlated with strong [O III] in the nebulosity; in some cases the nebular [O III] had a greater total luminosity than the nuclear [O III]. They found that the permitted lines had broader and more irregular profiles in the steep-spectrum radio source objects, in agreement with the study of Miley and Miller (1979). Also, in agreement with their first paper, they found that Fe II emission was much weaker in the objects whose nebular spectrum shows strong lines (the extended radio source objects). They were able to rule out conclusively for these objects that the weakness of Fe II was a result of large line widths making the lines difficult to detect and measure, an idea discussed at the Workshop by B. Wills. Though there was a bit more evidence for stellar absorption lines in the nebulosity of QSOs, especially 3C 273, in the second paper, one can still say that convincing evidence in their data for stellar absorption lines in the nebulosities is lacking for all QSOs except 3C 48. These matters will be discussed further in the next section.

IV. CONCLUDING REMARKS

Several conclusions can be drawn from the discussion in § III. It is clear that the majority of low redshift ($z \lesssim 0.5$) QSOs and active galaxies show nebulosities around their star-like active regions. Since the nuclei of many, if not most, of these objects investigated so far in imaging studies are of luminosities comparable to or less than bright Seyfert galaxies, this result is to be expected; it is highly likely many of them would have been classified as Seyfert galaxies if their redshifts had been very small. However, the situation for the luminous objects, the true quasars, is quite confusing. One would have expected the radio loud QSOs to be in giant ellipticals, but the evidence for this is marginal. In the published literature to date there is only one absolutely convincing case of spectroscopic detection of stars in the nebulosity around a quasar, 3C 48. In that case the spectrum is that of hot stars, and the luminosity of these stars is extremely high. Clearly the nebulosity associated with 3C 48 is not a normal elliptical galaxy if it is an elliptical at all. Furthermore, the studies of Boroson, Oke, and Persson show that for quasars with extended, low-frequency radio sources – just those one would most expect to be associated with giant ellipticals – the surrounding nebulosities have a relatively blue continuum. I feel these data indicate strongly that quasars cannot in general be considered to be the active nuclei of otherwise more-or-less normal galaxies.

If the galaxies associated with QSOs and, perhaps, many active galactic nuclei are in some way peculiar, the question is what is the cause and what is the effect? Are active galaxies active because of the peculiarity of the galaxy or its environment, or does the presence of an active nucleus cause major disturbances in what would otherwise be a normal galaxy? There is evidence that Seyfert galaxies are more common in interacting galaxies (see for example Dahari 1984), but there are many Seyfert galaxies that appear to be completely isolated, so interaction cannot be the sole cause of activity.

So this discussion must end with a series of as yet unanswerable questions. What kinds of galaxies are associated with QSOs? Is the QSO and active nucleus phenomena a result of normal processes within galaxies, or does it arise from the peculiarities of abnormal galaxies? Do all luminous galaxies, or at least nearly all, pass through an active phase at some time in their life? What effect does an active nucleus have on the evolution of its host galaxy? We ask these questions because at present we have very little if any understanding of the relationship between active nuclei and the galaxies in which they reside. Further observational progress on these matters can be made with modern instruments in dark sites, but probably more definitive studies require observations from above the Earth's atmosphere.

REFERENCES

Balick, T. and Heckman, T. M. 1983, *Ap. J.*, **265**, L1.

Borosin, T. A., and Oke, J. B. 1984, *Ap. J.*, **278**, 11.

Borosin, T. A., Oke, J. B. and Green, R. G. 1982, *Ap. J.*, **263**, 32.

Dahari, O. 1984, *A. J.*, **89**, 966.

Gehren, T., Fried, J., Wehinger, P. A., and Wyckoff, S., 1984, *Ap. J.*, **278**, 11.

Hutchings, J. B., Crampton, D., and Campbell, B. 1984, *Ap. J.*, **280**, 41.

Kristian, J. 1973, *Ap. J. (Letters)*, **179**, L129.

Mackenty, J. W., and Stockton, A. 1984, *Ap. J.*, **283**, 64.

Malkan, M. A., Margon, B., and Chanan, G. A. 1984, *Ap. J.*, **280**, 66.

Miley, G., and Miller, J. S. 1979, *Ap. J. (Letters)*, **228**, L55.

Miller, J. S. 1981, *Pub. A.S.P.*, **93**, 681.

Morton, D. C., Williams T. B., and Green, R. G. 1978, *Ap. J.*, **219**, 381.

Richstone, D. O., and Oke, J. B. 1977, *Ap. J.*, **213**, 8.

Romanishin, W., Ford, H., Ciardullo, R., and Margon, B. 1984, *Ap. J.*, **277**, 487.

Stockton, A. 1976, *Ap. J. (Letters)*, **205**, 115.

Stockton, A. 1979, in *Objects of High Redshift*, IAU Symposium No. 92, p. 89.

Tyson, J. A., Baum, W. A. and Kreidl, T. J. N. 1982, *Ap. J. (Letters)*, **257**, L1.

Wampler, E. J., Robinson, L. B., Burbidge, E. M., and Baldwin, J. A. 1975, *Ap. J. (Letters)*, **198**, L49.

Wyckoff, S., Wehinger, P. A., Spinrad, H., and Boksenburg, A. 1980, *Ap. J.*, **240**, 25.

THE RADIO TO X-RAY CONTINUA OF AGN

W.A. Stein

University of Minnesota

Minneapolis, MN

S.L. O'Dell

Virginia Tech

Blacksburg, VA

ABSTRACT

The spectral distribution of continuum emission of strongly nonthermal AGN is adequately described by synchrotron self-Compton models. However, significant questions remain regarding the origin of relativistic particles and the possible origin of beaming. Separation of potential radiation components in AGN in which gas is present is difficult in practice. One example is the question of the origin of the blue bump. Models involving a power law plus Balmer continuum and Fe II emission, as well as those based on thermal accretion disk emission are discussed. There is no definitive resolution of this problem at present. The variable nonthermal emission, X-rays, and observable consequences of accretion disks are primary examples of ways in which the innermost core of AGN can be studied.

I. INTRODUCTION

Most of the luminosity of QSOs and AGN is radiated in the form of a continuum extending from radio frequencies through those at X-ray photon energies. Up to 10^{48} erg sec^{-1} is emitted in some cases. It is imperative that we understand the origin of this continuum in order to explain the relative importance of thermal versus nonthermal processes in various objects, the origin of relativistic particles, accretion by supermassive objects, the importance of obscuration and thermal reradiation by dust, and the origin of the photoionizing continuum. That is, by understanding the origin of this continuum we are able to investigate the physical environment in the vicinity of the energy generator.

The emission and absorption line regions of QSOs and AGN occur at distances from the source of energy of the order of a parsec and greater. When we ask ourselves how we may best be able to understand the core emission region, we conclude that one means may be through investigating the origin of jets observed at radio frequencies and visual wavelength. In addition, the variable nonthermal visual-infrared emission, the featureless photoionizing continuum (be it either thermal or nonthermal emission) and the X-ray emission all arise as a direct result of the core object. All of these observable characteristics may originate within volumes with linear size of $10^{15} - 10^{16}$ cm. Most other observed phenomena associated with these objects are determined as a result of the physical processes occurring in this core region.

We intend to summarize our view of what we understand and do not understand about the continuum emitted by AGN. We do not wish to discuss phenomena associated with systems in which the activity observed is most likely to be attributed to star formation, although we are aware that at least some characteristics of many objects may be the spatially unresolved superposition of activity of this type as well as those processes that are associated with the most luminous sytems. Can we understand the origin of the luminosity of the most energetic systems within essentially one physical model, or are there fundamentally different types of objects, for example, those with a supermassive compact core and those without?

II. THE MOST SIMPLE CASE — SOURCES WITH STRONGLY NONTHERMAL CHARACTERISTICS

Some sources, the BL Lacertae objects, exhibit characteristics that are clearly explained primarily by nonthermal processes. These AGN, when observed at relatively modest distances, are seen to be the nuclei of elliptical galaxies (Ulrich *et al.* 1975,

Miller *et al.* 1978). They are strongly variable, upon occasion erupting with enormous luminosity outbursts extending from X-rays to radio frequencies (Kinman *et al.* 1974, Rieke *et al.* 1976) that may exceed 10^{48} erg sec^{-1} (if the radiation is isotropic). The degree of linear polarization, especially during periods of high activity, has been found to be very large (e.g., 0235+164, Impey *et al.* 1982) and strongly variable in degree and position angle on short time scales (Angel *et al.* 1978). All of this information leads to the conclusion that the X-ray to radio frequency continuum of these objects is to be explained through the synchrotron self-Compton (SSC) emission (see §II.b) from a compact region in the nucleus of a galaxy. Many of these same characteristics are also observed to be associated with optically violent variable (OVV) QSOs (Miller and French 1978) (or highly polarized QSOs, HPQs; Moore and Stockman 1981; Moore 1982) and the physical description of these objects is thought to be similar to that of the BL Lac objects. An earlier review (Stein, O'Dell, and Strittmatter 1976) summarized many of the properties of these objects and here we will briefly update information obtained during recent years.

a) Observations – Recent Studies of Some Objects

i) AO 0235+164

Impey *et al.* (1982) have observed a strong polarization phase in the visual-infrared luminosity of this object. During this phase the degree of polarization at V (0.55μm) reached 43.9% and a small rotation of the position angle of polarization ($\Delta\Theta \sim 10°$) was observed over the wavelength interval 0.44 μm to 2.2 μm. The flux observed during this phase was modest ($\sim$0.5 mJy at $\lambda = .44$ μ) compared to a previous large luminosity outburst with peak flux of $\sim$3 mJy at $\lambda = .44$ μm (Rieke *et al.* 1976).

ii) OI 090.4 (0754+101)

This object was one of the first found in which an apparent rotation of the plane of polarization from infrared through visual wavelengths was observed (Rieke *et al.* 1977, Puschell and Stein 1980). Polarization studies at visual wavelengths also indicate rapid variability of degree and position angle on time scales less than one day (Angel *et al.* 1978). Thus, polarization observations at various wavelengths must be done simultaneously.

iii) OJ 287 (0851+202)

A rapid outburst of this object was observed in January 1983 by Holmes *et al.* (1984). The visual wavelength spectral index was about the same $(\alpha \sim 1.2,\ F(\nu) \propto \nu^{-\alpha})$ during the outburst as when measured during previous, more quiescent, periods. Polarization degree and position angle changed rapidly (1 day) and wavelength dependence of position angle was observed.

iv) 1156+295

An enormous outburst was observed in 1981 in which an object that previously had exhibited a rather normal QSO spectrum increased in brightness to an integrated luminosity exceeding 10^{47} erg sec^{-1}. During this phase 1156+295 exhibited the characteristics of a BL Lac object (Wills *et al.* 1983). Spectral features disappeared and linear polarization increased to about 30 percent at visual wavelengths. A radio outburst was observed several months later and it is not clear whether this activity was related to the earlier optical outburst or to a later one. This ambiguity in relationship between visual-infrared and radio outbursts is similar to results obtained on 1308+326 (Mufson *et al.* 1985).

v) 1308+326

This object has been one of the most violently variable known. An outburst in 1978 was observed in detail by Moore *et al.* (1980). The polarization studies indicated very short-term fluctuations (1 day). An extensive review of the luminosity fluctuations indicates that enormous outbursts occur regularly (with a typical duration of only ~2 weeks), although it is not known yet whether or not there is a periodic component due to lack of comprehensive coverage (Mufson *et al.* 1985). Polarization studies during the outburst of March-June 1983 exhibit clear wavelength dependence of both degree and position angle at visual wavelengths (Sitko *et al.* 1984). The high frequency radio emission (8 GHz) exhibits strong fluctuations as well, but they occur on much longer time scales and the relationship of these fluctuations to the visual-infrared outbursts is not clear.

vi) BL LAC (2200+420)

An extensive series of continuous observations of flux and polarization at visual-infrared wavelengths over a one week period was conducted by Moore *et al.* (1982). Short-term, small-amplitude fluctuations were observed on time scales of hours, but an analysis indicates that they may be modeled by random changes with time. A model of multiple, independent sources of synchrotron emission has been suggested as being an appropriate description of these data. It should be noted however, that BL Lac was not in a strong eruptive phase at the time of these studies (L $\sim 10^{45}$ erg sec^{-1}), in contrast to observations of strong outbursts of other sources in which L $\sim 10^{48}$ erg sec^{-1}, assuming isotropic radiation.

vii) Multifrequency Studies

Since the strongly variable objects are observed to vary at all wavelengths from radio to X-ray frequencies, there have been a series of determined efforts to obtain simultaneous observations at all wavelengths in order to properly delineate the continuum spectral distribution of several objects. Studies of this type (from radio through visual wavelengths) have been successfully completed on a number of sources by Landau *et al.* 1983, for 0735+178 by Bregman *et al.* (1984), for OJ 287 (0851+202) by Worrall *et al.* (1982), for 3C371 by Worrall *et al.* (1984), for 1413+135 by Bregman *et al.* (1981), and for IZw 187 by Bregman *et al.* (1982) and others. All these studies confirm the continuity of spectra over the radio to X-ray frequency region and provide information on the relative luminosities radiated in the various spectral bands. Specific papers should be consulted on the details of results obtained on individual sources.

b) Physical Interpretation

We believe that all the observational data for blazars, i.e., BL Lac objects and high-polarization (or OVV) quasars – point toward a synchrotron origin for the radio-through-ultraviolet continua of these objects. The X-ray emission from blazars seems to be comprised of two components, with a range of relative strengths. These are a steep soft-X-ray component, which is reasonably consistent with an extrapolation of the infrared-to-ultraviolet synchrotron emission, and a flatter hard-X-ray component (see Mushotzky *et al.* 1978; Hearn, Marshall, and Jernigan 1979; Riegler, Agrawal, and Mushotzky 1979; Ledden *et al.* 1981; Bregman *et al.* 1982; Urry *et al.* 1982; Ulmer *et al.* 1983; Maccagni *et al.* 1983).* There are several plausible X-radiation processes which might account for this hard-X-ray component (see, e.g., O'Dell 1978, 1979), the most frequently cited (see, e.g., Margon, Jones, and Wardle 1978; Mushotzky *et al.* 1978; Schwartz *et al.* 1979; Urry and Mushotzky 1982; Madejski and Schwartz 1983) being the synchrotron self-Compton (SSC) mechanism (Jones, O'Dell, and Stein 1974a,b; Burbidge, Jones, and O'Dell 1974).

While one expects SSC X-rays to appear at some level, other mechanisms may conceivably dominate the X-ray emission in given sources. Nevertheless, the observed X-ray emission is in any case an upper limit to the SSC X radiation. Even as an upper

---

* However, see Elvis and Lawrence in this volume for some interesting cases related to the subject of ultraviolet–X-ray continuity.

limit to the SSC emission, the X-ray observations place important constraints on models for the synchrotron radio emission (e.g., Jones *et al.* 1974b; Burbidge *et al.* 1974; Condon *et al.* 1979; Dennison *et al.* 1981; Marscher and Broderick 1981a,b; Bregman *et al.* 1981, 1982). Generalized model calculations (Jones *et al.* 1974a,b; Burbidge *et al.* 1974) and specific model calculations for inhomogeneous spherical sources (Marscher 1977) and for jets (Königl 1981; Reynolds 1982a,b) all require at least modestly relativistic motion ($\gamma_0 \gtrsim 2$) to reduce the SSC emission, predicted on the basis of the observed radio synchrotron emission, to a level at or below that of the observed X-ray emission (see below). Other theoretical arguments (see O'Dell 1979; Condon *et al.* 1979; Dennison *et al.* 1981) – such as variability time scales, departure from equipartition, and radiative lifetime – also point to the likelihood of modestly relativistic bulk motion. Since the SSC emission must be less than or equal to the observed X-ray spectral flux S_x (in μJy) at an X-ray photon enejrgy E_x (in keV), the kinematic Doppler factor $\delta_k \equiv [\gamma_0(1 - \beta_o \cos\theta)]^{-1}$ must satisfy (Marscher *et al.* 1979; Condon *et al.* 1979; Burbidge *et al.* 1974)

$$\delta_k > \frac{0.8(1+z)[\frac{S_r}{Jy}]}{[\frac{E_x}{keV}]0.1[\frac{S_x}{\mu Jy}]0.2[\frac{\nu_r}{GHz}]1.3[\frac{\theta_s}{mas}]1.4} \, ,$$

where S_r is the radio spectral flux (in Jy) at the frequency ν_r (in GHz), θ_s is the equivalent angular radius of a spherical component (in milliarcseconds), and z is the redshift of the source. (We have assumed a spectral index $\alpha_r \approx 0.5$ for the transparent synchrotron emission, which seems to be typical; however, similar results are found for other reasonable values of the spectral index.)

We wish to emphasize that for most strong compact radio sources, SSC X-rays are expected at observed levels or greater unless some effect such as relativistic motion plays a major role. Indeed, we believe one must not only account for the origin of X-rays in given sources, but must also explain (at least in the strong radio sources) why the SSC X-rays are no stronger than they are.

The biggest uncertainties in our application of these theories to interpretation of the observations of strongly nonthermal QSOs involve the questions of the importance of beaming, the degree to which relativistic bulk motion is involved, and the inhomogeneity of the SSC source. These aspects of the sources will be difficult to understand in detail. However, the degree of polarization observed in some outbursts certainly indicates a high degree of *coherent* activity involving magnetic fields and relativistic particle injection. The SSC description includes BL Lac-OVV characteristics as well as the very red QSOs (Smith and Spinrad 1980; Stein and Sitko 1984; Rieke *et al.* 1982), in which steep visual wavelength spectral distributions are observed and the so-called blank field compact radio sources (Rieke *et al.* 1979; Ledden and O'Dell 1983).

c) Evidence for Beaming?

There has been much discussion of beaming in application to nonthermal sources because of a number of observed characteristics and theoretical problems. In extragalactic objects jets are commonly observed in high angular-resolution radio observations and relativistic motion is invoked to explain superluminal motions and as a solution to the Compton scattering problem. On the scale of individual stars, pulsars and SS433 observations are explained through beaming associated with neutron stars. We have already discussed the theoretical arguments involving the possibilities of beaming in compact nonthermal sources. What additional observational evidence is available favoring models of this type?

We believe that some of the polarization characteristics at visual-infrared wavelengths of the strongly nonthermal sources may be explained by beaming. In some cases sources exhibit wavelength dependence of degree and position angle of polarization (Rieke *et al.* 1977; Impey *et al.* 1982; Puschell *et al.* 1983; Sitko *et al.* 1984). We believe that the key to understanding the polarization characteristics of the strongly active nonthermal sources may lie in the geometrical relationship of emission regions as a function of time relative to the line of sight within the core of these QSOs. As an example, we can consider two spatially separate regions along lines of magnetic field that are filled with relativistic particles at the same time during an outburst. Relative to the line of sight the changes in particle energy and pitch angle, as well as strength and orientation of magnetic field, may be different for the two regions. As a result we may have a situation in which the synchrotron radiation spectrum, as well as the polarization degree and position angle of one region may be different than the same characteristics of another region. Yet as observed from earth these regions may be spatially unresolved.

The scheme described above for producing wavelength-dependent polarization characteristics from the nonthermal emission region of blazars may be similar to that of pulsars. It is well known that the pulsed radiation from these latter objects is strongly polarized both at radio frequencies (e.g., Radhakrishnan *et al.* 1969) and at visual wavelengths (Cocke *et al.* 1973) although the emission mechanisms are different. One of the interesting characteristics of pulsar radiation is the rotation of position angle as the hypothesized beam of radiation sweeps through the line of sight of the observer. Presumably this rotation of position angle is to be attributed to the relative geometry of the emission region with respect to the magnetic field, beaming direction, and the line of sight.

d) Summary

We have attempted to summarize the observational and theoretical evidence that supports the interpretation of the characteristics of the strongly nonthermal QSOs (blazars) through the synchrotron self-Compton mechanism. While the evidence is strong, there still are significant questions remaining about this interpretation. Some of these are as follows:

(1) Can we explain the detailed relationship of variable flux at all

wavelengths during outbursts?

(2) What is the physical origin of the beaming if it exists? The explanation of the origin of beaming, if it can be definitively proven, must imply the existence of a supermassive compact object.

(3) The enormous luminosity of these objects – up to 10^{48} erg $\sec^{-1}$ radiated by relativistic particles – implies some interesting nonthermal physics. What are the processes involved in acceleration of the relativistic particles?

III. COMPLICATIONS ARISING FROM THE EXISTENCE OF A NONTHERMAL SOURCE IN THE NUCLEUS OF A GALAXY WITH GAS

a) Photoionization, Emission Lines and the Thermal Continuum

It has been widely hypothesized that the source of photoionizing photons responsible for the excitation of the emission lines of QSOs is a power-law continuum that extends into the ultraviolet (Strittmatter and Williams 1976, Oke *et al.* 1984). A large flux of hard ultraviolet photons is necessary in order to provide for excitation of highly ionized species of gas constituents that are observed in QSO spectra. (An alternative view is that the photoionizing photons originate from an optically thick, hot, thermal accretion disk (Shields 1978). This will be discussed in § IV – Alternative Emission Processes.)

Evidence that the featureless continuum is power-law in nature has come from many sources. Direct observation of QSO continua is generally described as a power law (Oke *et al.* 1984). Detailed studies of polarization as a function of wavelength with relatively high spectral resolution of the nucleus of NGC 4151 indicate that the polarized component of the continuum which is described by a very hard power law $F(\nu) \propto \nu^{-0.33}$ (Schmidt and Miller 1980). Similar studies of the nucleus of NGC 1068 also indicate a power-law description of the polarized component, although in this case the spectral distribution is steeper than for NGC 4151 (Miller and Antonucci 1983).

If it is assumed that a nonthermal power-law source of photons exists in the nucleus of a galaxy along with thermal gas, we can describe the observable consequences that will result. Emission lines from photoionized species will be seen although detailed line intensities are the subject of debate because of questions of emission-line cloud densities and how they should be treated (Kwan and Krolik 1981; Canfield and Puetter 1981), and a thermal continuum from the gas will be visible. These thermal radiation components have been well studied in the cases of hot thermal photoionizing spectra (as in gaseous nebulae, Osterbrock 1974) as well as in cases in which the exciting continuum has a power-law shape (see review by Strittmatter and Williams 1976). These thermal radiation components from the gas must be removed in order to proceed with any discussion of the intrinsic nature of the photoionizing continuum. This task ought to be possible but, in fact, is difficult because of the complications resulting from optically thick emission-line clouds. Another well understood radiation component that is difficult to remove from spectra of the less luminous AGN is that of residual starlight in any observing aperture (Stein, Rudy, and Tokunaga 1985). Efforts in this direction have been made for Seyfert galaxies such as NGC 4151 (Rieke and Lebofsky 1981).

b) Dust and Thermal Infrared Emission

The nuclei of galaxies may contain dust that absorbs short wavelength radiation and reradiates the absorbed energy in the infrared. Recent reviews have discussed the evidence related to the degree of modification of the intrinsic AGN or QSO spectral distribution that may be attributed to this process (Rieke and Lebofsky 1979; Stein and Soifer 1983). Thus, we will not repeat details here. In some sources it is widely believed that dust is important in terms of extinction and thermal reradiation (leading to a large flux of infrared radiation), but for most AGN, the degree to which dust is involved is unknown. There is no evidence for dust as a major constituent in terms of severe modification of the intrinsic spectrum in blazars.

One example that illustrates the problem of deciding about the importance of dust in AGN is the case of the nucleus of NGC 4151. As surprising as it may seem it is still not clear how important dust may be in determining the observed characteristics of the nucleus of this Seyfert galaxy. This bright object is an important example because, if we could decide upon appropriate observational tests for determining the abundance of dust in this object, perhaps the tests could be applied to other AGN as well.

A brief review of the observations of this object is appropriate. Tests for reddening imply that a small degree is required to explain the Balmer decrement (Oke and Sargent 1968; Boksenberg *et al.* 1975; Osterbrock and Koski 1976; H.E. Smith, private communication — note that results are not in excellent agreement), as well as the sulfur line ratios (Wampler 1968). Visual wavelength polarization of the narrow component of the emission lines is observed and is attributed to scattering by dust (Thompson *et al.* 1979, Schmidt and Miller 1980). The 8-13 μm spectrum which exhibits structure in dusty H II nuclei of galaxies (e.g., Phillips *et al.* 1984), a weak feature in NGC 1068 (e.g., Roche *et al.* 1984) and a strong feature in MK 231 (Jones *et al.* 1984) exhibits only a very weak feature in NGC 4151 if any feature is present at all (Jones *et al.* 1984). The flux observed from the nucleus at visual wavelengths is strongly variable (Lyutyi 1973) and it is strongly variable at 2.2μm (Rieke and Lebofsky 1979), but the degree of variability decreases at longer infrared wavelengths (Penston *et al.* 1974, Stein *et al.* 1974).

Based on all the evidence available for the nucleus of NGC 4151, Rieke and Lebofsky (1981) separated emission components with the conclusion that most of the 10μm emission from the nucleus was to be attributed to thermal reradiation by dust. However, Ferland and Mushotsky (1982) argue that although dust is mixed with the gas in the narrow-line region, thermal reradiation by this dust is insufficient to account for the infrared radiation observed. Malkan and Filippenko (1983) also argue on the basis of the shape of the continuum spectrum, after elimination of the light of the galaxy, that the near infrared is not dominated by emission from dust grains.

One test of the hypothesis that thermal dust emission is responsible for most of the 10μm radiation of NGC 4151 is the measurement of the angular size at this wavelength. It is expected that the angular size should be greater than 0.25 seconds of arc and methods of measuring this quantity at a flux level of about 1.5×10^{-26} watt m^{-2} Hz^{-1} should be explored (Stein 1984).

c) Influence on Radio Emission

Thermal gas in AGN can, in principle, affect the (synchrotron) radio emission in several ways (e.g., Jones *et al.* 1974b; Marscher 1979; Condon *et al.* 1981). Depending on the geometry and physical conditions, thermal gas might alter the radio synchrotron radiation through Faraday depolarization, free-free absorption, or dielectric suppression (Razin-Tsytovich effect) if cospatial; or it might inhibit the formation of radio sources by confining the relativistic electrons to volumes too small to produce observable synchrotron emission or to speeds too little to produce relativistic enhancement. Thus, the presence of thermal gas is possibly a contributing factor along with beam orientation (Blandford and Rees 1978; Scheuer and Readhead 1979; Marscher 1980) and intrinsic differences among nonthermal sources, in determining the overall spectral-flux distribution of a given source — such as the distinctions between "radio-loud" and "radio-quiet" quasars, and between blazars, "normal" quasars, and other AGN. Here, we discuss only the nuclear thermal gas whose presence is already demonstrated — namely, that responsible for the broad-line emission in AGN. Although it is quite plausible — indeed, likely — that other phases also exist in the nuclear region of AGN, the properties of only the line-emitting regions are thus far established.

Analyses of the broad-line emission from active galaxies indicate that the emission originates in clouds or filaments with the following properties (see, e.g., MacAlpine 1976; Davidson 1977; Netzer 1978; Baldwin and Netzer 1978): temperature $T \approx 10^4$ K; number densities 10^9 cm$^{-3} \lesssim n \lesssim 10^{10}$ cm^{-3}; and ionization parameters $0.002 \lesssim \Upsilon \lesssim 0.03$, where

$$\Upsilon(r) \equiv \frac{F_{v*}^{*LC_{(r)}}}{nhc}$$

is the (approximate) ratio of Lyman-continuum photons to hydrogen. Since the broad-line emitting regions are probably radiation bounded (see, e.g., Oke 1974; Strittmatter and Williams 1976; and Kwan and Krolik 1979), the depth of the H II region in each cloud or filament is

$$\ell \approx \frac{75\Upsilon \, T_4^{1/2}}{n_9} \, ,$$

where $\ell_{12} \equiv \ell(10^{12}$ cm$)$, $T_4 \equiv T/(10^4$ K$)$, and $n_9 \equiv n/(10^9$ cm$^{-3})$. Consequently, the depth to free-free absorption at a frequency $\nu_9 \equiv \nu/(10^9$ Hz$)$ is (Condon *et al.* 1981)

$$\tau_{ff} \approx (8.8 \times 10^4)\frac{n_9^2 \ell_{12}}{T_4^{3/2}\nu_9^2(1+z)^2} \approx (6.6 \times 10^6)\frac{n_9\Upsilon}{T_4\nu_9^2(1+z)^2} \, .$$

Clearly, these H II regions are opaque to radio emission below about 300 GHz. Furthermore, except perhaps for the strongest radio sources (relative to the optical radiation), the broad-line emitting regions probably lie outside the volume occupied by any compact radio source emitting at centimeter wavelengths (see Condon *et al.* 1981).

Although the above calculations suggest that free-free absorption might attenuate the radio emission in AGN, there are other considerations which argue against this hypothesis (see Condon *et al.* 1981). Firstly, the angular covering factor of the broad-line clouds or filaments — at least those thick to Lyman continuum radiation — is probably less than unity (e.g., Baldwin and Netzer 1978; Soifer *et al.* 1981), implying that compact radio sources are not totally covered by free-free-thick clouds or filaments — unless these clouds are much more numerous than the (larger) ones opaque in the Lyman continuum. Secondly, while centimeter-wavelength components are sufficiently compact to lie in a volume bounded by broad-line emitting regions, meter-wavelength components are not; thus, another mechanism would be required to suppress the low-frequency radio emission.

It therefore seems unlikely that free-free absorption by the broad-line emitting regions alone can account for the total absence of radio emission in many AGN. On the other hand, the presence of thermal gas might act to restrict the development of a synchrotron emitting source by confining the relativistic electrons to small volumes or by providing sufficient inertia to limit the high speed flows which could lead to (relativistic) jets or at least allow a synchrotron component to become transparent (at radio frequencies) before radiative losses become catastrophic. Since the inferred (minimum) energy content of compact-radio-source components is nearly always less than 10^{57} ergs and typically 10^{54} ergs (Burbidge *et al.* 1974), 1 to 10^3 solar masses of thermal plasma is sufficient to retard the flow of relativistic plasma (if the momenta of the two plasmas can be coupled, e.g., through the magnetic field). Since this is comparable to the mass of the broad-line regions, it is conceivable that the thermal plasma can influence the evolution of a compact radio source.

d) X-ray Absorption

Sufficient gas may be present in the line of sight to the X-ray source in AGN to produce low-energy X-ray absorption. In fact such absorption has been observed in some objects for which X-ray spectra have been obtained (Ives *et al.* 1976). It is required that the line-of-sight gas have column densities $<N_e\ell>$ $\gtrsim 10^{22}$ m^{-2} of normal chemical composition in order to produce observable X-ray spectral turnover in the hν $\lesssim$ 3 keV region. It is not difficult to imagine this condition being satisfied in AGN H II regions, but it is more difficult to know in which cases gas in sufficient abundance is present *in the line of sight* (see Condon *et al.* 1981). The inhomogeneous nature of QSO gas clouds adds considerable uncertainty in predicting observable X-ray absorption for any given source.

IV. ALTERNATIVE EMISSION PROCESSES

a) *The Blue Bump Controversy*

There has been a great deal of discussion in recent years about the interpretation of the broad 3600Å continuum emission feature in AGN spectra. The debate is directed at deciding between the model of this feature as the sum of a flat power-law continuum plus Balmer continuum and Fe II emission (Puetter *et al.* 1982) or alternatively, emission from an optically thick, thermal accretion disk (Shields 1978; Malkan and Sargent 1982). The most serious weakness of the nonthermal power-law (plus Balmer continuum and Fe II) interpretration is that we do not understand the physical origin of the relatively flat photoionizing continuum (e.g., $F(\nu) \propto \nu^{-0.3}$ for NGC 4151, Schmidt and Miller 1980). The difficulty with the thermal accretion disk hypothesis is that the observed shape of the visual-ultraviolet continuum is generally thought to be described best by a power law up to a maximum photon energy; thus multiple temperature components of a thermal accretion disk must be invoked in attempts to reproduce this shape (Malkan 1983).

Since it is important for interpretation in both models, let us review the evidence for the power-law nature of the visual-ultraviolet continuum of AGN. Of nontrivial importance is the matter of proper correction for the starlight in the surrounding galaxy of an AGN. The shape of the inferred continuum of the active nucleus of a galaxy cannot be determined without correction for light from the host galaxy (Penston *et al.* 1974; Stein *et al.* 1985). In the case of most QSOs, the correction for galactic starlight is not significant by comparison with the brightness of the central object. However, caution must be exercised with regard to observations of low-luminosity ($\lesssim 10^{43}$ erg sec^{-1}) objects especially if active star formation may be occurring.

Let us examine the observational evidence on the shape of QSO continuum spectral distributions. Considerable detailed quantitative data has been assembled over the frequency range 3×10^{13} Hz – 10^{15} Hz (3000Å $< \lambda < 10\mu$m) by Neugebauer *et al.* (1979). Although it cannot be stated that the $\lambda < 10,000$Å continua are clearly simple power laws (because of wiggles and small bumps), it is very clear that all spectral distributions have increasing flux per unit frequency interval at longer wavelengths. This is contrary to predictions of any optically thick thermal accretion disk model for the continuum emission of QSOs. If a thermal accretion disk is to explain the blue-ultraviolet part of the spectrum, then another component must be invoked to explain the red part of the spectrum. What is the proposed source of this red continuum? More recently Oke *et al.* 1984 also conclude that the best description of the continuum distribution of a number of QSOs is that of a power-law plus Balmer continuum (probably from optically thick emission regions) plus Fe II emission (Netzer and Wills 1983).

Among AGN an object that has been studied in great detail is the nucleus of NGC 4151. Schmidt and Miller (1980) have obtained spectropolarimetry of the active nucleus concluding that the polarized component over the wavelength range 3700Å $< \lambda < 7100$Å is best described by a power law of the form $F(\nu) \propto \nu^{-\alpha}$ $\alpha \approx 0.33$. This result is also in agreement with results of Thompson *et al.* (1979).

Additional uncertainty about the nature of the shape of the intrinsic photoionizing continuum, especially in the ultraviolet, has been raised by MacAlpine (1981), Eastman *et al.* (1983) and MacAlpine *et al.* (1984). In exploring explanations for the He II $\lambda1640/\lambda4686$ ratio in AGN, these investigators have found difficulty accounting for observed equivalent widths in any spectrum with a far-ultraviolet steepening. Thus, they are led to search for absorption and reddening as explanations for the potential differences between observed and intrinsic far-ultraviolet flux.

The terminology of blue bumps has now evolved to include reference to little bumps and big bumps. It now appears to be agreed that the Balmer continuum plus Fe II emission are present in spectra and these together are referred to as the little bump because the emission does not extend to the far ultraviolet. It is the question about the origin of the big bump that is still debated. Note that a big ultraviolet bump, as referred to by some investigators in terms of νF_ν, does result from a flat power law in $F_\nu \propto \nu^{-\alpha}$ if $\alpha < 1$.

The physical origin of the photoionizing continuum usually described as a power law in spectra of AGN has been of interest since the early days of QSO spectroscopy. Demoulin and Burbidge (1968) discussed synchrotron emission and Compton scattering as possible explanations of the relatively flat power law, concluding that synchrotron emission was the most promising explanation. The blazars (Stein *et al.* 1976) are clear examples of sources of this type. The problem with interpreting the flat photoionizing continuum of AGN as Compton scattered radiation is that the low flux of radio emission observed from most sources (e.g., especially Seyfert galaxies and radio-quiet QSOs) requires that most of the luminosity (by large factors) be in the form of Compton scattered X-ray photons, which is not consistent with observations. In the radio-loud objects, the possible Compton origin seems more plausible. However, we must then question why the flat photoionizing continuum of a radio-loud object such as 3C273 is so similar in character to that of a relatively radio-quiet object such as the nucleus of NGC 4151. Excluding blazars, radio-loud and radio-quiet objects are similar in spectral distribution for $\nu >$ 10^{13} Hz (Neugebauer *et al.* 1979; Capps *et al.* 1982) and perhaps for $\nu > 10^{12}$ based on recent IRAS data (Neugebauer *et al.* 1984). Therefore, a Compton scattered origin of optical continuum would require scattering of infrared photons to the visual-ultraviolet part of the spectrum (DeMoulin and Burbidge 1968). We would then expect that since the visual-ultraviolet emission varies strongly (e.g., NGC 4151) the infrared emission would as well. Infrared monitoring of even the brightest AGN has been sporadic, but if anything can be said, it is that in NGC 4151 variability is less pronounced in the infrared than at visual-ultraviolet wavelengths (Stein *et al.* 1974; Penston *et al.* 1974; Lyutyi 1973). This is true for other active galaxies and quasars as well (Rieke and Lebofsky 1979). Furthermore, in many AGN there seems not to be sufficient infrared flux to produce the observed ultraviolet flux by first-order Compton scattering without at the same time, generating an un-acceptably large X-ray flux by second-order Compton scattering. We therefore conclude that Compton scattering from the infrared to visual-ultraviolet wavelengths is probably not the explanation of the photoionizing continuum.

The problem of explaining the origin of the flat photoion-izing power-law spectrum remains an embarrassment for those ad-vocating this model. If this continuum is synchrotron radiation, what is the relationship between the visual wavelength continuum to that at radio frequencies? In 3C273 a flat visual-ultraviolet continuum $F(\nu) \propto \nu^{-0.3}$, if extrapolated to lower frequencies, cannot explain the strength of the radio emission. In radio-quiet objects the radio spectrum is generally characteristic of that ob-served from extended emission regions of AGN (Rudnick *et al.* 1984) and it is quite steep ($\alpha \approx 0.7$). If such a spectrum is extrap-olated to higher photon frequencies it cannot explain the strength of visual-ultraviolet continuum. Thus, if the featureless power-law continuum at visual wavelengths is synchrotron emission it must originate in a component separate from that which is the source of the radio emission. It is puzzling, especially since this component of emission contains a large fraction of the luminosity of these objects!

An extreme example of the potentially large luminosity in the far-ultraviolet emission of a QSO is the case of PG 1211+143. In this object extrapolation of the X-ray spectrum to lower frequencies and the visual spectrum to higher frequencies would imply that most of the luminosity may be radiated in the form of 10-100 eV photons (Bechtold *et al.* 1985; Elvis and Lawrence 1984). This ultraviolet bump may be interpreted as a T $\sim 10^6$ K thermal accretion disk or as a flat power law extending to h$\nu \sim 40$ ev photon energies.

b) Thermal Comptonization

When the electron-scattering depth τ_{es} in a thermal plasma exceeds unity, low-energy (seed) photons (h$\nu_o \ll$ kT) are stochastically boosted, through multiple Thomson scattering, toward photon energies comparable to kT (Kompaneets 1957). This process, thermal Comptonization, has been investigated both for transmission geometries (e.g., Shapiro, Lightman, and Eardley 1976, Katz 1976, Payne 1980) and for reflection geometries (e.g., Lightman and Rybicki 1979a,b and 1980). Unsaturated Comptonization, $1 < \tau_{es} < [(mc^2)/(kT)]^{1/2}$, produces an approximately power-law spectrum ($\propto \nu^{-\alpha}$) out to photon energies h$\nu \approx$ kT; however, the spectral index $\alpha \approx 1$ only when $\tau_{es} \approx [(mc^2)/(kT)]^{1/2}$. Saturated Comptonization, $\tau_{es} > [(mc^2)/(kT)]^{1/2}$, produces a Wien hump at photon energies h$\nu \approx$ kT. In this regime, the power-law part of the spectrum is destroyed for transmission geometries (since photons have little chance of escaping before h$\nu \approx$ kT), while it persists (with $\alpha \approx 1$) for reflection geometries (since photons of energy h$\nu \ll$ kT can re-emerge after penetrating only a small skin-depth).

Katz (1976) suggested that unsaturated thermal Comptonization by transmission might account for the infrared-ultraviolet power-law continua of quasars. However, the quasars which exhibit simple power-law continua tend to be blazars, i.e., OVV quasars or HPQs and BL Lac objects. As already discussed, we believe that synchrotron emission is the most likely explanation for the infrared-ultraviolet, as well as radio, continuum emission from these objects. Thermal Comptonization does not naturally account for the high degree and variability of linear polarization, nor is it consistent with the rapidity and spectral character of flux variations unless the scattering medium has a temperature in excess of 1 keV (to avoid observable free-free absorption).

On the other hand, most quasars are not blazars, i.e., their emission is neither highly polarized, purely power-law, nor dramatically variable (O'Dell 1978, 1979). For these "ordinary" quasars, it is conceivable that thermal Comptonization plays a role at some photon energies; however, special geometrical configurations are required so that the thermal Comptonization acts effectively upon the seed photons (of unspecified origin), but not upon the spectral lines. In any case, it is difficult for (single-component) thermal Comptonization alone to account for the *entire* infrared-ultraviolet continuum, including the broad "blue bump." If the blue bump were a Wien bump, the temperature of the scattering plasma could be only a few electron volts, thus requiring electron-scattering depths of nearly a thousand for saturation. Such large depths would also produce free-free absorption at visible or infrared frequencies, unless the scattering region were quite large. Requiring that free-free absorption occurs longward of λ_{ff} for a temperature T, leads to the restriction that saturated Comptonization must originate in a region of size

$$[\frac{R}{10^{18} cm}] > 33 [\frac{\lambda_{ff}}{1\mu m}]^2 [\frac{1eV}{kT}]^3 .$$

For both the broad, blue bump and infrared emission to arise in the same Comptonizing region then requires a region tens of parsecs in size (with a mass in excess of 10^{10} solar masses), which would almost certainly scatter the line-emission and would allow flux variations only on time scale longer than about 10,000 years. More importantly such a region would produce an excessive free-free luminosity L_{ff},

$$[\frac{L_{ff}}{10^{48}\,erg\,sec^{-1}}] > 21[\frac{\lambda_{ff}}{1\mu m}]^2[\frac{1eV}{kT}]^{7/2} ,$$

which is inconsistent with observations.

It may, however, be possible to synthesize the entire infrared X-ray continuum (including the "blue bump") of some "ordinary" quasars, using multi-component, thermal Comptonization models (Ennis *et al.* 1982). The same, of course, can be said of other types of models or combinations of models. The primary difficulties with thermal Comptonization models for "ordinary quasars" are in thermalizing the continuum photons without doing the same to the line photons, in failing to account for the origin of the seed photons, and in maintaining the temperature of the Comptonizing electrons.

c) Infrared Free-Free-Emission

Puetter and Hubbard (1985) have suggested that strong near infrared emission near $\lambda \sim 3\mu m$ could explain the increased slope of QSO spectra in the wavelength range longward of $\lambda \approx 1\mu m$. This result depends strongly on very high emission-line cloud densities ($n_e > 10^{11}$ cm^{-3}). Such densities are in conflict with constraints on electron density ($n_e < 10^{10}$ cm^{-3}) imposed by other investigators (e.g., Kwan and Krolik 1981) on the basis of theoretical models of the clouds — particularly the frequent presence of semi-forbidden C III [$\lambda 1909$]. It is important that these disagreements be resolved.

d) Thermal X-rays

We have suggested earlier (in this discussion and elsewhere) that there is strong evidence that X-rays observed from blazars arise through the synchrotron and synchrotron self-Compton emission processes. However, these nonthermal X-rays may not necessarily dominate the high-energy continuum at all frequencies (see also Elvis and Lawrence 1984). We must remain alert to the possibility that hot gas resulting from accretion may emit thermal X-rays from AGN (Meszaros and Silk 1977). Unfortunately there is not much spectral information on AGN at X-ray or γ-ray energies. Such information, when available, may help discriminate between nonthermal and thermal X-ray emission process by the determination of spectral shape and the possible detection of ray line emission.

REFERENCES

Angel, J.R.P., *et al.* 1978, *Proceedings of Pittsburgh Conference on BL Lac Objects*, University of Pittsburgh, ed. A.M. Wolfe, p.117.

Baldwin, J.A., and Netzer, H. 1978, *Ap. J.,* **226**, 1.

Bechtold, J., Elvis, M., Green, R.F., and Fabbiano, G. 1985, AAS Society Meeting Abstract, Tucson, Arizona.

Blandford, R.D., and Rees, M.J. 1978, *Proceedings of Pittsburgh Conference on BL Lac Objects*, University of Pittsburgh, ed. A.M. Wolfe, p.328.

Boksenberg, A., Shortridge, K., Allen, D.A., Fosbury, R.A.E., Penston, M.V., and Savage, A., 1975, *M.N.R.A.S.,* **173**, 381.

Bregman, J.N., Lebofsky, M.J., Aller, M.F., Rieke, G.H., Aller, H.D., Hodge, P.E., Glassgold, A.E., and Huggins, P.J., 1981, *Nature,* **293**, 714.

Bregman, J.N., *et al.* 1982, *Ap. J.,* **253**, 19.

_____. 1984, *Ap. J.,* **276**, 454.

Burbidge, G.R., Jones, J.W., and O'Dell, S.L. 1974, *Ap. J.,* **193,** 43.

Canfield, R.C., and Puetter, R.C. 1981, *Ap. J.,* **243,** 390.

Capps, R.W., Sitko, M.L., and Stein, W.A. 1982, *Ap. J.,* **255,** 413.

Cocke, W.J., Ferguson, D.C., and Muncaster, G.W. 1973, *Ap. J.,* **183,** 987.

Condon, J.J., Ledden, J.E., O'Dell, S.L., and Dennison, B. 1979, *A. J.,* **84,** 1.

Condon, J.J., O'Dell, S.L., Puschell, J.J., and Stein, W.A. 1981, *Ap. J.,* **246,** 624.

Davidson, K., 1977 *Ap. J.,* **218,** 20.

Dennison, B., Broderick, J.J., Ledden, J.E., O'Dell, S.L., and Condon, J.J. 1981, *A.J.,* **86,** 1604.

Demoulin, M.-H., and Burbidge, G.R. 1968, *Ap. J.,* **154,** 3.

Eastman, R.G., MacAlpine, G.M., and Richstone, D.O. 1983, *Ap. J.,* **275,** 53.

Elvis, M., and Lawrence, A. 1984, Santa Cruz Workshop on Active Galactic Nuclei (this volume).

Ennis, D.J., Neugebauer, G., and Werner, M. 1982, *Ap. J.,* **262,** 460.

Ferland, G.J., and Mushotzky, R.F. 1982, *Ap. J.,* **262,** 564.

Hearn, D.R., Marshall, F.J., and Jernigan, J.G. 1979, *Ap. J. (Letters),* **227,** L63.

Holmes, P.A., *et al.* 1984 *M.N.R.A.S.,* to be published.

Impey, C.D., Brand, P.W.J.L., and Tapia, S. 1982, *M.N.R.A.S.,* **198,** 1.

Ives, J.C., Sanford, P.W., and Penston, M.V. 1976, *Ap. J. (Letters),* **207,** L159.

Jones, B., Worrall, D.M., Rodriguez-Espinosa, J., Stein, W.A., and Gillett, F.C. 1984, *Pub. A.S.P.*, **96**, 692.

Jones, T.W., O'Dell, S.L., and Stein, W.A. 1974a, *Ap. J.*, **188**, 353.

_____. 1974b, *Ap. J.*, **192**, 261.

Katz, J.I. 1976, *Ap. J.*, **206**, 910.

Kinman, T.D., Wardle, J.F.C., Conklin, E.K., Andrew, B.H., Harvey, G.A., Macleod, J.M., and Medd, W.J. 1974, *A. J.*, **79**, 349.

Kompaneets, A.S. 1957, *Soviet Phys.-JETP*, **4**, 730.

Königl, A. 1981, *Ap. J.*, **243**, 700.

Kwan, J., and Krolik, J.H. 1981, *Ap. J.*, **250**, 478.

Landau, R., Jones, T.W., Epstein, E.E., Neugebauer, G., Soifer, B.T., Werner, M.W., Puschell, J.J., and Balonek, T.J. 1983 *Ap. J.*, **268**, 68.

Ledden, J.E., and O'Dell, S.L., 1983 *Ap. J.*, **270**, 434.

Ledden, J.E., O'Dell, S.L., Stein, W.A., and Wisniewski, W.Z. 1981, *Ap. J.*, **243**, 47.

Lightman, A.P., and Rybicki, G.B. 1979a, *Ap. J. (Letters)*, **229**, L15.

_____. 1979b, *Ap. J.*, **232**, 882.

_____. 1980, *Ap. J.*, **236**, 928.

Lyutyi, U.M. 1973, *Sov. Ast. A. J.*, **16**, 763.

MacAlpine, G.M. 1976, *Ap. J.*, **204**, 694.

_____. 1981, *Ap. J.*, **251**, 465.

MacAlpine, G.M., Davidson, K., Gull, T.R., and Wu, C.-C. 1984, preprint.

Maccagni, D., Maraschi, L., Tanzi, E.G., Tarenghi, M., and Chiappetti, L. 1983, *Ap. J.*, **273**, 75.

Madejski, G.M., and Schwartz, D.A. 1983, *Ap. J.*, **275**, 467.

Malkan, M.A. 1983, *Ap. J.*, **268**, 582.

Malkan, M.A., and Filippenko, A.V. 1983, *Ap. J.*, **275**, 477.

Malkan, M.A., and Sargent, W.L.W. 1982, *Ap. J.*, **254**, 22.

Margon, B., Jones, T.W., and Wardle, J.F.C. 1978, *A. J.*, **83**, 1021.

Marscher, A.P. 1977, *Ap. J.*, **216**, 244.

_____. 1979, *Ap. J.*, **228**, 27.

_____. 1980, *Ap. J.*, **235**, 386.

Marscher, A.P., and Broderick, J.J. 1981a, *Ap. J. (Letters)*, **247**, L49.

_____. 1981b, *Ap. J.*, **249**, 406.

Marscher, A.P., Marshall, F.E., Mushotzky, R.F., Dent, W.A., Balonek, T.J., and Hartman, M.F. 1979, *Ap. J.*, **233**, 498.

Meszaros, P., and Silk, J. 1977, *Astr. Ap.*, **55**, 289.

Miller, J.S., and Antonucci, R.R.J. 1983, *Ap. J. (Letters)*, **271**, L7.

Miller, J.S., and French, H.B. 1978, *Proceedings of Pittsburgh Conference on BL Lac Objects,* University of Pittsburgh, ed. A.M. Wolfe, p.228.

Miller, J.S., French, H.B., and Hawley, S.A. 1978, *Proceedings of Pittsburgh Conference on BL Lac Objects,* University of Pittsburgh, ed. A.M. Wolfe, p.176.

Moore, R.L., and Stockman, H.S. 1981, *Ap. J.*, **243**, 60.

Moore, R.L. 1982, in IAU Symposium #97, *Extragalactic Radio Sources,* ed. D.S. Heeschen and C.M. Wade (Dordrecht: D. Reidel), p.341.

Moore, R.L., *et al.* 1980, *Ap. J.*, **235**, 717.

Moore, R.L., *et al.* 1982, *Ap. J.*, **260**, 415.

Mufson, S.L., Stein, W.A., Wisniewski, W.Z., Pollack, J., Aller, H.D., and Aller, M.F. 1985 *Ap. J.*, to be published.

Mushotzky, R.F., Boldt, E.A., Holt, S.S., Pravdo, S.H., Serlemitsos, P.J., Swank, J.H., and Rothschild, R.H. 1978, *Ap. J. (Letters)*, **226**, L65.

Netzer, H. 1978, *Ap. J.*, **219**, 822.

Netzer, H., and Wills, B.J. 1983, *Ap. J.*, **275**, 445.

Neugebauer, G., Oke, J.B., Becklin, E.E., and Mathews, K. 1979, *Ap. J.*, **230**, 79.

Neugebauer, G., *et al.* 1984, *Ap. J. (Letters)*, **278**, L83.

O'Dell, S.L. 1978, in *Pittsburgh Conference on BL Lac Objects*, ed. A.M. Wolfe (Pittsburgh: University of Pittsburgh), p.312.

_____. 1979, in *Active Galactic Nuclei*, eds. C. Hazard and S. Mitton (Cambridge, England: Cambridge University), p.95.

Oke, J.B. 1974, *Ap. J. (Letters)*, **189**, L47.

Oke, J.B., and Sargent, W.L.W. 1968, *Ap. J.*, **151**, 807.

Oke, J.B., Shields, G.A., and Korycansky, D.G. 1984, *Ap. J.*, **277**, 64.

Osterbrock, D.E. 1974, *Astrophysics of Gaseous Nebulae* (W.H. Freeman & Co., San Francisco).

Osterbrock, D.E., and Koski, A.T. 1976, *M.N.R.A.S.*, **176**, 61p.

Payne, D.G. 1980, *Ap. J.*, **237**, 951.

Penston, M.V., Penston, M.J., Selmes, R.A., Becklin, E.E., and Neugebauer, G. 1974, *M.N.R.A.S.*, **169**, 357.

Phillips, M.M., Aitken, D.K., and Roche, P.F. 1984, *M.N.R.A.S.*, **207**, 25.

Puetter, R.C., Burbidge, E.M., Smith, H.E., and Stein, W.A. 1982, *Ap. J.*, **257**, 487.

Puetter, R.C., and Hubbard, E.N. 1985, to be published.

Puschell, J.J., and Stein, W.A. 1980, *Ap. J.*, **237**, 331.

Puschell, J.J., Jones, T.W., Phillips, A.C., Rudnick, L., Simpson, E., Sitko, M., Stein, W.A., and Moneti, A. 1983, *Ap. J.*, **265**, 625.

Radhakrishnan, V., Cooke, D.J., Komesaroff, M.M., and Morris, D. 1969, *Nature,* **221**, 443.

Reynolds, S.P. 1982a, *Ap. J.*, **256**, 13.

_____ . 1982b, *Ap. J.*, **256**, 38.

Riegler, G.R., Agrawal, P.C., and Mushotzky, R.F. 1979, *Ap. J. (Letters)*, **233**, L47.

Rieke, G.H., Grasdalen, G.L., Kinman, T.D., Hintzen, P., Wills, B.J., and Wills, D. 1976, *Nature,* **260**, 754.

Rieke, G.H., and Lebofsky, M.J. 1979, *Ann. Rev. Astr. Ap.*, **17**, 477.

_____ . *Ap. J.*, **250**, 87.

Rieke, G.H., Lebofsky, M.J., Kemp, J.C., Coyne, G.V., and Tapia, S. 1977, *Ap. J. (Letters)*, **218**, L37.

Rieke, G.H., Lebofsky, M.J., and Kinman, T.D. 1979, *Ap. J. (Letters)*, **232**, L151.

Rieke, G.H., Lebofsky, M.J., and Wisniewski, W.Z. 1982, *Ap. J.*, **263**, 73.

Roche, P.F., Aitken, D.K., Phillips, M.M., and Whitmore, B. 1984, *M.N.R.A.S.*, **207**, 35.

Rudnick, L., Sitko, M.L., and Stein, W.A. 1984, *A. J.*, **89**, 753.

Scheuer, P.A.G., and Readhead, A.C.S. 1979, *Nature,* **277**, 182.

Schmidt, G.D., and Miller, J.S. 1980, *Ap. J.*, **240**, 759.

Schwartz, D.A., Doxsey, R.E., Griffiths, R.E., Johnston, M.D., and Schwarz, J. 1979, *Ap. J. (Letters)*, **229**, L53.

Shapiro, S.L., Lightman, A.P., and Eardley, D.M. 1976, *Ap. J.,* **204**, 187.

Shields, G. 1978, *Nature,* **272**, 706.

Sitko, M.L., Stein, W.A., and Schmidt, G.D. 1984, *Ap. J.,* to be published.

Smith, H.E., and Spinrad, H. 1980, *Ap. J.,* **236**, 419.

Soifer, B.T., Neugebauer, G., Oke, J.B. and Matthews, K. 1981, *Ap. J.,* **243**, 369.

Stein, W.A. 1984, *Proceedings of Conference on Techniques of Ground Based Infrared Astronomy,* University of Wyoming, Laramie, Wyoming.

Stein, W.A., Gillett, F.C., and Merrill, K.M. 1974, *Ap. J.,* **187**, 213.

Stein, W.A., O'Dell, S.L., and Strittmatter, P.A. 1976, *Ann. Rev. Astr. Ap.,* **14**, 173.

Stein, W.A., Rudy, R.J., and Tokunaga, A. 1985, *Pub. A.S.P.,* to be published.

Stein, W.A., and Sitko, M.L. 1984, *A. J.,* **89**, 1688.

Stein, W.A., and Soifer, B.T. 1983, *Ann. Rev. Astr. Ap.,* **21**, 177.

Strittmatter, P.A., and Williams, R.E. 1976, *Ann. Rev. Astr. Ap.,* **14**, 307.

Thompson, I., Landstreet, J.D., Angel, J.R.P., Stockman, H.S., Woolf, N.J., Martin, P.G., Maza, J., and Beaver, E.A. 1979, *Ap. J.,* **229**, 909.

Ulmer, M.P., Brown, R.L., Schwartz, D.A., Patterson, J., and Gruddace, R.G. 1983, *Ap. J. (Letters),* **270**, L1.

Ulrich, M.-H., Kinman, T.D., Lynds, C.R., Rieke, G.H., and Ekers, R.D. 1975, *Ap. J.,* **198**, 261.

Urry, C.M., and Mushotzky, R.F. 1982, *Ap. J.,* **253**, 38.

Urry, C.M., Mushotzky, R.F., Kondo, Y., Hackney, K.R.H., and Hackney, R.L. 1982, *Ap. J.*, **261**, 12.

Wampler, E.J. 1968, *Ap. J. (Letters)*, **154**, L53.

Wills, B.J., *et al.* 1983, *Ap. J.*, **274**, 62

Worrall, D.M. 1984, *Pub. A.S.P.*, to be published.

Worrall, D.M., *et al.* 1982, *Ap. J.*, **261**, 403.

_____. 1984, *Ap. J.*, **278**, 521.

ACCRETION DISKS IN ACTIVE GALACTIC NUCLEI

Mitchell C. Begelman[*][†]

Joint Institute for Laboratory Astrophysics
University of Colorado and National Bureau of Standards
Boulder, Colorado

ABSTRACT

The qualitative features of an accretion flow orbiting a massive black hole depend principally on the ratio $\dot{m}$ of the accretion rate to the Eddington accretion rate $\dot{M}_E = L_E/c^2$. For $\dot{m} \gg 1$, the flow traps its radiative output and becomes an inefficient radiation torus, the luminosity of which is limited to a few times L_E. At $\dot{m} \ll 1$, the flow may be unable to cool, and may become an ion torus supported by gas pressure. At intermediate values of $\dot{m}$, the flow may settle into a thin accretion disk. Each of these modes of accretion has its characteristic spectral properties and radiative efficiencies, which are discussed and compared with the observed properties of quasars, Type I Seyferts, and radio galaxies. It is argued that different modes of accretion may account for the widely differing manifestations of activity in the nuclei of galaxies.

[*]Presidential Young Investigator

[†]Also at Department of Astrophysical, Planetary and Atmospheric Sciences, University of Colorado, Boulder, CO 80309

I. INTRODUCTION

At the Cambridge AGN meeting seven years ago, Dick McCray presented his now-famous cartoon depicting the spherical accretion of theoretical astrophysicists onto a fashionable new idea (Fig. 1; McCray 1979). He described how they are first attracted to the idea when they innocently venture inside the accretion radius. Many fly through on their hyperbolic orbits without getting trapped. Occasionally, however, two astrophysicists collide, generating a great deal of heat (but not always much light). These

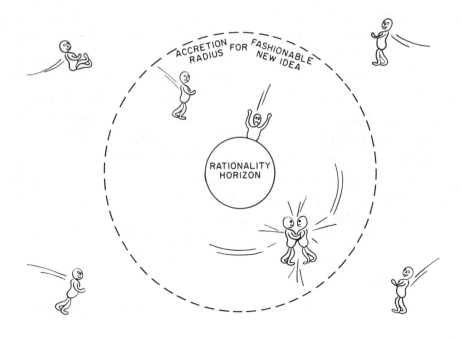

Figure 1. The response of astrophysicists to a fashionable new idea, after McCray (1979).

hapless souls can no longer leave the sphere of influence of the fashionable new idea, but are fated to slip ever closer to the "rationality horizon," within which the idea ceases to be an interesting hypothesis and becomes an article of faith. At the time, this seemed like a particularly good metaphor for the ascendance of the "black-hole bandwagon" in AGN studies. Indeed, black holes are still an article of faith for most of us, and the question of the day has shifted from "what is the central engine?" to "how does it work?"

The current situation is illustrated in Figure 2. Instead of falling in radially, the unsuspecting theorists are swept into a

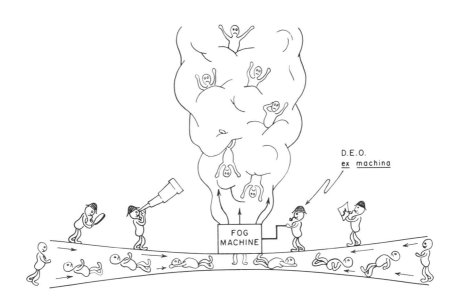

Figure 2. The fate of theorists trying to understand the "central engines" of AGN, circa 1984.

disk. As the theorists swirl inward toward the rationality horizon, observers clamber all over the disk, looking for clues to the whereabouts of their missing colleagues. Occasionally, one of the observers notices a fleeting "blue bump" on the surface of the disk, another spots an unmistakable profile, but the fragments of evidence don't quite cohere. Before they can reach a comfortable consensus inside the rationality horizon, the theorists are swept away in a poorly collimated, one-sided jet of fog. Some of them interact with the broad line or narrow line region on their way out, and stay at a few parsecs forever; others are expelled from the field entirely.

The theorists' dispersion to larger scales is hardly surprising, since few observations point unambiguously to the inner workings of the central engine. The best spatial resolution now available brings us to just within five orders of magnitude of the event horizon, and the only direct access to the (alleged) primary energy source is through the interpretation of integrated spectra, polarization and variability. The rich diagnostics of the broad and narrow emission-line regions are lacking, and measurements of variability to date have provided few clear indications of which frequencies are emitted by gas near the black hole. Therefore, most models of the central engine have evolved through "pure thought," constrained by some very general observational requirements. The best I can do in this review is to summarize some of the main possibilities and show how they can be placed in a coherent framework. Observations of the "blue bump" and inferences about radiative efficiencies can help us to distinguish between these possibilities, but it may be the emission line studies that really pin things down, once we learn how to interpret them. In this respect, the D[on] E[.] O[sterbrock] ex machina who turns the crank on the fog machine may be doing us a favor.

II. MODES OF ACCRETION

It is now widely believed that energetic activity in the nuclei of galaxies arises from the interaction of matter with a massive black hole. Although it is possible that some of the energy is extracted electromagnetically from the spin of the hole (Blandford and Znajek 1977; Macdonald and Thorne 1982; Phinney 1983), the "best bet" (at least for optically and X-ray active sources) is still that most of the energy is released during accretion of gas with a substantial amount of angular momentum. If the specific angular momentum exceeds $\sqrt{12}\,r_g c$ with $r_g = GM/c^2$ (for a Schwarzschild hole of mass M), then the gas must give up some of its angular momentum via viscous (or other) torques before it can cross the event horizon. In the process, it dissipates a certain amount of binding energy, which may be either radiated away or retained by the gas in the form of heat. An accretion flow which is able to radiate away most of its binding energy forms a thin *accretion disk*. Thin disks have been studied extensively in connection with cataclysmic variables and X-ray binaries (see Pringle 1981 for a review), and it is natural to ask whether such systems can be scaled up to account for activity in the nuclei of galaxies.

The answer is not known, partly because we do not understand some of the physics (e.g., the viscosity mechanism and the role of nonthermal emission processes) and partly because we lack some crucial observations. It is certainly possible for a theorist to speculate on any or all of these missing links, but it is probably most fruitful to dwell on those aspects which (in principle) can be resolved observationally. Fortunately, the qualitative "mode" of accretion is one such aspect, since it depends mainly on the accretion rate and the mass of the black hole.

Radiation pressure and electron scattering play important roles in disks around stellar-mass objects, and the structures of such disks are largely governed by the ratio ($\dot{m}$) of the actual accretion rate to the "Eddington accretion rate," $\dot{M}_E = L_E/c^2$, where $L_E = 1.3 \times 10^{38}(M/M_\odot)$ ergs s^{-1} = $1.3 \times 10^{46}\,m_8$ ergs s^{-1} is the Eddington limit. If the ratio of inflow speed to Keplerian speed is fixed, then flows with similar values of $\dot{m}$ should be qualitatively similar. In particular, accretion rates, timescales t and length scales ℓ should all scale with M for similar disks. Thus the characteristic density in a disk scales as $\rho \propto \dot{M}t/\ell^3 \propto \dot{m}/M$. The cooling timescale is inversely proportional to density, so the ratio of cooling time to dynamical time is inversely proportional to $\dot{m}$ and is independent of M. In other words, an accretion flow may not be able to cool and form a thin disk if $\dot{m}$ is too small. Such a flow may instead puff up to form an *ion torus* supported by gas pressure (Rees *et al.* 1982). Alternatively, consider a flow with $\dot{m}$ very large. The electron scattering optical depth scales as $\tau \propto \ell\rho \propto \dot{m}$. This is also proportional to the ratio of photon diffusion time (Kelvin-Helmholtz time) to dynamical time, so radiation is unable to leak out of a flow with $\dot{m}$ too large. Such a flow is also unable to cool, and puffs up to form a *radiation torus* supported by radiation pressure. Because the luminosity required to inflate a radiation torus is $\gtrsim L_E$, such structures may form whenever $\dot{m}$ is larger than a few.

The generic properties of the three modes of accretion are summarized in Table 1, and expanded upon in subsequent sections. One obvious difference between them is in the quality of spectra they produce. Thin disks and radiation tori are primarily thermal emitters, with spectra peaking in the ultraviolet. Surrounded by a corona, either of them seems capable of producing both an ultraviolet thermal component and a power-law continuum, in varying ratios (§III). The decomposition of quasar and Seyfert spectra into these two components by Malkan and Sargent (1982) and Malkan (1983) does not by itself discriminate between the two models, although the details of the decomposition (when they can be agreed upon) may. Specifically, thin disks are broadband emitters, with a gently sloping spectrum built up from emission at a range of temperatures. The integrated spectrum of a radiation torus cannot be predicted with such theoretical certainty, but Blandford (1984a) has suggested that radiation tori may have star-like photospheres, with spectra resembling single temperature blackbodies (§IV). Malkan (1983) has fitted his data for six luminous quasars to both broadband and blackbody spectra, and prefers the broadband model because of the flatness in the thermal component just shortward of the Balmer continuum. Narayan, however, has re-plotted some of Malkan's published data in terms of νF_ν vs ν (see Blandford 1984b), revealing a well-defined hump that looks very much like single-temperature blackbody at 27,500 K. Both results are sensitive to the assumed spectrum of the nonthermal contin-uum, and other observational uncertainties, but it is curious that all of the Malkan's quasars can be fitted by single-temperature blackbodies in the range 25,000–30,000 K. In trying to interpret this, one should bear in mind that the observed spectrum may have been substantially modified by reprocessing or by conversion of kinetic or magnetic energy to radiation at some distance from the black hole (e.g., in a jet; see Shields and Ferland, this volume). Polarization may be a further discriminant between radiation tori and thin disks: we expect disks to exhibit a higher degree of po-larization (at least a few percent due to scattering) than nearly spherical tori, a feature which is not seen in quasars (Angel and Stockman 1980) and may or may not be present in Type I Seyferts (Antonucci 1983).

A second difference between the modes of accretion is in the radiative efficiency of the flow. For example, the weakness of the radiation from the nuclei of many radio galaxies, compared with the inferred kinetic energy fluxes into the jet and lobes, sup-ports the ion torus as the dominant mode of accretion in these objects (Rees *et al.* 1982; §§V,VI).

It would clearly be advantageous if we had some indepen-dent means of determining $\dot{m}$ in a given object. The best quantita-tive diagnostics for quasars and Seyferts are provided by the broad emission lines, which appear to have remarkably similar character-istics (density, ionization parameter, velocity dispersion, covering factor) over a huge range of luminosities. At present, we do not know whether the velocity dispersions σ_{BLR} of the broad emission lines are local Keplerian velocities, or substantially exceed v_{Kep}. However, writing the Keplerian speed in the form

TABLE 1

Modes of Accretion

DETERMINANTS	(Two-Temperature) Ion Torus	Thin Disk	Radiation Torus
Inflow time	$\sim \alpha^{-1} t_{Kep} \propto \alpha^{-1}M$	$\sim \alpha^{-1}(h/R)^{-2} t_{Kep}$	$\sim \alpha^{-1} t_{Kep} \propto \alpha^{-1}M$
Local cooling time	$\propto \frac{1}{\rho} \propto \sim \frac{\alpha M^2}{\dot{M}}$	Short	Short
Radiative transfer time	Short	Short	$\sim \frac{\tau r}{c} \propto \rho r^2 \propto \sim \frac{\alpha M^2}{\dot{M}}$
$\dot{M}$	$< 50\,\alpha^2\,\dot{M}_E$ $\leftarrow$ overlap $\rightarrow$	$< \dot{M}_E$	$> \dot{M}_E$
Radiative efficiency	$0.1(\frac{\dot{M}}{\dot{M}_E})(1 + 3\times10^{-3}\frac{\dot{M}_E}{\dot{M}})(<<1)$	~ 0.1	$\gtrsim (\dot{M}/\dot{M}_E)^{-1}(<<1)$ $[\lesssim (\dot{M}/\dot{M}_E)^{-2/3}$ if radiation released from trapped wind]

RADIATION			
Basic input radiation	Mostly nonthermal (synchrotron and Compton)	Thermal (Comptonized bremsstrahlung)	Thermal (Comptonized bremsstrahlung)
Basic radiation output	IR (self absorbed synchrotron) γ-rays (Comptonized synchrotron and bremsstrahlung)	Opt + UV (soft -X)	UV + X (soft)
Coronae	Basic flow resembles corona	Ion corona (inner radii) Electron corona, wind (outer radii) (X-ray heated wind)	Electron corona, wind
Nonthermal/ thermal ratio	High	Variable $\gtrless 1$ (Nonthermal synchrotron, Compton, SSC in ion corona; Thermal Compton in electron corona)	Variable, $\lesssim 1$
Optional accessories	Funnels, exotic MHD and plasma processes, jets		Funnels, radiation pressure-driven wind, jets

$$v_{Kep}(BLR) \sim 900 \left(\frac{L_E}{L}\right)^{1/2} \left(\frac{L}{10^{46} ergs\ s^{-1}}\right)^{1/4}$$

$$\left(\frac{n}{10^{10}\ cm^{-3}}\right)^{1/4} \Xi^{1/4}\ km\ s^{-1}, \qquad (1)$$

where Ξ is the ionization parameter $\sim$0.1-1 (Krolik, McKee and Tarter 1981) and n is the density of the line-emitting gas, reveals that at least we have a clear choice: If $\sigma_{BLR} \sim v_{Kep}$, then quasars and Seyferts must be substantially sub-Eddington, with $\dot{m} \ll 1$. The appearance of the thermal component in the spectrum then argues for a thin disk/corona model. If on the other hand, it can be shown that the clouds substantially exceed the local escape speed (e.g., they are swept out in a wind or injected by supernova explosions), then L is much closer to L_E and could even exceed L_E by a small factor. The conclusion that $L \sim L_E$ for all quasars and Seyfert I's would have important implications for quasar evolution, since it would rule out downward luminosity evolution in a single source. Perhaps an analysis such as D. Weedman's (this volume), performed on a deeper sample, will be able to rule out the $L \sim L_E$ hypothesis. Alternatively, if quasars are all very sub-Eddington, then there must be some 10^{10} M$_\odot$ black holes lurking in contemporary galaxies; perhaps Space Telescope will tell us where they are or are not. A third possibility is that quasars are radiation tori while Seyfert I's are sub-Eddington; we should then expect to find systematic differences between the spectra and polarization properties of quasars and Seyferts.

At least we do not expect σ_{BLR} to be *smaller* than v_{Kep}; this places a lower limit on $\dot{m}$ in the range $10^{-2} - 10^{-3}$.

III. THIN DISKS AND CORONAE

A thin disk is by definition an efficient radiator (efficiency $\epsilon \equiv L/\dot{M}c^2 \sim 0.1$), hence most of the radiation comes from deep within the potential well of the accreting black hole, at $r \sim 20\ r_g$

(for a Kerr hole with a/M $\ll$ 1). I will concentrate on the quality of the radiation which may be emitted in this region, rather than on the integrated emission of the entire disk or secondary emission resulting from processes at r $\gg$ r_g (e.g., the thermalization of a wind or jet). The radiation energy density above and below the disk is insensitive to the value of the viscosity, and is given approximately by

$$U_{disk} \sim \frac{m_p c^2 \dot{m}}{100 \; \sigma_T \; r_g} \sim 1.5 \times 10^6 \; \frac{\dot{m}}{m_8} \; ergs \; cm^{-3} \qquad (2)$$

where σ_T is the Thomson cross section and I have assumed an efficiency of 0.1. This quantity provides a fiducial value for energy densities in a disk corona, such as the energy density in magnetic fields, relativistic electrons or thermal plasma. A second fiducial value is associated with the mean energy density inside the disk, but this, unfortunately, depends on the still-unknown behavior of the viscous stress.

I will follow the standard practice of using the α-parametrization for the viscosity (Shakura and Sunyaev 1973; Pringle 1981), in which the viscous stress is assumed to be αp where $\alpha \lesssim$ 1 and p is the pressure inside the disk. The radial behavior of this parametrization is not crucial, since I am only considering conditions over a limited range in r. Since electron scattering provides most of the opacity inside the disk, the characteristic internal radiation density if $\tau_{disk} U_{disk}$, where τ_{disk} is the electron scattering optical depth integrated vertically from the central plane of the disk. Characteristic densities and opacities inside the disk depend further on whether the internal energy density is dominated by gas pressure or radiation pressure. If radiation pressure dominates the central pressure, then the half thickness of the disk is h $\sim$ $\dot{m}$ r_g and parameters characterizing the internal disk structure are given by

$$\text{inflow time}: t_{in} \sim \alpha^{-1} \left(\frac{h}{r}\right)^{-2} \frac{r}{v_{Kep}} \sim 0.6 \frac{m_8}{\alpha \dot{m}^2} \; yr \qquad (3a)$$

$$\text{electron scattering opacity}: \tau_{disk} \sim \frac{100}{\alpha \dot{m}} \qquad (3b)$$

$$\text{electron density}: n \sim \frac{100}{\alpha \dot{m}^2 \sigma_T r_g} = 10^{13} (\alpha \dot{m}^2 m_8)^{-1} \; cm^{-3}. \qquad (3c)$$

Gas pressure dominates at 20 r_g if the central temperature T_c exceeds $T_g = 1.4 \times 10^9 \; \dot{m}^2$ K, in which case the values of t_{in}, τ_{disk} and n given in equations (3) must be multiplied by $(T/T_g)^{-1}$, $(T/T_g)^{-1}$, $(T/T_g)^{-3/2}$, respectively.

One can determine the quality of the emitted radiation in principle by comparing the various emission and absorption processes. The temperature is determined self-consistently by balancing heating and cooling. In practice, this procedure is complicated by the uncertain role of nonthermal processes. However, by using the fiducial energy densities judiciously, we can suggest plausible scaling laws for these mechanisms.

The dominant radiation mechanisms in a disk consisting primarily of electron-ion plasma are thermal bremsstrahlung and nonthermal synchro-Compton radiation produced by a small population of highly relativistic electrons. Much of the nonthermal radiation may arise in a disk corona which is heated mechanically (Liang and Price 1977). If the disk or corona is heated to temperatures in excess of a few $\times\ 10^9$ K, it is also possible that a substantial quantity of electron-positron pair plasma will be created. The observable consequences of this are being explored by Rees and by Phinney; they will not be discussed further here.

a) Thermal Radiation

Bremsstrahlung is not only able to cool a thin disk, but for $\dot{m}$ or $\alpha \lesssim 0(1)$ the radiation is thermalized with a central temperature

$$T_c \sim \begin{cases} 4.5 \times 10^5 (\alpha m_8)^{-1/4} K & \text{radiation pressure dominated} \\[2em] 2.2 \times 10^6 (\alpha m_8)^{-1/5} \dot{m}^{2/5} K & \text{gas pressure dominated.} \end{cases} \quad (4)$$

Gas pressure dominates in the disk if $\dot{m} \lesssim 0.016 \, (\alpha m_8)^{-1/8}$. Electron scattering opacity exceeds the free-free opacity at all heights above the disk plane, hence the escaping thermal radiation will be diluted blackbody, with a color temperature T_{disk} in the range $T_c > T_{disk} > T_c / \tau_{disk}^{1/4} \sim 1.4 \times 10^5 (\dot{m}/m_8)^{1/4}$ K. Temperatures at the lower end of this range are consistent with the broadband spectral fits to the "UV bump" preferred by Malkan (1983), but they are much higher than the $25{,}000 - 30{,}000$ K indicated by the single-temperature blackbody fits (see §II; Malkan 1983; Malkan and Sargent 1982; Blandford 1984b) unless $\dot{m}/m_8 < 10^{-3}$. In any case, the insensitivity of T_{disk} to $\dot{m}$, m_8 or α makes it very risky to use the observed spectrum to infer anything about disk parameters or the mass of the black hole.

A thermal corona at $T_{cor} \lesssim 10^9$ K may produce a quasi-power-law component of the spectrum by Comptonizing soft radiation from the disk (e.g., Katz 1976; Takahara, Tsuruta and Ichimaru 1981). The resulting spectral index depends sensitively on the "Compton y-parameter" $y = 4kT_{cor}/m_e c^2 \max [\tau, \tau^2]$, which must be $\sim 0(1)$ to form a power law over an appreciable range of frequencies shortward of the injection frequency (UV-X-ray if the injected radiation is the quasi-blackbody disk spectrum). Production of a standardized spectrum would require some kind of sensitive feedback which regulates the optical depth and/or temperature of the corona (e.g. Ionson and Kuperus 1984). For a spectral index s $\equiv -[\text{d log } F_\nu/\text{d log } \nu]$ between 0 and 1, the ratio of Comptonized (power law) to thermal flux from the disk is

$$\frac{F_{comp}}{F_{disk}} \sim min[1, \tau_{cor}]e^{\tau_{cor}} \left(\frac{T_{cor}}{T_{disk}}\right)^{1-s} \tag{5}$$

where τ_{cor} is the electron scattering optical depth of the corona. The catastrophic cooling that the corona must suffer if s < 1 (for y $\gtrsim$ 1) suggests a natural mechanism for producing a standard ν^{-1} power law. If T_{cor} is maintained at $\sim 10^9$ K (e.g., by pair processes), then the value of τ_{cor} required to give y = 1 will hover around unity. The sensitivity of F_{comp}/F_{disk} to both τ_{cor} and s would account for the wide range of "nonthermal to thermal" flux ratios inferred by Malkan and Sargent (1982). Presumably, the heating of the corona is accomplished through shocks or magnetic phenomena in the underlying disk. Progressive quenching of this energy supply at increasing Ṁ would show up observationally as a positive correlation betwen the total luminosity and the ratio of quasi-blackbody to power-law flux. The existence of such a correlation is claimed by Malkan and Sargent (1982).

b) Nonthermal Radiation

It is an observational fact that the energy density residing in ultrarelativistic particles is often competitive with that contained in other reservoirs. This is particularly the case in dilute astrophysical plasmas – the interiors of supernova remnants, extended extragalactic radio sources, the cosmic rays in the interstellar medium – so it should not be surprising if the thermal corona of a quasar or Seyfert accretion disk contained a healthy admixture of relativistic electrons. Indeed, there is no reason why a substantial fraction of the energy density within the disk itself could not reside in relativistic electrons, and we must therefore examine the contributions of such particles to the overall spectrum.

Relativistic particles are generally thought to have non-thermal distribution functions, with energies distributed according to a power law $n(\gamma) \propto \gamma^{-p}$, where γ is the Lorentz factor. A power-law distribution of particles produces a power-law spectrum, with a spectral index $(p-1)/2$, regardless of whether the emission is associated with synchrotron radiation, inverse Compton scattering, or the so-called "synchrotron self-Compton" (SSC) process.

The emissivity of a group of relativistic electrons in a logarithmic bin of Lorentz factors around γ may be written

$$\epsilon(\gamma) \sim \gamma U_{rel}\,(\gamma) U_{inj}\, \frac{c\sigma_T}{m_e c^2} \qquad (6)$$

where $U_{rel}(\gamma) \sim n(\gamma)\, \gamma^2\, m_e c^2$ and U_{inj} is the "injected" energy density. For synchrotron radiation, $U_{inj} = U_{mag} = B^2/8\pi$, while for inverse Compton scattering of the thermal disk spectrum $U_{inj} = U_{disk}$ outside the disk and $\sim \tau U_{disk}$ at optical depth τ inside the disk. First consider nonthermal emission from particles mixed in with a disk corona. As we saw earlier, such a corona is unlikely to be very optically thick in thermal particles, so it is safe to assume that the scattering optical depth in highly relativistic electrons is quite small. We can scale the magnetic field strength in terms of the radiation energy density, $U_{mag} = \eta_{mag} U_{disk}$; η_{mag} may be as large as τ_{disk} if the field is anchored in the disk (larger if the disk is gas pressure-dominated). The ratio of synchrotron to Compton emissivity for a given group of electrons is simply η_{mag}. The field strength is given by

$$B \sim 6 \times 10^3 \left(\frac{\dot{m}\eta_{mag}}{m_8} \right)^{1/2} G \qquad (7)$$

and electrons with Lorentz factors $\sim \gamma$ produce synchrotron radiation at a characteristic frequency

$$\nu(\gamma) \sim 7.4 \; \gamma^2 \left(\frac{\dot{m}\eta_{mag}}{m_8} \right)^{1/2} GHz. \qquad (8)$$

For s $\sim$ 1, the integrated emissivity is given by

$$\epsilon_{synch} \sim \gamma_{min}\eta_{mag} \left(\frac{U_{rel}}{U_{disk}} \right) \frac{U_{disk}^2 c\sigma_T}{m_e c^2} \qquad (9)$$

where γ_{min} is the smallest Lorentz factor that contributes to the power law and U_{rel} is the total energy density in relativistic electrons with $\gamma > \gamma_{min}$.

In practice, γ_{min} will be set by synchrotron self-absorption, which limits the brightness temperature to

$$kT_b \sim \epsilon_{synch} h_{cor} \frac{c^2}{2\nu^2(\gamma)} < \frac{\gamma m_e c^2}{3} \qquad (10)$$

where h_{cor} is the scale height of the corona. Without explicit knowledge of h_{cor}, we can express γ_{min} (and ν_{min}) in terms of the total energy density of synchrotron emission in the corona, $U_{synch} \sim \epsilon_{synch} h_{cor}/c$:

$$\frac{U_{synch}}{U_{disk}} \sim \frac{\nu_{min}^3(\gamma_{min})\gamma_{min} m_e c^2}{c^3 \, U_{disk}}. \qquad (11)$$

Using (7), (8), and (9) and (2) we obtain

$$\nu_{min} \sim 7.8 \times 10^{13} \eta_{mag}^{1/14} \left(\frac{\dot{m}}{m_8} \right)^{5/14} \left(\frac{U_{synch}}{U_{disk}} \right)^{2/7} Hz \qquad (12a)$$

and

$$\frac{U_{synch}}{U_{disk}} = \frac{F_{synch}}{F_{disk}} \sim 2.2 \times 10^5 \; \eta_{mag}^{11/12} \; \dot{m}^{13/12} m_8^{1/12}$$
$$\left(\frac{U_{rel}}{U_{disk}} \right)^{7/6} \left(\frac{h_{cor}}{20 r_g} \right)^{7/6}. \qquad (12b)$$

If the corona is dominated by thermal particles at $T \sim 10^9$ K, the factor $2.2 \times 10^5 \ (h_{cor}/20 \ r_g)^{7/6}$ in equation (12b) can be replaced by 5.6×10^3. Thus a very modest energy density $U_{rel}/U_{disk} \sim 10^{-4} \ \dot{m}^{-1}$ in relativistic electrons is all that is required to produce a synchrotron flux comparable with the thermal disk flux, shortward of infrared wavelengths.*

Now consider inverse Compton scattering of the thermal disk radiation by the same relativistic particles. The emissivity is again given by equation (9), with $\eta_{rad} = 1$, and this time there is no lower limit on γ imposed by self-absorption. For an $s \sim 1$ spectrum the Compton emissivity is essentially η_{mag}^{-1} times the synchrotron emissivity, but $U_{rel}(\gamma)$ must continue to Lorentz factors below γ_{min} to produce photons with energies in the range $kT_{disk} < h\nu < \gamma_{min}^2 \ kT_{disk}$. Photons in this energy range could also be produced by the synchrotron process, if $n(\gamma)$ extends to high enough energies.

The synchrotron self-Compton process, in which the same relativistic electrons produce the synchroton photons and subsequently Comptonize them, will also operate in the corona, and will be particularly important if $U_{synch} > U_{disk}$. The power laws produced by the first-order (synchrotron) and second-order (Compton) processes will be the same, but the two continua will join to form a single power law only if $U_{synch} \sim U_{mag} \ (=\eta_{mag}U_{disk})$. Thus, necessary conditions for the synchrotron self-Compton process to form a single power law from the infrared to X-rays include (1) that $\eta_{mag} > 1$; and (2) that the nonthermal flux at least be comparable with the thermal flux from the underlying disk.

Nonthermal energy production inside the disk is much more complicated than analogous processes in the corona, since

---

* It is well known that observable radio and submillimeter flux cannot come from stationary gas this near the black hole, but rather must come from gas at larger radii or from an ultrarelativistic jet.

photons must run the gamut of free-free absorption and multiple electron scattering before they can escape. We do not expect U_{mag} to exceed the radiation energy density in this region unless the disk is gas pressure-dominated [and some authors – e.g., Coroniti (1981) – have proposed even more stringent limits on U_{mag}], and in any case, most synchrotron-produced photons with $h\nu < kT_{disk}$ will be absorbed. On the other hand, if a thermal photon suffers one relativistic Compton scattering at a modest optical depth τ within the disk, it is unlikely to be absorbed subsequently, since the free-free absorption cross section declines rapidly with frequency $(\propto \nu^{-3})$. The real enemy of a Comptonized photon trying to escape the disk is Compton cooling by the thermal gas, which is effective if

$$\frac{\tau^2 h\nu}{m_e c^2} > 1. \tag{13}$$

If we define a γ-dependent optical depth to Compton scattering

$$\tau(\gamma) \sim \frac{\gamma n_{rel}(\gamma)}{n_{thermal}}\tau \sim \frac{U_{rel}(\gamma)}{U_{thermal}} \frac{kT_{disk}}{\gamma m_e c^2}\tau, \tag{14}$$

and set $h\nu \sim \gamma^2 kT_{disk}$ in equation (13), then we obtain an upper limit on the fraction $f(\gamma)$ of photons which may escape with an energy $\sim \gamma^2 kT_{disk}$:

$$f(\gamma) \lesssim [\tau(\gamma)\tau]_{max} \sim \left(\frac{U_{rel}(\gamma)}{U_{thermal}}\right)\gamma^{-3}. \tag{15}$$

If $\tau(\gamma)\tau < [\tau(\gamma)]_{max}$, then the Comptonized part of the spectrum will be a power law with $s = (p-1)/2$. Where $\tau(\gamma)\tau > [\tau(\gamma)\tau]_{max}$, the Comptonized flux will saturate at

$$F_{Comp}(\gamma) \sim \left(\frac{U_{rel}(\gamma)}{U_{thermal}}\right)\gamma^{-1} F_{disk} \propto \gamma^{1-p} F_{disk}, \tag{16}$$

giving a spectrum with the form

$$F_{Comp,\nu} \propto \nu^{-[(p+1)/2]} \propto \nu^{-(s+1)} \tag{17}$$

where s is the "normal" spectral index (p-1)/2.

IV. RADIATION TORI

The fate of a rotating accretion flow with $\dot{m} \gg 1$ is still hotly debated. Shakura and Sunyaev (1973) conjectured that any influx in excess of $\dot{m} \sim$ a few would be blown away in a radiation pressure driven wind, as the flux of binding energy released by the accreted material exceeded L_E. Meier (1982a,b,c) computed models for the radiative properties of such winds, but did not delve into the details of their creation. An alternative viewpoint was developed by Abramowicz, Paczyński, Wiita and collaborators, who suggested that inflowing gas with arbitrarily large $\dot{m}$ could settle into a quasistationary *radiation torus*.

The qualitative features of radiation tori are sketched in Figure 3. A transition from thin disk to torus occurs where pressure forces become comparable with gravity. Since a radiation pressure dominated thin disk with a fixed $\dot{m}$ has a uniform vertical scale height (§III), the torus must extend at least as far as r ~ $\dot{m}r_g$ (Fig. 3a), but in fact it may extend further (Fig. 3b). It is a small step conceptually to go from Figure 3b to a truly isolated torus, which might form after a black hole tidally disrupts a star or captures a gas cloud with a small but nonnegligible angular momentum (Frank 1979). Pressure forces point outward in the outer parts of a torus, but they must point inward in the innermost region, because the black hole is a perfect drain for bound material with angular momentum smaller than a threshold value. Thus, a torus must contain a pressure maximum (Fig. 3c), where material orbits the hole at the local (relativistic) Keplerian speed. This pressure maximum is usually assumed to lie at a few gravitational radii, but it must lie outside the radius of the marginally stable

orbit $(r_{ms} = 6\,r_g$ for a Schwarzschild black hole), because there are
no pressure forces acting on the gas at the pressure maximum. Inside the pressure maximum, pressure forces augment gravity, and
material may be able to orbit the black hole at radii as small as
the marginally bound orbit $(r_{mb} = 4r_g$ for a Schwarzschild black
hole).

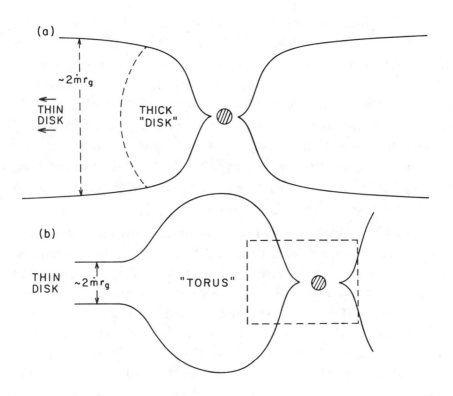

Figure 3 (a) and (b): It is unclear how a radiation "torus" would join
onto an outer, thin accretion disk. Outside the torus, the disk will be supported
by radiation pressure, and have a uniform thickness, $\sim 2\,\dot{m}r_g$. The torus may
begin at a radius comparable to that thickness (a) or at a larger radius (b).
Dashed line in (b) encloses region shown in (c).

(c)

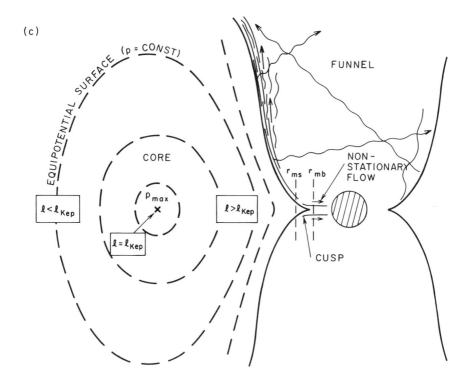

Figure 3c: The inner part ("core") of a stationary torus has a pressure maximum where the specific angular momentum ℓ equals the Keplerian value. Inside this radius, $\ell > \ell_{Kep}$ and inward-directed pressure forces allow material to remain in stable orbits down to a radius which is somewhat smaller than the normal marginally stable orbit (r_{ms}) but larger than the marginally bound orbit (r_{mb}). The cusp is like a Lagrangian point in a mass-transferring binary, and marks the transition from a slow inward drift to nearly radial free fall. The centrifugally dominated funnel is filled with radiation [enhanced by the "reflection effect" (Sikora 1981)] and with material stripped off the funnel walls (Narayan *et al.* 1983), and is a possible site of jet formation. Outside the pressure maximum, the pressure forces point outward and $\ell < \ell_{Kep}$. At large r, the structure of a radiation torus may resemble that of a radiation pressure-supported star.

In practice, a quasistationary torus is expected to have an inner surface with an equatorial cusp (Kozlowski, Jaroszyński and Abramowicz 1978; Abramowicz, Jaroszyński and Sikora 1978; Jaroszyński, Abramowicz and Paczyński 1980) located somewhere between r_{mb} and r_{ms}. The exact location of the cusp r_{cusp} determines (or is determined by) the amount of binding energy that must be radiated away by the torus, ranging from $> 0.057 \dot{M}c^2$ for a cusp at r_{ms} (thin disk limit) to an arbitrarily small fraction of $\dot{M}c^2$ as the cusp near r_{mb} (Paczyński and Wiita 1980). It can be shown that the total luminosity of a radiation torus can exceed the Eddington limit at most by a factor $\sim \ln (h_t/r_{cusp})$, where h_t is the total height of the torus (Abramowicz, Calvani and Nobili 1980); consequently, tori with $\dot{m} \gg 1$ must have cusps lying close to r_{mb}.* The radiative efficiency of a radiation torus is therefore $\sim 10/\dot{m}$ times the logarithmic factor.

What is the quality of the radiation produced by a radiation torus? We can make some crude guesses by thinking of the torus as a toroidal star supported by radiation pressure. Granted, we do not know the run of angular momentum or entropy, but this is partly made up for by the fact that we do not have to worry about the self-gravity of the star. The "core" will be a donut surrounding the pressure maximum, with a total thickness com-

---

* Most of the logarithmic enhancement of L over L_E occurs in the "funnel" which surrounds the rotation axis (Sikora 1981). For a torus with a small binding energy, this funnel may be quite narrow and contain a high radiation flux density, giving rise to the hope that it would engender and collimate a radiation pressure driven jet (Abramowicz and Piran 1980). However, recent investigations (e.g., Sikora and Wilson 1981; Narayan, Nityanda and Wiita 1983) have revealed severe limitations on jet powers, speeds and collimations obtainable in this way. It now appears that more complicated and less well understood processes must be operating if powerful jets do emerge from radiation tori (e.g. Begelman and Rees 1983, 1984).

parable with the radius of the pressure maximum (say, 6 r_g). The condition of hydrostatic equilibrium then implies a relation between the maximum pressure and maximum density, $p_{max} \sim 0.1$ $\rho_{max}c^2$. Figure 4 shows the physical state of the core as a function of ρ_{max} and $M/M_\odot$. In the lower left-hand corner, where the optical depth to electron scattering is <1, the viscous α parameter exceeds one, so radiation tori do not really occur in this region of the parameter plane. Below and to the left of the line labeled "$\tau \sim 10^3$," the radiation field is that of Comptonized bremsstrahlung; only above the line is the opacity great enough to fully thermalize the radiation. In this region, the right-hand ordinate is labeled to show the maximum temperature in the torus. When T_{max} exceeds $\sim 10^8$ (for $10^6 < m < 10^9$), the energy output due to thermonuclear fusion (mainly the CNO cycle) exceeds L_E. Since the efficiency of fusion is nearly 0.01, it is clear that *inefficient* tori cannot exist above this line in the parameter plane. Finally, in the upper right-hand corner of the graph, the mass of the torus becomes comparable with the mass of the black hole, and dynamical instabilities will prevent the establishment of a quasistationary flow.

The dashed lines in Figure 4 are lines of constant photospheric temperature for an isentropic torus. Note that temperatures in the range inferred by Malkan and Sargent (1982) and Malkan (1983) for the "blue bump" require rather high central densities. In fact, for AGN with $L \sim L_E < 10^{46}$ ergs s^{-1}, the central mass must be less than 10^8 $M_\odot$, so we see that these tori fall not too far below the hydrogen-burning limit. Begelman (1984) suggested that the onset of hydrogen burning regulates the central density in radiation tori. If the entropy in the torus is not uniform, it must increase outward (entropy decreasing outward would lead to convection and/or large-scale circulation under most circumstances). The density would then drop off more rapidly than in the isentropic torus, and the photospheric temperature would be *higher* than for an isentropic torus with the same central density.

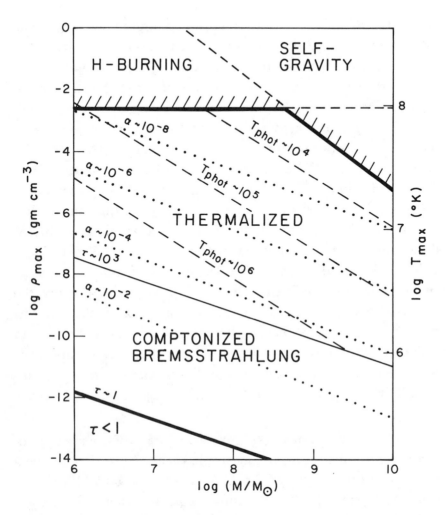

Figure 4: Conditions in the "core" of a radiation torus, in terms of the maximum density (ρ_{max}) and the mass of the black hole. Tori are excluded from the upper region of the parameter plane by the onset of nuclear energy generation at a rate exceeding L_E, and from the upper right-hand corner by the onset of gravitational instabilities. Radiation in the interior of the torus is thermalized when the electron scattering optical depth is $\gtrsim 10^3$, above the solid line marked "$\tau \sim 10^3$." Central core temperatures in the thermalized regime are marked on the right-hand ordinate. Photospheric temperatures for an isentropic envelope are indicated by dashed sloping lines: if the torus is not isentropic (but is convectively stable) then these lines will be shifted upwards. Lines of constant α (consistent with dissipative energy generation at a rate $\sim L_E$) are dotted.

Thus, lack of isentropy exacerbates the difficulty of finding a niche in parameter space that will accommodate Malkan's results, particularly if one adopts the single-temperature blackbody fits (Blandford 1984a).

Now consider radiation tori as accretion flows. As in the thin disk case (§III), we resort to the α-model for the viscous stress, but refrain from applying it anywhere except in the core. The viscous dissipation rate per unit volume equals the viscous stress times the rate of strain, and we expect the total emissivity of the core to be of order L_E, i.e.,

$$10\alpha\rho_{max}c^3\, r_g^2 \sim L_E. \tag{18}$$

Thus, α is uniquely determined by ρ_{max} and m; loci of constant α are plotted as dotted lines in Figure 4. Apparently, a radiation torus capable of producing a "blue-bump" must have an extremely small viscosity, $\alpha \lesssim 10^{-8}$. Such small values of α may seem unpalatable, since turbulent or magnetic viscosities are generally thought to yield $\alpha \gtrsim 10^{-3}$ (e.g. Coroniti 1981; Sakimoto and Coroniti 1981; Lynden-Bell and Pringle 1974). However, they do not seem unreasonably small if an analogy is made with the molecular viscosity in a differentially rotating star, such as the Sun.

Finally, it is worth noting that the relation between α, ρ_{max} and m implies that the inflow speed scales as $\alpha\dot{m}v_{Kep}$. This contrasts with the extrapolation of thin disk theory, according to which $v_{in} \sim \alpha(h/r)^2 v_{Kep} \sim \alpha v_{Kep}$ for a torus with h $\sim$ r. The difference arises from the fact that the inflow speed is proportional to the viscous stress divided by the angular momentum gradient. For a given angular momentum, the *gradient* in the core of a radiation torus must be smaller than that in a thin disk by a factor $\sim \dot{m}^{-1}$. Since only a small amount of angular momentum need be transferred to drive the inflow, a large $\dot{M}$ can be sustained without the dissipation rate exceeding a few times L_E.

Like thin disks, radiation tori probably possess coronae

containing a mixture of thermal and nonthermal particles. The radiative properties of these coronae can be analyzed in much the same way as those which surround thin disks, and the details will not be repeated here.

V. ION TORI

The thin disk flow described in §III can persist to very low values of ṁ. As ṁ decreases, so does the flux of energy that needs to be radiated. As a result, the disk is cooler, (h/r) is smaller, and the density inside the disk remains sufficiently large that bremsstrahlung can continue to cool the disk. However, if a disk with $\dot{m} < 50\,\alpha^2 \min[1,(2000\,r_g/r)^{1/2}]$ is ever heated to its local virial temperature $T_{vir} \sim (GM_p/3kr)$ at r, then the regions inside this radius may never cool back down. In other words, accretion flows with sufficiently low ṁ may have two stable thermal states.

Wherever cooling is ineffective, the disk must swell into a torus supported by gas pressure, with a temperature comparable to the virial temperature of the protons. Inside 2000 r_g, however, this temperature approaches and exceeds the temperature associated with the rest mass energy of the electrons, and a range of very efficient cooling processes (especially relativistic synchrotron emission and relativistic Compton scattering) "turn on." Thus, if the electrons and protons are thermally coupled ($T_e \sim T_p \sim T_{vir}$), the electrons will rapidly drain energy from the protons at $r < 2000\,r_g$ and radiate it away, and the torus will deflate. If, however, the electrons and protons are thermally decoupled ($T_e \ll T_p$) the torus can survive, supported almost entirely by the thermal pressure of the ions. "Two-temperature" bistable disks were first proposed by Shapiro, Lightman and Eardley (1976) to account for the "high" and "low" states of the Galactic X-ray source Cygnus X-1.

Electrons and protons are coupled *at least* by Coulomb collisions, and the minimal condition for thermal coupling is roughly the same as for the failure of bremsstrahlung cooling at

2000 r_g,

$$\dot{m} < 50 \; \alpha^2 \tag{19}$$

(Rees *et al.* 1982). It is not known whether plasma collective effects, perhaps resulting from shear-induced anisotropies, will couple the electrons and protons on a shorter timescale. [To my knowledge, no plasma physicist has yet responded to Sterl Phinney's challenge at the 1981 Varenna Summer School, to come up with an instability that would kill the model (Phinney 1981).]

Structurally, ion tori share many features in common with radiation tori, including a core (surrounding the pressure maximum), a cusp, and (if the binding energy is small) a funnel. Like radiation tori, ion tori are inefficient radiators of the energy released through accretion. If the electron-ion coupling is entirely due to Coulomb collisions, then the radiative inefficiency declines linearly with $\dot{m}$ from 0.1 at $\dot{m} \sim 50 \; \alpha^2$, but levels off when it reaches $\epsilon \sim 3 \times 10^{-4}$ because energy input into the electrons is then dominated by adiabatic heating rather than Coulomb energy transfer. The quality of the radiation emitted by an ion torus is very different from that of a radiation torus or thin disk. The torus will be optically thin to electron scattering, and opaque to incoherent synchrotron or cyclotron emission, in fact, to any photons longward of the far infrared. Relativistic thermal bremsstrahlung may be a source of γ-ray photons, and Compton upscattering of synchrotron and bremsstrahlung photons may produce photons at all wavelengths shortward of the far IR. Much of the Compton power may be contributed by a nonthermal distribution of ultrarelativistic electrons, hence spectral details will depend sensitively on particle acceleration mechanisms. However, it is fair to say that the spectrum of an ion torus will have a nonthermal character.

The important feature of an ion torus, which was stressed by Rees *et al.* (1982), is not the spectral quality *per se*, but the low radiative efficiency. This property makes ion tori prime candidates for powering the jets in powerful radio galaxies, where the radiative output at all accessible frequencies seems puny compared with the inferred kinetic energy fluxes in the jets. In addition to the direct conversion of energy released through accretion into jet energy, perhaps through a hydromagnetic wind (Blandford and Payne 1982; cf. §VI), ion tori (as well as radiation tori and thin disks) can catalyze the extraction of spin energy from the black hole through the Blandford-Znajek effect (1977). Here, organized magnetic fields that pierce the ergosphere of the hole are supported by currents in the disk or torus, and the dragging of inertial frames by the spinning hole causes a Maxwell stress which carries energy (and angular momentum) away from the hole. The disk or torus merely provides inertia to hold the field in place, and in principle no accretion is necessary! In practice, however, it is likely that sufficient field will penetrate the disk or torus that the resulting accretion (due to the transfer of angular momentum to the field lines) will release energy at a rate comparable with the rate of energy extraction from the hole.

VI. "UNIFIED" AGN SCHEMES

If dissipative accretion flows and their characteristic spectra can be classified largely on the basis of one parameter, $\dot{m}$, it is tempting to construct a one-dimensional classification scheme for all forms of AGN, from optically quiet radio galaxies (e.g., M87 or Cygnus A) to the most luminous quasars. Such a scheme (Fig. 5) would associate increasing ratio of nonthermal to thermal emission with decreasing $\dot{m}$. Bright quasars, and possibly some Seyfert I's, might be associated with radiation tori (Fig. 5a). This would imply that the broad-line clouds are moving at speeds in excess of the local Keplerian speed (see §I), a prediction which could be checked, for example, by the detection of radial outflow. (However, disproof of outflow would not disprove the conjecture, since the clouds could be injected with isotropic velocities in local explosions.) I am comfortable with this prediction, but several other features of radiation tori make me uncomfortable:

a)

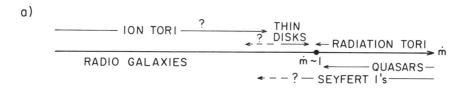

b)

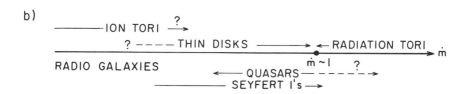

Figure 5: One-dimensional "unified" schemes for quasars, Seyfert 1s and radio galaxies, in terms of $\dot{m}$. In (a), quasars and most Seyfert 1s are assumed to contain radiation tori, which account for their spectral similarities. If this scheme is adopted, broad-line clouds must be in unbound orbits and Seyferts could not have evolved from quasars. Assumed scarcity of thin disks could be accounted for if $\alpha \gtrsim 0.1$, and sources with $\dot{m} < 1$ contained ion tori. In (b), some quasars and most Seyferts are assumed to contain thin disks, which occur over a wider range in $\dot{m}$. Seyferts could have evolved from quasars in this picture, and broad-line clouds may or may not be unbound.

1) The radiative efficiency of a torus with $\dot{m} \gg 1$ is very low ($\sim \dot{m}^{-1}$), exacerbating the already tough problem of finding enough fuel to "feed the monster."

2) The luminosity $\sim L_E$ essentially depends only on the mass of the black hole. If Seyfert I's contain radiation tori, they could not have evolved from more luminous quasars, as Weedman's analysis (this volume) suggests. If one skirts this problem by positing that the Seyferts are thin disks while quasars are radiation tori, then one might expect to find a higher ratio of nonthermal to thermal flux and a higher degree of polarization in Seyferts.

Malkan and Sargent (1982) report such a trend in their thermal vs. nonthermal decomposition; the polarization trend is uncertain because Seyferts are more heavily contaminated by starlight than are quasars (Antonucci 1983). It will be interesting to see whether the thermal components in Seyfert spectra are better characterized as broadband or single temperature blackbodies (provided this issue can be resolved for the quasars).

3) From the discussion of §IV it appears that radiation tori can produce a thermal spectrum with a color temperature in the range required by Malkan and Sargent (1982; Malkan 1983) only if the viscosity is very small. Such small values of α are at odds with the current wisdom on magnetic and turbulent viscosity in disks. More worrisome is the global nonaxisymmetric instability demonstrated recently by Papaloizou and Pringle (1984a,b) for tori with idealized boundary conditions. Several groups are now trying to evaluate the importance of this dynamical instability in more realistic systems. If the instability occurs in all tori, it may place a lower bound on α which would effectively rule out the production of the "blue bump" by a radiation torus.

Because of these reservations (and because radiation tori have not yet lived up to their promise as "jet engines"), I see no compelling reason to prefer them to thin disks plus coronae. One might therefore array the sources as shown in Figure 5b. In this picture, the broad line clouds may or may not move with super-Keplerian velocities. As I argued in §III, it is plausible that thin disks with comparable values of $\dot{m}$ could produce widely differing ratios of nonthermal to thermal flux; the same is probably true of radiation tori. If Seyfert I's evolved from quasars, then they would have systematically smaller values of $\dot{m}$, but it is not clear that this would show up in the spectral data, since the factors governing energy injection into the corona are unknown. One difficulty with the thin disk picture is that it leads one to expect relatively high percentage polarizations $\lesssim 10\%$, whereas most quasars have polarizations $\lesssim 1\%$ (Angel and Stockman 1980). Standard thin disks would also be in trouble if it is confirmed that quasar (and Seyfert I) spectra contain a single-temperature blackbody component at 25,000-30,000 K.

The overlap between Seyferts and quasars in Figure 5 points out the fundamental limitation in this type of diagram: we distinguish different classes of AGN not only by radiative efficiency and spectral qualities, but also by absolute energy output. What we really need is a two-parameter diagram, say, in the $\dot{m}$-M or $\dot{M}$-M plane. Figure 6 is an illustrative example of the latter, with diagonal lines of constant $\dot{m}$ labeled. Seyferts which have evolved from quasars lie to the left of their progenitors, while Seyferts which have never been quasars would tend to lie below and to the left of spectrally similar quasars, along lines of constant $\dot{m}$. Presumably, LINERs are also found at similar values of $\dot{m}$, but at much lower values of M.

Predominantly nonthermal sources, such as radio galaxies and the nucleus of the Milky Way, would contain ion tori and occupy the region with $\dot{m} \ll 1$. Even if most of the energy powering these objects were extracted electromagnetically from a "black-hole flywheel" (Phinney 1983), one would still expect a strong correlation between $\dot{M}$ and the *total* energy output $\dot{E}$, because inflowing material is still needed to "anchor" the magnetic field in the ergosphere of the hole (Rees *et al.* 1982). The most naive scaling arguments suggest that the *total* efficiency $\dot{E}/\dot{M}c^2$ is of order unity. If this is true then the most powerful radio galaxies (e.g., Cygnus A), which appear to spew forth in jet kinetic energy what bright quasars emit in radiation, should lie vertically above these quasars in Figure 6. These radio galaxies would have to contain black holes that are more massive than quasar black holes by a factor $\sim \dot{m}_{quasar}/\dot{m}_{rad.gal.} \gtrsim 10^3$. Even if quasars were tucked up against the Eddington limit, the most powerful radio galaxies would have to have black hole masses in excess of $10^{11} M_\odot$. I find this hard to swallow, and it may be possible to disprove it with existing spectra of the weak emission lines often found in the nuclei of active ellipticals. There are some conjectural ways out of

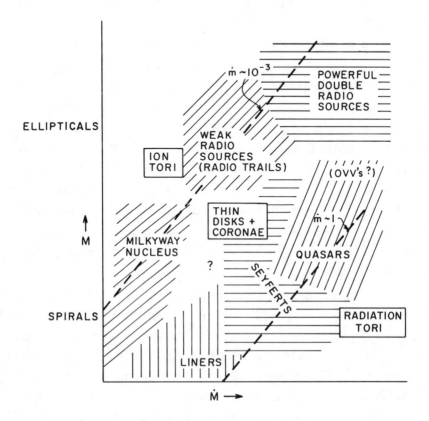

Figure 6: Two-dimensional "unifed" AGN scheme is displayed schematically in the Ṁ-M plane. Possible parameter space for optically active AGN (quasars, Seyferts, LINERs) lies on either side of the diagonal (dashed) line of constant $\dot{m} \sim 1$. Seyferts that evolved from quasars would lie to the left of the quasar region (cf. Fig. 5). Parameter space for predominantly nonthermal sources, including giant elliptical radio galaxies and the nucleus of the Milky Way, straddles the dashed line of constant $\dot{m} \sim 10^{-3}$. Note that powerful double radio sources must have very massive black holes if they are powered by accretion at $\dot{m} \ll 1$. Optically violently variable quasars (OVV's) are shown tentatively at an intermediate point between quasars and radio sources. Ordinate labels indicating galaxy type suggest that correlations between galaxy type and types of activity may result from a correlation of galaxy type with hole mass. See text for a critical discussion of this type of unified scheme.

this conclusion (Rees *et al.* 1982), but their plausibility remains to be seen. Weaker radio galaxies do not present these difficulties, and indeed there is evidence for mass concentrations in excess of 10^9 M$_\odot$ in the nuclei of M87 (Young *et al.* 1978) and NGC 6251 (Young *et al.* 1979).

If we believe that these sources are ion tori, then from the fact that strong radio galaxies are ellipticals while Seyferts and quasars seem to be in spirals, we could draw the conclusion that ellipticals contain more massive central black holes than do spirals, while the supply of accreting matter is comparable or smaller. The former property may be due to the lower specific angular momentum of material in ellipticals, while the latter could be correlated with the apparent lack of cool interstellar gas in ellipticals. The properties may also be correlated with the ability of the galaxy to produce a large-scale collimated jet (Sparke and Shu 1980).

Nevertheless, there remains the unsolved problem of whether ion tori can exist at all (§V). In addition to the fundamental question of ion-electron coupling, there is also the question of why most of the material would go into an ion torus at low $\dot{m}$, when an ordinary thin accretion disk appears to be a viable alternative. This question was addressed by Shapiro, Lightman and Eardley (1976) in their two-temperature disk model for Cygnus X-1. Their motivation for studying an apparently bistable system was the observed switching of Cyg X-1 between "high" and "low" states, and their model assumed that the system was capable of switching spontaneously between the two modes of accretion. But there is no evidence that giant elliptical radio galaxies ever become quasars, and it is virtually certain that Seyferts and radio galaxies are very different beasts.

In view of these uncertainties, it is worth considering the possible existence of "nondissipative" accretion disks. Blandford and Payne (1982) showed that open magnetic field lines piercing a disk could efficiently remove angular momentum and binding energy, transferring it to a hydromagnetic wind. The magnetic field required to drive a mass flux $\dot{M}$ through radius R (actually, the geometric mean of the poloidal and toroidal components, or, equivalently, the square root of the Reynolds stress) scales as

$$B \sim \left(\frac{\dot{M}^{1/2}}{R}\right)\left(\frac{GM}{R}\right)^{1/4} \propto R^{-5/4} \tag{20}$$

and attains a value comparable with that given by equation (7) at $R \sim 20\ r_g$, $B(20\ r_g) \sim 10^4\ (\dot{m}/m_8)^{1/2}$ G.

Fields of this strength, or higher (since the pressure associated with this field is still smaller than the pressure inside the disk) could have been created by shear and reconnection within the disk (e.g., Eardley and Lightman 1975; Coroniti 1981; Pudritz 1981), but it is not clear that these processes would lead to the desired forest of open field lines. However, if the accreted gas starts out with a substantial net magnetic flux, then it might retain this flux all the way into the nucleus. The typical magnetic flux density found in the interstellar medium of the Milky Way would be sufficient to drive a respectable accretion rate. The ratio of dissipative to dissipationless energy loss might be related to the ratio of magnetic flux density to column density in the accreted gas, and differences in the latter ratio could determine whether a given flow produces an extended radio source or a quasar. Admittedly, there is a great deal of doubt about whether the sheared magnetic field could carry away so much angular momentum and energy without producing a comparable amount of dissipative heating within the disk.

To complete a classification scheme for AGN, one would like to insert all of the other beasts in the AGN zoo – Lacertids, Type II Seyferts, etc. – into their $\dot{M}$-M plane niches. I leave this as an exercise to the reader, who may wish to add (or grind) additional axes (e.g., to take account of relativistic beaming effects, etc.) as needed.

VII. AGN DISKS IN THE LARGE

In this review, I have focused on the innermost regions of the central engines in active galactic nuclei, and have tried to show how different "modes" of accretion with angular momentum may account for the diverse manifestations of galactic activity. But disk-like accretion flows, if they occur very close to the black hole, may well extend to radii beyond the 1-1000 a.u. within which the primary radiation is emitted and incipient jets are accelerated. Even where I have compared the radiative properties of disks and tori with the observed properties of quasars and Seyferts, it has been with the caveat that much of the observed radiation shortward of the infrared may be energy that is reprocessed far outside the furnace which supplies it. Few observations of variability constrain the emission at these wavelengths to come directly from a few Schwarzschild radii;[*] radio emission almost certainly comes from larger scales. I do not want to discuss specific means of reprocessing the energy, e.g., through a radiative jet or irradiation of the disk; these possibilities are discussed by Shields and Ferland (this volume). However, the extension of a disk-like accretion flow to large radii has other, largely dynamical consequences, which we must address if we hope to understand how material reaches the vicinity of the black hole.

One byproduct of disk accretion is the angular momentum that is carried outward by viscous stresses. The outer parts of a finite disk will spread indefinitely until this excess angular momentum is removed (Lynden-Bell and Pringle 1974). In bina-

---

[*] Perhaps the the strongest evidence for direct emission from a compact disk would be the detection of short-term *periodic* variability. Several groups have reported tentative detections of $\sim$15-minute periodicity in the Lacertid 0J287 (e.g., Carrasco, Dultzin-Hacyan and Cruz-Gonzalez 1984), which is consistent with $M < 6 \times 10^7 \ M_\odot$. Carrasco *et al.* point out that a mass this low would give $L/L_E \gg 1$ for 0J287, perhaps indicating that beaming is important.

ries undergoing mass transfer, it is believed that the excess angular momentum is transferred to the binary orbit via tidal stresses (e.g., Smak 1976; Paczyński 1977), but such a mechanism is unlikely to operate in an active galactic nucleus. Instead, AGN disks must rely on some other agent to remove the excess angular momentum, such as (1) friction or instabilities at the interface between the disk and a nonrotating hot medium (Gunn 1979); (2) dynamical friction against a nonrotating star cluster (Ostriker 1983); (3) hydromagnetic winds (Blandford and Payne 1982); and (4) Compton-heated winds, which occur when the outer disk is irradiated by X-rays from the nucleus (Begelman, McKee and Shields 1983; Begelman and McKee 1983).

Compton-heated winds may have other dynamical consequences. If the Compton temperature of the incident radiation is 10^8 T_{IC8}K, the wind will be significant at radii exceeding 0.05 m_8/T_{IC8} pc (Shields *et al.* 1985), and there its mass flux may greatly exceed the accretion rate necessary to produce the X-rays in the first place. A sufficiently large mass flux in the wind, compared with the accretion rate, can drive the disk unstable and lead to intermittency in the luminosity (Begelman, McKee and Shields 1983), but a more detailed analysis (Shields *et al.* 1985) indicates that the conditions for this instability are probably not met in AGN. Nevertheless, the large rate of mass loss can exacerbate the already difficult problem of finding a mass supply capable of fuelling the more luminous AGN. One might say that Compton-heated winds decrease the "effective efficiency" of extended accretion disks.

A further complication in the modeling of large-scale accretion disks in AGN is their tendency to become self-gravitating perpendicular to the disk plane, at radii comparable with and exceeding the radius of the broad-line region. Paczyński (1978a,b) exploited this tendency by suggesting that weak turbulence driven by gravitational instabilities could transfer angular momentum within the disk and provide a minimum viscosity. He did not consider the possibility of star formation as result of these instabilities. Sakimoto and Coroniti (1981) and Shore and White (1982) also considered self-gravitating thin disks in AGN. One way to avoid self-gravitation on scales greater than a few parsecs is for the disk to be clumpy, and to be thickened by random motions of the clumps. Perhaps some kind of self-regulation exists in which energy input from recently formed stars keeps the disk thickened and the clumps at marginal gravitational instability [e.g., as suggested by Norman and Silk (1980) for molecular cloud complexes]. One might then bring to bear the theory of the multi-phase interstellar medium on the problem of large-scale disks in AGN.

There need be no intrinsic limitation on the size of an AGN disk, and no reason why the disk could not merge smoothly into the interstellar medium itself, on scales of a kiloparsec or larger. Bailey and Clube (1978) and Bailey (1980) suggested that AGN are fed intermittently, when a large scale "storage disk" becomes self-gravitating and dumps its fuel into the nucleus. Gunn (1979) similarly explored the relationship between an accreted gaseous disk in the host galaxy and activity in the nucleus. Less attention has been paid to the fact that enormous outputs of energy from the nucleus can have a dramatic impact on the host galaxy (Begelman 1985). In particular, the mass loss due to X-ray heating may peak on scales as large as a kiloparsec for luminous quasars inside otherwise "normal" spirals, further lowering the "effective efficiency" of the accretion disk if the fuel for the AGN comes from the interstellar medium. What is more, X-rays from Seyferts and quasars more luminous that $\sim 10^{44}$ ergs s $^{-1}$ may be able to *eliminate* any cool component of the interstellar medium out to several kioparsecs, on a timescale of 10^8 - 10^9 years. The energetics of the ISM on even larger scales could be dominated by X-ray heating, and the multi-phase medium we know in the Milky Way replaced by something more akin to the two-phase structure that is supposed to characterize the broad-line region (e.g., Krolik, McKee, and Tarter 1981).

Placing the above speculations on a firm quantitative footing will require a great deal of work, but at least we know the X-rays are there and we have some idea of how gas behaves when irradiated by them in an interstellar environment. What we may see, when we study the interstellar medium in active galaxies using Space Telescope and other space-based observatories could reflect the integrated history of activity in the nucleus. How long-lasting is the damage done by a luminous quasar or Seyfert in the nucleus of an otherwise normal spiral? Does it disrupt the galactic ecosystem to the extent that metal enrichment is affected? How is the duty cycle of activity affected by the reaction of the ISM to the activity itself? These are certainly among the questions that we must answer if we wish to understand active galaxies. If a large proportion of galaxies are active, as Keel (1983) concludes, and if active galaxies undergo strong luminosity evolution, as Weedman suggests (this volume), then these answers could be central to understanding the evolution of so-called "normal" galaxies as well.

Many of the views discussed above have been incubating during a long-term collaboration with Roger Blandford, Chris McKee, Sterl Phinney, Martin Rees, and Greg Shields. I am grateful to Deborah Dultzin-Hacyan, Martin Gaskell, Matt Malkan, Laura Maraschi, Bohdan Paczyński, and Paul Wiita for their input. Chris McKee and Richard Klein also deserve a large share of credit for Figure 2 and the associated patter. This work was supported in part by the National Science Foundation under Grant AST83-51997, and by a grant from Ball Aerospace Systems Division.

REFERENCES

Abramowicz, M.A., Calvani, M. and Nobili, L. 1980, *Ap. J.*, **242**, 772.

Abramowicz, M.A., Jaroszyński, M., and Sikora, M. 1978, *Astr. Ap.*, **63**, 221.

Abramowicz, M.A., and Piran, T. 1980, *Ap. J. (Letters)*, **241**, L7.

Angel, J.R.P., and Stockman, H.S. 1980, *Ann. Rev. Astr. Ap.*, **18**, 321.

Antonucci, R.R.J. 1983, *Nature*, **303**, 158.

Bailey, M.E. 1980, *M.N.R.A.S.*, **191**, 195.

Bailey, M.E., and Clube, S.V.M. 1978, *Nature*, **275**, 278..

Begelman, M.C. 1984, in Proceedings of IAU Symposium 110, *VLBI and Compact Radio Sources*, eds. R. Fanti, K. Kellermann and G. Setti (Dordrecht, Holland: Reidel), p. 227.

_____. 1985, in preparation.

Begelman, M.C., and McKee, C.F. 1983, *Ap. J*, **271**, 89.

Begelman, M.C., McKee, C.F., and Shields, G.A. 1983, *Ap. J.*, **271**, 70.

Begelman, M.C., and Rees, M.J. 1983, in *Astrophysical Jets,* eds. A. Ferrari and A. G. Pacholczyk (Dordrecht, Holland: Reidel), p. 215.

_____. 1984, *M.N.R.A.S.*, **206**, 209.

Blandford, R.D. 1984a, in *Numerical Astrophysics,* eds J. Centrella, R. Bowers and J. Le Blanc, in press.

_____. 1984b, in *Proceedings of the Manchester Conference on Active Galactive Nuclei*, ed. J. Dyson, in press.

Blandford, R.D., and Payne, D.G. 1982, *M.N.R.A.S.*, **199**, 833.

Blandford, R.D., and Znajek, R. L. 1977, *M.N.R.A.S.*, **179**, 433.

Carrasco, L., Dultzin-Hacyan, D., and Cruz-Gonzalez, I. 1984, preprint.

Coroniti, F.V. 1981, *Ap. J.*, **244**, 587.

Eardley, D.M., and Lightman, A.P. 1975, *Ap. J.*, **200**, 187.

Frank, J. 1979, *M.N.R.A.S.*, **187**, 883.

Gunn, J.E. 1979, in *Active Galactic Nuclei*, eds C. Hazard and S. Mitton (Cambridge Univ. Press), p. 213.

Ionson, J.A., and Kuperus, M. 1984, *Ap. J.*, **284**, 389.

Jaroszyński, M., Abramowicz, M.A., and Paczyński, B. 1980, *Acta. Astr.*, **30**, 1.

Katz, J.I. 1976, *Ap. J.*, **206**, 910.

Keel, W.C. 1983, *Ap. J.*, **269**, 466.

Kozlowski, M., Jarosynński, M., and Abramowicz, M.A. 1978, *Astr. Ap.*, **63**, 209.

Krolik, J.H., McKee, C.F., and Tarter, C.B. 1981, *Ap. J.*, **249**, 422.

Liang, E.T.P., and Price, R.H. 1977, *Ap. J.*, **218**, 247.

Lynden-Bell, D., and Pringle, J.E. 1974, *M.N.R.A.S.*, **168**, 603.

Macdonald, D., and Thorne, K.S. 1982, *M.N.R.A.S.*, **198**, 345.

Malkan, M.A. 1983, *Ap. J.*, **268**, 582.

Malkan, M.A., and Sargent, W.L.W. 1982, *Ap. J.*, **254**, 22.

McCray, R. 1979, in *Active Galactic Nuclei*, eds. C. Hazard and S. Mitton (Cambridge Univ. Press), p. 227.

Meier, D.L. 1982a, *Ap. J.*, **256**, 386.

_____ . 1982b, *Ap. J.*, **256**, 681.

_____ . 1982c, *Ap. J.*, **256**, 693.

Narayan, R., Nityanda, R., and Wiita, P.J. 1983, *M.N.R.A.S.*, **205**, 1103.

Norman, C.A. and Silk, J.I. 1980, *Ap. J.*, **238**, 158.

Ostriker, J.P. 1983, *Ap. J.*, **273**, 99.

Paczyński, B. 1977, *Ap. J.*, **216**, 822.

_____ . 1978a, *Acta Astr.*, **28**, 91.

_____ . 1978b, *Acta Astr.*, **28**, 241.

Paczyński, B. and Wiita, P. 1980, *Astr. Ap.*, **88**, 23.

Papaloizou, J.C.B., and Pringle, J.E. 1984a, *M.N.R.A.S.*, **208**, 721.

_____ . 1984b, preprint.

Phinney, E.S. 1981, in *Plasma Astrophysics*, ed. T. Guyenne, ESA SP-161, p. 337.

_____ . 1983, Ph.D. Thesis, University of Cambridge.

Pringle, J.E. 1981, *Ann. Rev. Astr. Ap.*, **19**, 137.

Pudritz, R.E. 1981, *M.N.R.A.S.*, **195**, 881.

Rees, M.J., Begelman, M.C., Blandford, R.D., and Phinney, E.S. 1982, *Nature*, **295**, 17.

Sakimoto, P.J., and Coroniti, F.V. 1981, *Ap. J.*, **247**, 19.

Shakura, N.I., and Sunyaev, R.A. 1973, *Astr. Ap.,,* **24**, 337.

Shapiro, S.L., Lightman, A.P., and Eardley, D.M. 1976, *Ap. J.*, **204**, 187.

Shields, G.A., McKee, C.F., Lin, D.N.C., and Begelman, M.C. 1985, in preparation.

Shore, S.N., and White, R.L. 1982, *Ap. J.*, **256**, 390.

Sikora, M., and Wilson, D.B. 1981, *M.N.R.A.S.*, **197**, 529.

Smak, J. 1976, *Acta Astr.*, **76**, 277.

Sparke, L.S., and Shu, F.H. 1980, *Ap. J. (Letters)*, **241**, L65.

Takahara, F., Tsuruta, S., and Ichimaru, S. 1981, *Ap. J*, **251**, 26.

Young, P.J., Sargent, W.L.W., Kristian, J., and Westphal, J.A. 1979, *Ap. J.*, **234**, 76.

Young, P.J., Westfell, J. A., Sargent, W.L.W., Kristian, J., Wilson, C.J., and Landauer, F.P. 1978, *Ap. J.*, **221**, 721.

CENTRAL RADIO SOURCES

E. S. PHINNEY

The Institute for Advanced Study
Princeton, NJ

We make to ourselves pictures of facts.

Ludwig Wittgenstein, Tractatus Logico-philosophicus

ABSTRACT

The compact radio sources in the nuclei of most active galaxies lie closer to their centers of activity than any other region accessible to observation, excepting only the broad emission line region. They provide uniquely strong evidence for bulk motion of matter at relativistic velocities, encouraging the belief that the activity originates in a gravitational potential well whose escape velocity is of order the speed of light. We review the observational facts and several theoretical pictures of them. We do not repeat the excellent reviews of the early observations (Kellerman and Pauliny-Toth 1981) or the basic physics of compact radio sources (Begelman, Blandford, and Rees 1984), nor do we show VLBI maps (which the reader may enjoy in the proceedings of IAU Symposium 110, 1984). Instead, we have tried to emphasize those places where systematic observations could help to distinguish the true theoretical picture from the many competing forgeries.

I. INTRODUCTION

Compact radio source; central radio source; flat-spectrum radio source; nuclear radio source. These terms have become practically synonymous as observations have revealed that extragalactic radio sources with a flat spectrum ($S_\nu \propto \nu^{-\alpha}$, $\alpha \lesssim 0.4$ at frequencies 100 MHz$\lesssim \nu \lesssim$ 10 GHz) nearly always have a linear size <1 kpc and coincide in position with the nucleus of an active galaxy. Conversely, sufficiently sensitive observations of an active galaxy discovered by some other technique generally reveal a small flat-spectrum radio source in the nucleus.

The optical continuum luminosity of active galactic nuclei (AGNs) ranges over some seven orders of magnitude. Optical astronomers have subdivided this range into two-order of magnitude pieces named 'Quasar', 'Seyfert', and 'LINER'. By contrast, the single name 'compact radio source' embraces objects differing in radio luminosity by twelve orders of magnitude —from the 10^{34} erg s^{-1} of our Galactic center to the 10^{46} erg s^{-1} of 2134+004. This range of luminosity is even greater than that spanned by the objects we call stars (the luminosity of an O-type supergiant being some 10^{10} times that of a brown dwarf at the edge of the hydrogen-burning main sequence). Unfortunately the additional orders of magnitude have not produced a corresponding increase in the depth of our understanding; it would be charitable to describe the theory of compact radio sources as 'less developed' than the theory of stellar structure.

This underdevelopment is due in large measure to the fact that the objects in question are in neither hydrostatic nor local thermodynamic equilibrium. Non-equilibrium physics is poorly understood; such scratches as have been made on its surface reveal a bewildering richness of phenomena, phenomena which tend to be ill-conditioned, in the sense that infinitesimal changes in the boundary conditions lead to large changes in the results. The perennially unsolved problems in the theory of stellar structure are largely those associated with departures from equilibrium (convection, rotation-induced circulation, coronal heating, stellar winds, non-LTE effects). Yet even to lowest order, compact radio sources are far from equilibrium.

Despite these depressing prospects, one may find some comfort in the fact that the most interesting phenomena in another famous non-equilibrium system—the earth's atmosphere—can be understood on the basis of dimensional analysis alone. So, while awaiting the coming of self-contained and predictive theories of magnetohydrodynamic turbulence, non-linear saturation of plasma instabilities, and relativistic particle acceleration, it seems worthwhile to examine the phenomenology and the energetics, and try what we can learn from simple physics and dimensional analysis.

II. INTENSITIES AND SPECTRA

a) Emission Mechanisms

The most striking feature of the radio sources in the inner tens of parsecs of active galactic nuclei is the flatness of their spectra ($S_\nu \sim \nu^\alpha$, $-0.3 \lesssim \alpha \lesssim 0.3$) and their variability on timescales t_{var} ranging from months to tens of years. Estimates of the angular size of the emitting region as $\theta \lesssim ct_{var}/D$ (where D is the angular-diameter distance to the source) first showed that the brightness temperature of these compact sources generally lay in the range 10^{10} K $\lesssim T_b \lesssim 10^{14}$ K, clearly demonstrating that the radiation was nonthermal. Two possibilities suggested themselves for the radiation mechanism: coherent processes (due to stimulated emission, as in masers, or due to particle bunching, as in pulsars) and incoherent sychrotron radiation. There is no natural reason why coherent processes should lead to brightness temperatures near 10^{12} K (though with some ingenuity, a saturation mechanism could probably be concocted for contrived models). There *is*, however, an obvious reason why incoherent synchrotron radiation should limit itself to brightness temperatures near 10^{12} K, and it is for this reason that it is now generally believed to be the relevant radiation mechanism. Relativistic electrons of Lorentz factor γ in a magnetic field of B Gauss self-absorb their own radiation of characteristic frequency

$$\nu \simeq 0.3\gamma^2 \left(\frac{eB}{2\pi m_e c} \right) \simeq \gamma^2 B \text{ MHz} \tag{1}$$

when the brightness temperature reaches

$$T_{sa} \simeq \gamma m_e c^2 / k \simeq 6 \times 10^9 \gamma \, \text{K}. \qquad (2)$$

Synchrotron radiation may be thought of as inverse-Compton scattering of the virtual photons of a magnetic field. Hence the average rate of energy loss per particle by an isotropic distribution of particles with velocity βc is $\dot{E} = -(4/3)\sigma_T c \gamma^2 \beta^2 U_{TOT}$, where $U_{TOT} = U_{mag} + U_{phot}$. Here $U_{mag} = B^2/8\pi$, which contributes to synchrotron radiation, and $U_{phot} = 4\pi J/c$ is the total energy density in radiation, which contributes to inverse Compton scattering. When the energy density in the synchrotron spectrum radiated by the particles exceeds the magnetic energy density, the particlez0cegin to inverse Compton scatter their own radiation (the so-called synchrotron self-Compton, or SSC process), leading to a rate of energy loss $\propto \gamma^4 U_{mag}$. A slight further increase in the brightness temperature will cause the energy density in this scattered radiation to exceed that in synchrotron radiation, leading to energy loss $\propto \gamma^6 U_{mag}$, and the process quickly runs away — until the last-scattered photons have energies $> \gamma^{-1} m_e c^2$, at which point energy conservation and the Klein-Nishina cross-section prohibit further up-scattering. Since the hard gamma-ray background flux does not allow the gamma-ray luminosity of each compact radio source to be much greater than its radio luminosity, it is clear that this runaway has not occurred. Thus we deduce that if the radiation from compact radio sources is incoherent synchrotron radiation, the brightness temperature (measured in a Lorentz frame in which the radiation electrons have an isotropic distribution — i.e. in their fluid rest-frame) cannot much exceed the one which causes the runaway to begin: $kT_b \nu_s^3/c^3 < B^2/8\pi$. Relating γ and T_b by equation (2), and using the expression equation (1) for ν_s, one finds that for a self-absorbed source, $\gamma < 400 \, B^{-1/7}$, corresponding to $T_b < 2 \times 10^{12} B^{-1/7} \text{K}$ (more sophisticated calculations which allow for a distribution of electron energies may be found in Jones, O'Dell, and Stein 1974; the existence of this limit was first pointed out by Hoyle, Burbidge and Sargent in 1966). Some powerful and rapidly variable sources have brightness temperatures exceeding this limit by two or three orders of magnitude. These sources are generally BL Lac objects and optically violently variable quasars, but at least one powerful broad-emission-line radio galaxy (3C111) exceeds the limit (but by a smaller factor; Hine and Scheuer 1980). The probable reasons for this are discussed below in the subsections on low- and high-frequency variability.

b) Source Structure

The astrophysical signatures of synchrotron radiation are high ($\gtrsim 30\%$) linear polarization and a characteristic $S_\nu \propto \nu^{-0.7}$ spectrum. The first is inherent in the emission mechanism when the magnetic field is anisotropic (but not necessarily *ordered* — Laing 1980); the second signature is probably due to a universal mechanism of accelerating electrons to relativistic energies (by scattering them back and forth in the converging flow maintained by a shock front —*cf.* Bell 1978; for a recent review, see Drury 1983). The radiation from compact radio sources has neither of these characteristic signatures: it has low ($\sim 3\%$) polarization and a flat $S_\nu \propto \nu^{-\alpha}$, $-0.3 \lesssim \alpha \lesssim 0.3$) spectrum. The fact that the brightness temperatures cluster about the Compton limit (§II.*a*) encourages the belief that the emission is nevertheless synchrotron. It therefore behooves us to inquire into the reasons for its disguise.

The synchrotron radiation from a homogeneous box containing magnetic field and relativistic electrons with a suitably truncated powerlaw distribution of Lorentz factors $N(\gamma)d\gamma \propto \gamma^{-p}d\gamma$ (Fermi acceleration in non-relativistic shocks gives $p \gtrsim 2$) has flux density $S_\nu \propto \nu^2\gamma \propto \nu^{5/2}$ [using eq. (1)] for $\nu < \nu_*$, and $S_\nu \propto \nu^{-(p-1)/2}$ for $\nu > \nu_*$, where ν_* is the frequency at which the box becomes optically thick to synchrotron self-absorption. To order of magnitude, ν_* is just the frequency at which S_ν — calculated on the assumption that the source is optically thin— becomes equal to the source function $S_\nu \simeq \gamma m_e c^2(\nu^2/c^2)$ [where γ is to be related to ν by (II.1)].

Since no compact radio source exhibits the characteristic $\nu^{5/2}$ spectrum, the nuclear sources are evidently *not* homogeneous. The characteristic flat spectrum must therefore result from a superposition of many homogeneous boxes whose luminosities and self-absorption frequencies are carefully adjusted so that the sum has a flat spectrum. That this should be universally so seems quite remarkable, and has become known as the "Cosmic conspiracy." Multifrequency VLBI observations strongly suggest that this is nevertheless the correct explanation. They show that the sources are typically resolved into several blobs of emission, all but one of which have at high frequencies the steep spectra characteristic of synchrotron radiation elsewhere in the universe. Summing the spectra from the observed blobs magically reproduces the flat spectrum of the unresolved source (Cotton *et al.* 1980; Wittels *et al.* 1982; Unwin *et al.* 1983; Bartel *et al.* 1984a; see also the cleverly made spectral index maps of a close pair of quasars in Marcaide and Shapiro 1984). This universal conspiracy is a clue to the structure of the source.

Consider a free jet or a spherical wind. In the absence of shear or dynamo action, the magnetic field $B \propto r^{-1}$. At a given frequency, the flux from the source will come mainly from the synchrotron photosphere (radius $r_*(\nu)$) whose source function $S_\nu \propto \gamma \nu^2$. Thus $F_\nu^{TOT} \propto S_\nu(r_*)r_*^2 \propto \gamma^5 B^2(r_*)r_*^2$. In a source with a flat spectrum and $B \propto r^{-1}$, at every frequency the observer is looking at electrons of the same Lorentz factor (a few hundred for typical parameters), and the source size (photospheric radius) $r_* \propto \nu^{-1}$. There is therefore a well-defined *radius–frequency relation.* Flux at higher frequencies comes from deeper in the source.

The simple model considered above predicts that the source size would be proportional to the observing wavelength, and therefore that VLBI observations with a fixed baseline should show the same fractional resolution of the source at all wavelengths. More complicated models (Reynolds and McKee 1980; Marscher 1980; Königl 1981) make different predictions, and may thus be testable. If the magnetic field falls more steeply than r^{-1}, then $r_* \propto \lambda^\beta$, $\beta < 1$, and the source will be more resolved at high frequency. If the jet is collimating rather than conical, $r_* \propto \lambda^\beta$, $\beta > 1$, and the source will be more completely resolved at low frequency than at high.

The spectra of active galactic nuclei invariably steepen above 10^{13} Hz. The radius-frequency mapping tells us that this implies the existence of some characteristic *inner* radius in the source. Scaling from $r_* \sim 10\mathrm{pc}$ at 1 GHz according to the simple $r_* \propto \nu^{-1}$ relation, we infer that the inner edge is at a radius of order $10^{15.5}$cm, which is not inconsistent with the expectations of black hole models.

A 'humped' spectrum (deficient at low frequencies) would, in this simple picture, imply the existence of a characteristic *outer* radius. In fact sources with this type of spectrum are identified with "compact doubles" (Phillips and Mutel 1982; Pearson *et al.* 1984). These appear to be more distant animals of the species whose nearby representatives are classified as stifled jets (van Breugel 1984; van Breugel *et al.* 1984 and references therein; Wilson and Ulvestad 1983 and references therein). Wright (1983) has made the interesting observation that QSR's of very high redshift are much more likely to exhibit this type of spectrum than low redshift QSRs (cf. also Menon 1983). This is consistent with one's natural prejudice that galaxies at high redshifts should have more gas at higher pressure and thus be more apt to stifle their jets. VLBI mapping of high-redshift quasars (combined with long-slit spectroscopy at Space Telescope resolution) has much to teach us about the evolution of the interstellar medium in galaxies.

III. LOW FREQUENCY VARIABLES — A RED HERRING?

The reality of low frequency variability of compact extragalactic radio sources is now well established (cf. papers in Cotton and Spangler 1982). Since for a given flux density S_ν, the brightness temperature T_b inferred for a source variable on timescale

t_{var} varies as $T_b \propto S_\nu \nu^{-2} t_{var}^{-1}$, rapid variability at low frequencies causes the greatest embarassment to the 'Compton limit'. Low frequency variability is seen exclusively in flat-spectrum compact sources, which often (but certainly not always) exhibit high frequency variability as well. It might appear that there was thus a watertight case for an intrinsic origin. Suspicions were, however, aroused by the fact that there was no apparent correlation between source variability at frequencies above 1 GHz and that below 1 GHz (Fanti *et al.* 1982).

Following the elegant demonstration by Sieber (1982) that the timescale for low-frequency variability of *pulsars* was strongly correlated with their dispersion measure, there has been a flurry of theoretical activity examining light propagation through large-scale density fluctuations in the interstellar medium (Rickett, Coles and Bourgois 1984; Coles and Felice 1984; Blandford and Narayan 1985; Goodman and Narayan 1985). As a result, it now seems likely that refractive effects in the interstellar medium of our own galaxy are the cause of most low-frequency variability. The small–amplitude ($\sim$ 2%) flickering on timescales of a week seen at intermediate frequencies (Heeschen 1984) is probably of the same origin.

Seen through an inhomogeneous medium (bad window glass or the local interstellar medium) a point source will appear both blurred and displaced. The blurring is caused by *diffraction* by irregularities with a scale smaller than the Fresnel radius $R_F \simeq \sqrt{\lambda D} = 10^{11.7} \lambda_m^{1/2} D_{kpc}^{1/2}$ cm (λ_m is the wavelength measured in meters; D_{kpc} is the distance D from the observer to the middle of the scattering medium, measured in kpc). The displacement is caused by *refraction* by irregularities with a scale larger than R_F.

It is conventional to assume that the fluctuations of electron density in the interstellar medium have a three-dimensional power spectrum $\Phi(k) \propto k^{-\beta}$, where k is the wave-number of the fluctuation (which here has characteristic scale $a \sim 2\pi/k$). Unconvincing physical arguments and consistency with data on pulsar scintillation suggest that $3 \lesssim \beta \lesssim 5$. If the interstellar medium were homogeneous, unmagnetized, and everywhere sub-sonic, one might expect turbulence with a Kolmogorov spectrum, giving $\beta = 11/3$. For the given scale-free power-spectrum, the electron density fluctuations near wavenumber k have amplitude given by $\langle \delta n_e^2 \rangle \propto k^3 \Phi(k) \propto k^{3-\beta}$. Hence on a scale a, $\delta n_e \propto a^{\frac{\beta-3}{2}}$.

The index of refraction n for an electromagnetic wave of wavelength λ propagating through a sea of free electrons (density n_e) is

$$n = 1 - \frac{n_e r_0 \lambda^2}{2\pi}, \tag{3}$$

where $r_0 = e^2/m_e c^2$ is the classical radius of the electron. Snell's law shows that in passing through a blob of size a whose index of refraction differs from that of the surroundings by an amount δn, a light ray will be deflected by an angle

$$\delta\theta \sim \delta n \sim \delta n_e \frac{r_0 \lambda^2}{2\pi}. \tag{4}$$

In propagating through a distance D, the ray will encounter $\sim D/a$ blobs of size a. Their density fluctuations have random sign and a characteristic magnitude given by the power spectrum. The ray's random walk leads to an rms scattering angle caused by fluctuations of scale a

$$\theta_{rms}(a) \sim \left(\frac{D}{a}\right)^{1/2} \delta\theta \propto a^{\frac{\beta-4}{2}} D^{1/2}\lambda^2. \tag{5}$$

If $\beta < 4$, the smallest scales dominate the scattering; if $\beta > 4$, the largest scales dominate. Observations of pulsars indicate that the integral effect of diffractive scattering by irregularities with scales $a < R_F$ is to smear the image to an angular size

$$\theta_d \sim \lambda_m^2 D_{kpc}^{1/2} \text{mas}. \tag{6}$$

The rays contributing to this image had a maximum separation $\theta_d D \sim 10^{13} \lambda_m^2 D_{kpc}^{3/2}$cm. For $D \sim 1$ kpc and $\lambda > 10$ cm, $\theta_d D$ exceeds R_F, so the scintillation will be strong. The diffraction pattern at the earth has a spatial scale $\sim \lambda/\theta_d$; when observed through a sufficiently narrow bandpass (typically ~ 0.2 MHz for $\lambda \sim 1$ m), the earth's motion relative to the scattering interstellar medium (at velocity $v \sim 100$ km s^{-1}) will cause the flux to vary (scintillate) on a timescale $\sim \lambda/v\theta_d \sim 10^3$s. This scintillation will be observed only if the true angular size of the source is sufficiently small: less than θ_F^2/θ_d, where $\theta_F = R_F/D$.

Refraction of the image by irregularities of scale $\sim \theta D$ will alternately focus and defocus it, causing the *broadband* flux to vary by a fractional amount

$$\frac{\delta I}{I} \sim \frac{\theta_{rms}(a = \theta D)}{\theta} . \tag{7}$$

Here θ is the apparent angular size of the source, which is the larger of its true angular size and the angular size θ_d [cf. eq. (6)] of the blurred spot created by diffractive scattering. As the earth moves through the refraction pattern, the source will vary on a timescale $\sim \theta D/v \sim 10^6 \theta_{mas} D_{kpc}$s. From equations (5) and (7) we see that $\delta I/I \propto \theta^{\frac{\beta-6}{2}}$, so that larger sources will show smaller intensity variations. This plausibly explains the correlation that only flat-spectrum sources exhibit low-frequency variablity: only they are small enough to be significantly focussed by the weak "lenses" in the interstellar medium. The predicted timescales and amplitudes of variation agree with those seen in low frequency variables and Heeschen's (1982) intermediate frequency flickering (Rickett *et al.* 1984). Goodman and Narayan (1985) have explicitly demonstrated that in the strong-scintillation limit the properties of diffractive *scintillation* depend only upon $|\beta - 4|$, but that for $\beta > 4$ a source of angular size $\theta < \theta_d$ will have a fractal structure (rather than the smooth gaussian profile produced if $\beta < 4$) and will vary by $\delta I/I \sim 1$, independent of wavelength. Observations at low frequency of pulsars and compact extragalactic radio sources may tell us more about the structure of turbulence in the local interstellar medium than they tell us about the sources themselves.

IV. MAPPING AND VLBI

By a happy accident, the lifetime of an astronomer, measured in units of the Hubble time, is slightly greater than the reciprocal of the radius of the earth, measured in centimeters. This means that Very Long Baseline Interferometry (VLBI) at centimeter wavelengths* can resolve at cosmic distances objects known to be variable on their light-crossing times. These measurements have confirmed the angular sizes and brightness temperatures deduced from (high-frequency) variability arguments. Most spectacular, however, has been the observation that several of the objects whose brightness temperature exceeds the Compton limit of 10^{12} K exhibit superluminal motion. This confirmed the prediction (Rees 1967) that the high brightness temperature was due to bulk motion of the emitting regions at relativistic velocities. For reviews of the observations, the reader may consult Kellerman and Pauliny-Toth (1981) and the proceedings of IAU Symposium No. 110, *VLBI and Compact Radio Sources*.

The observations there described have taught us that on the 1–100 pc scales probed by VLBI,

- the radio sources are one-sided in their emission (to jet/counterjet brightness ratios exceeding 50 to 1 —cf. D.L. Jones *et al.* 1985).

- the radio emission is asymmetrical in the same sense as the large-scale structure is asymmetrical, in each of a dozen well-studied cases. This strongly suggests that the asymmetry

* Short enough to be unaffected by refraction in the interstellar medium!

is not due to asymmetries in the jets' environment, since the interstellar medium deep in the nucleus of the galaxy would be unlikely to know of or share any asymmetry in the extragalactic medium. Either the jet is truly created one-sided (at least in its emission properties), or the asymmetry is only apparent, an effect of relativistic beaming.

- the jets are knotty and curved, not smooth and straight.

- the flat spectra are the result of adding the fluxes from a compact core with a rising spectrum and an extended 'jet' or 'blob' with a descending spectrum (cf. §II).

- except in isolated unconfirmed cases, superluminal motion is always an expansion, the extended blob moving away from the stationary core (cf. §VIII.c).

- besides the core-dominated flat-spectrum radio sources and the large-scale ($\gtrsim 50$ kpc) steep-spectrum radio sources with weak flat-spectrum cores, there is a large population of steep-spectrum compact sources, most of whose flux comes from a region of complex morphology and a scale of a few kiloparsecs (Peacock and Wall 1982; Simon 1983; Pearson *et al.* 1984). They are very similar to the radio sources seen in nearby Seyferts and interacting gas-rich radio galaxies (van Breugel 1984).

The next three sections discuss fluid phenomena involving relativistic bulk motion. These appear to provide the most promising explanation of the observations.

V. DRY WATER JETS

Due to aberration, time compression and Doppler shifts, emitting regions moving at relativistic velocity in directions close to the line of sight tend to be over-represented in our observations. To illustrate the consequent selection effects we consider in turn:

a) Standard Candles at Random Angles to the Line of Sight

In a steady flow, emitting material moving with velocity $\vec{\beta}c$ at an angle θ to the direction of the line of sight $\vec{n}$ will have an apparent brightness $A(\theta) = (1 - \vec{\beta} \cdot \vec{n})^{-(2+\alpha)}$ times greater than it would if seen face-on ($\theta = \pi/2$). This is strictly valid only if the source is optically thin, with spectral index α, but it is approximately correct for a self-absorbed source in a scale-free atmosphere, provided one uses the *observed* integrated spectral index ($\simeq 0$ for compact radio sources) rather than the spectral index of local emission ($\simeq 0.7$).

On the authority of Ryle and Longair (1967), many authors persist in using an exponent of $(3 + \alpha)$ instead of $(2 + \alpha)$. This is *never* correct in a steady flow (e.g. a smooth jet), which necessarily occupies a well-defined volume in the observer's frame. It is appropriate *only* if all the emission comes from a moving (and hence non-steady) *spherical* blob —as might be the case for a short time after an outburst near the photosphere of an optically thick source. If the emitting blob is non-spherical, different lines of sight will have different (aberrated) path-lengths through the blob and the exponent $(3 + \alpha)$ will no longer be appropriate.* If the blob is very optically thick, the flux depends on the projected surface area. If the non-spherical blob is only marginally optically thick (as seems likely: the knots seen with VLBI become visible as they move out of the optically thick core), the angular dependence of

---

* In fact, if the blob is highly elongated in the direction of its motion, the angle-dependent path-length causes the exponent to become $(2 + \alpha)$ again!

the flux can be very complicated, since some lines of sight will be optically thin, and others optically thick (*cf.* Lind and Blandford 1985).

Consider an ensemble of smooth, bipolar flat-spectrum jets, identical in every way except for the orientation of their axes with respect to the line of sight. The flux $S(\theta)$ from a jet at angle θ is $S(\theta) = S_\perp \frac{1}{2}[(1 - \beta\cos\theta)^{-(2+\alpha)} + (1 + \beta\cos\theta)^{-(2+\alpha)}]$, where $S_\perp = S(\pi/2)$. This being a monotonic function of θ, the fraction of sources $P(> S)$ with flux greater than some value $S(\theta)$ is just the probability that a source's axis lies within θ of the line of sight: $(1 - \cos\theta)$. For $\gamma = (1 - \beta^2)^{-1/2} \gg 1$, one thus finds (Scheuer and Readhead 1979)

$$P \simeq \left(\frac{2S}{S_\perp}\right)^{-1/(2+\alpha)} - \frac{1}{2\gamma^2}, \tag{8}$$

for $S_\perp < S < 0.5(2\gamma^2)^{2+\alpha}S_\perp$. We shall see in § VI that this $S^{-1/2}$ distribution is completely inconsistent with the observations, so that at least one of the following must be false: A) all quasar jets have the same ratio of radio emissivity to optical luminosity, B) all quasar jets have the same velocity, C) all quasar jets are narrow, homogeneous, and all the emitting material in them moves with the same *vector* velocity. We explore the consequences of relaxing each in turn.

b) A Luminosity Distribution of Candles at Random Angle to the Line of Sight

We continue to assume that all the sources are narrow jets with identical velocities, but we now allow the jets to have a *distribution* of luminosities $n_\perp(L)dL$ when viewed from $\theta = \pi/2$. Then the number of sources per unit volume with *apparent* luminosity greater than L_a is

$$N_a(> L_a) = n_\perp (L > L_a) + \int_{L_a/A_{max}}^{L_a} P(A(\theta) > L_a/L) n_\perp (L) d\, L$$

$$(9)$$

$P(A > L_a/L)$ is given by equation (8) with $S/S_\perp$ replaced by L_a/L. Suppose that $n_\perp(L)$ is a broken powerlaw

$$n \perp (L) = f L_*^{r-1} L^{-r}, \quad L < L_* \qquad (10a)$$

$$n \perp (L) = f L_*^{s-1} L^{-s}, \quad L > L_* \qquad (10b)$$

where $f = (1 - r)(s - 1)/(s - r)$ gives unit normalization, and we must have $r < 1$ (to give a finite number of sources) and $s > 2$ (to give a finite total luminosity). Hence

$$N_a(>L_\alpha) \simeq f f_1 \gamma^{(2s-2)(2+\alpha)-2} (L_a/L_*)^{1-s}$$

$$\text{for } L_a > 2^{1+\alpha} \gamma^{2(2+\alpha)} L_*, \qquad (11)$$

where f_1 is a number of order unity. For $L_a > 2^{1+\alpha} \gamma^{2(2+\alpha)} L_*$, the sources are mainly maximally beamed ones (i.e. seen at angles $\theta \lesssim \gamma^{-1}$) and the luminosity function has the same slope as the unbeamed one, but with amplitude increased by the factor $\gamma^{(2s-2)(2+\alpha)-2}$.

For $L_* < L_a < 2^{1+\alpha} \gamma^{2(2+\alpha)} L_*$, the sources are predominantly those with $L \sim L_*$ seen at intermediate angles $\theta \sim (L_*/L_a)^{1/(4+2\alpha)}$, and the integral luminosity function

$$N_a(> L_a) \simeq f f_2 (L_a/L_*)^{-1/(2+\alpha)}$$

$$\text{for } L_* <L_a <2^{1+\alpha} \gamma^{2(2+\alpha)} L_*, \qquad (12)$$

has the same slope that it would if all the sources had $L_\perp = L_*$; f_2 is a number of order unity.

For $L_a < L_*$ the sources are predominantly unbeamed, $L_a \sim L$, seen at angles $\theta \sim \pi/2$. The luminosity function is, up to factors of order unity, the same as equation (10a).

The observed integral source counts of flat-spectrum quasar cores (see § VI) have a slope of 1.5 at the bright end, and ~ 0.2 at the faint end. Interpreted along the above lines, this would require $s \simeq 2.5$, $r \simeq 1.2$ and $\gamma \lesssim 1.5$ [to avoid a significant range of apparent luminosities where the number counts vary as in eq. (12)]. Since the high apparent brightness temperatures and superluminal motions in some compact cores require $\gamma \gtrsim 5$, we deduce that if hypothesis (A) is false, then hypothesis (B) must also be false. Thus we are led to consider

c) Standard Candles with a Distribution of Speeds.

Since there is no reason to suppose that jets with different speeds should have the same emissivities, we suppose that the apparent luminosity at $\theta = \pi/2$ of a jet is some arbitrary function $L_\perp(\gamma)$ of its Lorentz factor, and consider a distribution $N(\gamma)$ of Lorentz factors. In general, one would expect a two-dimensional distribution $N(\gamma, L_\perp)$ with a range of $L_\perp$ at any given γ. We restrict ourselves to the case when the effect of the spread in $L_\perp$ is small compared to that of the spread in γ; the opposite limit was treated in the previous subsection.

To explore the consequences, let us suppose that $L_\perp(\gamma) = L_o\gamma^p$ and that $N(\gamma)d\gamma \propto \gamma^{-q}d\gamma$ for $1 \lesssim \gamma < \gamma_M$. Then defining $L_1 = L_o\gamma_M^p$ and $L_2 = L_o\gamma_M^{p+2(2+\alpha)}$, one finds that if $\sigma \equiv 1 - q + p/(2 + \alpha) > 0$, then

$$N_a(> L_a) \simeq (L_a/L_o)^{-1/(2+\alpha)}\gamma_M^\sigma \qquad L_1 < L_a < L_2 \quad (13a)$$

$$N_a(> L_a) \simeq (L_a/L_o)^{\frac{1-q}{p}} \qquad\qquad L_o < L_a < L_1 \quad (13b)$$

while if $\sigma < 0$, then

$$N_a(> L_a) \simeq (L_a/L_o)^{-\frac{1+q}{p+2(2+\alpha)}} \qquad L_o < L_a < L_2 \qquad (14)$$

For all plausible values of p and q, the luminosity function is flat for high luminosities, in conflict with the observations (see below). Thus we deduce that if hypothesis (B) is false, then hypothesis (A) must be false too.

VI. LIES, DAMN LIES, AND BEAMING STATISTICS

Assume, for the sake of argument, that the optical line emission from quasars is equally detectable from all directions (this assumption is examined more closely below). Then an optically-selected ensemble of quasars will have their putative preferred axes oriented at random on the sky. To be definite, consider quasars with B-magnitude $m_B < 17.0$. The most complete optical surveys (Mitchell *et al.* 1984) find 0.09 such objects per square degree.

All-sky surveys of radio sources with flux at 5 GHz $S_{5000} \gtrsim 1$ Jy (Ulvestad *et al.* 1981; Perley 1982) identify $\sim 2 \times 10^{-3} \deg^{-2}$ or 2% of these quasars with compact, flat-spectrum ($\nu^{-\alpha}$, $\alpha < 0.5$) radio sources. The morphology of these sources is quite different from that of the "classical-double" 3C quasars. The median source in Perley's (1982) list has less than 1% of its flux at 1.4 GHz coming from regions more distant from the core than ~ 1" ($= 15h^{-1}$ kpc for a quasar at $z \sim 1$). Such resolvable structure as there is is usually in the form of asymmetrical blobs or convoluted corkscrews (Browne *et al.* 1982a; Perley it et al. 1982; claims by the first set of authors of diffuse halos with $\sim 10\%$ of the flux are disputed by the second set). The remaining 99% of the flux comes from a compact flat-spectrum core which is typically only slightly resolved (Zensus *et al.* 1984) at 5 GHz with an angular resolution of ~ 1 mas ($\sim 15h^{-1}$ pc for $z \sim 1$).

These morphological characteristics have led several authors (Scheuer and Readhead 1979; Blandford and Königl 1979;

Orr and Browne 1982) to suggest that there is a large population of quasars whose nuclei contain highly relativistic radio-emitting jets, and that the core-dominated flat-spectrum sources are merely those few oriented so that we have a view down the jet.

We have compiled data on the radio properties of quasars with $15.0 < m_B < 17.0$. The sources were the following: $S_{178} > 10$ Jy, Laing, Riley and Longair 1983; $S_{5000} > 1$ Jy, Perley 1982 and Ulvestad *et al.* 1981; $S_{408} > 0.5$ mJy, Condon *et al.* 1981. The integral counts at 5 GHz are presented in Figure 1.

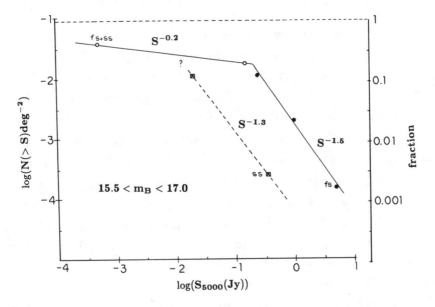

Figure 1. Radio luminosity function at 5 GHz of quasars with $15.5 < m_B < 17.0$. The filled circles are number densities of flat spectrum quasars. The crosses are number densities of steep-spectrum quasars. The open circles are detection fractions at 5 GHz (i.e. both flat spectrum and steep spectrum sources). The detection fractions have been put on a common scale with the number densities, assuming a total quasar number density of 0.09 deg^{-2}. See text for references.

The $N(> S_{5000})$ curve varies as $S_{5000}^{-1.5}$ for $S_{5000} > S_* \simeq$ 0.1 Jy (corresponding to a radio/optical luminosity ratio $(\nu f_\nu)_{5GHz}$∎

$/(\nu f_\nu)_B \simeq 4 \times 10^{-4})$, but flattens to $S_{5000}^{-0.2}$ for $S_{5000} < S_*$. The shape of the radio luminosity function is quite similar to the luminosity function of galaxies. The break in the luminosity function at S_* allows one to cleanly separate quasars into two subspecies: the radio-quiet $(S < S_*)$ and the radio-loud $(S > S_*)$. About 10% of quasars are radio-loud in this sense.

Figure 1 allows us to draw the following conclusions. If (as claimed by Browne *et al.* 1982a) flat-spectrum core-dominated quasars with $S_{5000} > 1$ Jy were surrounded by a diffuse, isotropically emitting halo whose flux at 1400 MHz was 10% that of the core (implying that the halo, with a spectral index ~ 1, would have $S_{5000} \sim 0.03$ Jy and $S_{408} \sim 0.3$ Jy), then the halos would have been detected in the survey by Fanti *et al.* (1975). If the flat-spectrum cores are beamed, then their unbeamed counterparts should have appeared as steep-spectrum quasars. Such objects are only three times more numerous than the flat-spectrum sources with $S_{5000} > 1$ Jy. Thus one must conclude that *either* a)the beaming is *very* broad (into ~ 2 steradian), or b) the optical line emission from quasars is very anisotropic and most of the 'unbeamed' couterparts of the flat-spectrum quasars are not normal quasars but a large population of red quasars (Beichman *et al.* 1981; Bregman *et al.* 1981), dusty radio galaxies, or empty field IRAS sources, or c) the 10% halos do not exist, or are relativistically beamed. If one accepts that the flat-spectrum core-dominated quasars with $C(S \sim S_*)$ are significantly beamed, then one is again forced to conclusion (a) or (b), whether the isotropic halos exist or not. The prescient paper by Strittmatter *et al.* (1980) derived (for fainter prism-selected quasars) a radio luminosity function similar to the one shown in Figure 1, and pointed out that its shape was quite inconsistent with the predictions of simple 'unified scheme' beaming models.

In §V, we showed that the shape was inconsistent even with slightly more complicated models. Thus at least one of the following must be true: 1) unbeamed quasars aren't classified as quasars; 2) there is no 'unified theory' and orientation is not the primary cause of the apparent differences between quasars; or 3) the emitting jet material is not smooth and homogeneous with a top-hat velocity profile. We suspect both 2) and 3), and thus discuss

VII. REALISTIC JETS

a) What Do We See?

We observe only synchrotron radiation. Synchrotron emission requires the presence of both magnetic fields and relativistic particles. Magnetic fields are amplified in shear flow. Shear flow occurs around obstacles, downstream of curved shocks, and near the boundaries of a jet. Relativistic particles are accelerated in shocks, by turbulence, and by diffusive pumping. It is thus to be expected that synchrotron radiation will be a tracer of the most dissipative (complicated and chaotic) regions of a flow.

If the flow is even mildly relativistic, the problem of diagnosing the flow from the observed emission is further complicated, since the motion greatly enhances the brightness of regions moving rapidly at small angles to the line of sight. For example, consider a large volume V_r of fluid at rest. Let it have some emissivity $j_\nu \propto \nu^{-\alpha}$. Suppose that inside this volume of stationary fluid is a small blob (volume V_m) of fluid with identical (rest-frame) emissivity, moving with speed βc at an angle θ to the line of sight to a distant observer. The ratio of the observed flux S_m from the small blob to that from the large volume of fluid at rest is

$$\frac{S_m}{S_r} = \frac{\gamma}{[\gamma(1 - \beta \cos \theta)]^{3+\alpha}} \frac{V_m}{V_r - V_m}. \qquad (15)$$

This simple result has rather stunning consequences: only one part in 10^3 of the fluid volume need move toward the observer with a Lorentz factor $\gamma = 2.8$ for it to dominate the observed flux. Only one part in 10^6 need move toward the observer with a Lorentz factor of 12.6 for it to appear more luminous than the other 99.9999% of the fluid! From the point of view of an observer with a line of sight at right angles to these, of the total flux only 0.008% will come from the blob moving with $\gamma = 2.8$, and only 0.0000002% from the blob with $\gamma = 12.6$.

In a real jet, shocks and instabilities will guarantee that fluid elements in the jet will have a rather wide range of speeds and directions of motion (cf. Norman *et al.* 1983; Blandford 1984; Lind and Blandford 1985). Our simple example illustrates the important point that *different observers will see different parts of a relativistic jet.* Unless the variations in emissivity between different parts of the jet are extremely large, most of the flux received by a given observer will have been emitted by those fluid elements which happen to be moving most rapidly towards him.

b) Bends and Wiggles

The interpretation of observations is further confused by the fact that in a time-dependent flow, streamlines (whose tangents are instantaneous velocity vectors), streaklines (paths of dye injected into moving fluid from fixed points), and particle paths are *not* the same. For example, a high-density (ballistic) jet whose nozzle is precessing or wiggling has *straight* particle paths, but wiggly streaklines. Relativistic jets must probably have densities much lower than ambient, and will therefore not be ballistic. Nevertheless, overly simple models of smooth jet flow in curved channels may make misleading predictions about the brightness variation in curved relativistic jets.

A jet of diameter h which is bent with radius of curvature R must have a proper Mach number

$$\mathcal{M} = \frac{\gamma_j \beta_j c}{u_s} \lesssim \sqrt{\frac{R}{h}} , \qquad (16)$$

where $u_s = c_s / \sqrt{1 - c_s^2/c^2}$ and c_s is the internal sound speed. If the jet has a relativistic speed and a relativistic internal equation of state, then $u_s = c/\sqrt{2}$ and equation (16) becomes $\gamma_j \lesssim \sqrt{R/2h}$. A plane curve with true radius of curvature R_T will have an apparent (projected) radius of curvature $R_a \simeq R_T \sin^2 \theta$ as seen by an observer whose line of sight lies in a plane which contains the tangent to the curve and the normal to the plane of the curve, with which plane the line of sight makes an angle θ (i.e. to an observer looking down the curved jet, except for a misalignment angle θ). The superluminal sources typically have $R_a \sim 4h$, so $\gamma_j \beta_j \lesssim 1.5/\sin\theta$. The statistics require $\theta \gtrsim 10°$; hence $\gamma_j \lesssim 10$. Notice that this is a limit on the Lorentz factor of the moving *fluid*; the apparent superluminal speed is determined by the speed of the emission *pattern* (§VII.c).

The brightness of a relativistic jet which seems to turn a sharp corner (i.e. bends with $R_a \sim h$) will not change significantly around the bend. In order to make the bend it must have $\gamma_j \lesssim 1/\sin\theta$. Its radiation will thus be beamed into an angle $\gtrsim \theta$. Since the true (deprojected) deflection angle is only $\sim \theta$, the brightness will change only slightly. Jets with gentler bends could show large brightness changes, if their flow were laminar, with a top-hat velocity profile. However, if 1) there are strong internal shocks (such as appear in the numerical simulations by Norman *et al.* 1983), or 2) the jet has a smooth velocity profile, then the jet will contain fluid elements moving with many different speeds and with velocity vectors covering a cone with opening angle much wider than $1/\bar{\gamma}$ (where $\bar{\gamma}$ is some mean Lorentz factor). In case 1), the jet might appear 'knotty'; in case 2) it would appear slightly edge-brightened.

c) What's Changing? -Superluminal Motion

As was first pointed out by Rees (1967), a source of photons moving with a speed close to the speed of light will, to some observers, appear to be moving across the sky with a speed exceeding the speed of light.

Consider a source of photons which at time $t = 0$ lies at

$x = 0$ and emits photon 1 in the direction of an observer at some very great distance D, at an angle θ to the x-axis. See Figure 2.

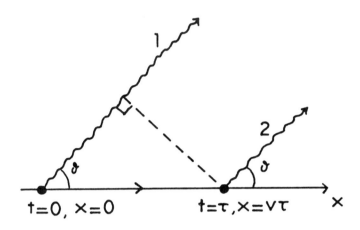

Figure 2. Superluminal motion.

At a later time τ the source is located at $x = v\tau$ and emits photon 2, also in the direction of the distant observer. This observer will receive photon 1 at time $t_1 = D/c$ and photon 2 at time $t_2 = \tau + [D - v\tau \cos \theta]/c = t_1 + \tau(1 - \frac{v}{c} \cos \theta)$. If $v > c$, observers at angles $\theta < \cos^{-1}(c/v)$ will receive photon 2 *before* photon 1. This is how tachyons wreak havoc with causality. There is, however, no objection to non-material sources of photons moving with velocities $v > c$. For example, let the x-axis be surrounded by some material able to scatter light (a white ribbon, or an electron-scattering jet). If a plane-wave pulse with wave-front normal velocity $v_w = c$ moves across this material at an angle α, then the source of scattered photons moves along the x-axis with a velocity $v_w / \cos \alpha > c$. See Figure 3. For α sufficiently close to $90°$, even subluminal $(v_w < c)$ wavefronts —e.g. shock waves— can produce regions of excitation moving with superluminal velocities.

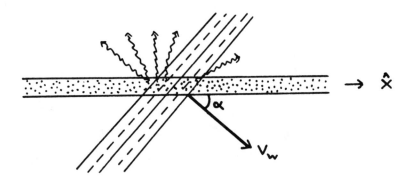

Figure 3. Scattering screen.

Return now to Figure 2. The distant observer will see the source of photons moving across the sky with an apparent velocity $(v\tau \sin\theta)/(t_2 - t_1)$:

$$v_{app} = \frac{v \sin\theta}{\left(1 - \frac{v}{c}\cos\theta\right)} . \tag{17}$$

For $v = c\sqrt{1 - \gamma^{-2}}$, v_{app} is maximized for observers at $\theta = \sin^{-1}(1/\gamma)$, who see $v_{app} = \gamma v$. Notice that the photons which reach these observers must be emitted perpendicular to the x-axis as seen in a frame moving with the source. Hence if the source is a plane sheet with normal along the direction of its motion (e.g. a perpendicular shock front), it will appear *edge-on* to those observers for whom it has the greatest apparent velocity.*

If $v < c$ all observers will agree on the direction of the photon source's motion. But if $v > c$, some observers will see the source moving backwards. For example, in the simple scattering-screen model illustrated in Figure 3 ($v = c/\cos\alpha$) observers at angles $\theta < \alpha$ will see the illuminated spot moving in the $-\hat{x}$ direction. The traditional argument against such screen models

---

* Recall that an object in relativistic motion is *measured* by a lattice of observers to be contracted but unrotated, yet to a single observer *looks* rotated but uncontracted.

has always been that the sources observed with VLBI exhibited only superluminal expansion, never contraction. Recent tentative reports of superluminal contractions in 0711+356 (Readhead *et al.* 1984) and in 4C39.25 (Shaffer 1984) suggest that things may not be quite so simple. It is nevertheless still the case that all of the well-studied sources with convincing evidence for superluminal motion show *only* steep-spectrum blobs moving *away* from the flat-spectrum core (—which in 3C 345 is now known to be at rest on the sky —Bartel *et al.* 1984).

The interpretation of these phenomena is unfortunately complicated by the fact that the observed properties of a source of waves depend not on one, but on several velocities:

- c, the speed of propagation of the observable radiation.

- v_{em}, the physical velocity of the material *em*itting the radiation.

- v_p, the velocity at which the *p*attern of emitting material moves.

- v_s, the velocity of propagation of the *s*ignal which excites the pattern.

These all interact to produce

- v_o, the *o*bserved apparent velocity of some identifiable feature.

The importance of distinguishing these velocities [emphasized by Blandford, McKee and Rees (1977)] is best illustrated by a simple example. Consider a line of taxi cabs of length ℓ waiting at a red light at an intersection. When the light turns green, an exciting signal propagates down the line at velocity $v_s = 186,000$ miles s^{-1}, until it reaches the first taxi driver in a bad mood. After a time τ (the reaction time of a typical taxi driver), he honks his horn. This infuriates the driver in front, who (after a time $\frac{\ell}{c_s} + \tau$) honks his horn, and the process repeats itself. Clearly $v_{em} = 0$. The wave of honks however, propagates up the line of cabs at a velocity $v_p = \left(\frac{1}{c_s} + \frac{\tau}{\ell}\right)^{-1}$, [where c_s is the speed of sound]. As heard by a distant pedestrian at an angle θ to the line of cabs, the honk-front seems to be running forward at a velocity

$$v_o = \frac{c_s \sin \theta}{(1 - \cos \theta) + \frac{c_s \tau}{\ell}}. \qquad (18)$$

If $c_s \tau / \ell < (\sqrt{2} - 1)$ [i.e. if the drivers' reaction time $\tau < 0.007(\ell/20$ ft) s], the honk-front can seem to propagate forward supersonically. Of course, there will be no sonic boom (the "beaming" phenomenon normally associated with supersonic motion), since it is only the wave of fury which is propagating forward, not the individual horns. In this example, as probably in real compact radio sources, all five velocities are physically and numerically distinct. In particular, notice that if there is a coupling between particles capable of emitting, it is very easy to excite a wave of excitation that can propagate at a velocity v_p quite different from v_{em} [this decoupling of v_p and v_{em} also occurs in screen models where the pattern of excitation is determined by an external signal]. Superluminal motion does not imply beaming, nor does beaming necessitate superluminal motion.

We now exhibit two physically reasonable mechanisms whereby a source can exhibit superluminal expansion, yet appear equally bright as seen from a range of angles as wide as a steradian. They make quite different predictions regarding the incidence of superluminal motion.

i) Sonic Booms

Suppose that the fluid in a compact radio source usually moves with nonrelativistic speed. If a "bullet" (which could be an intense stream of fluid) is fired through it with relativistic speed, it will be surrounded by a relativistic bow shock. The structure of such bow shocks is not difficult to determine with similarity techniques.

If the bullet is more-or-less spherical, of radius R and moving with Lorentz factor γ_b, then at a distance z downstream of the bullet the shock is found to have a transverse extent $r \simeq (Rz)^{1/2}$. In the shock-frame the shock-normal component γ_n of the incoming fluid's Lorentz factor (which determines the downstream pressure $p \sim \rho_e c^2 \gamma_n^2$) is $\gamma_n \simeq \gamma_b (R/z)^{1/2}$. The paraboloidal shock is thus relativistic to a distance $\sim \gamma_b^2 R$ downstream, where it has a transverse extent $\sim \gamma_b^2 R$.

If we piously assume that relativistic particles and magnetic fields are always in equipartition, with pressure proportional to the pressure downstream of a shock, then the local synchrotron emissivity $\propto p^{7/4}$. Adding up the Doppler-boosted emission from all the fluid elements downstream of the shock, one finds that the flux S from the bowshock of a spherical bullet varies as $\theta^{-1.5+\alpha}$. The emission is much less beamed than the emission from a spherical plasmoid, $S \propto \theta^{-(6+2\alpha)}$, θ being the angle between the observer's line of sight and the direction of bullet motion. If $\alpha = 0$, the resulting $P(> S) \propto S^{-4/3}$, quite close to the slope observed for radio-loud quasars (Section VI). A naïve unified scheme of such bullets would thus predict $P(> S) \propto S^{-4/3}$ for $S > S_*$, and $v_0/c \simeq (S/S_*)^{2/3}$, where $S_* \simeq 0.3 \mathrm{Jy}$ for quasars of apparent B magnitude ≈ 17 (*cf.* section VI).

Such predictions should not be taken too seriously. Repeating the calculation for the cylindrical bullet, one finds that the emission is now dominated by the nonrelativistic edges of the bow shock, so that S is nearly independent of θ. Achterberg (1984) has given reasons to suppose that a highly relativistic shock may be an inefficient accelerator of ultrarelativistic particles; if this is true, the flux from the bowshock of a spherical bullet could be independent of θ as well. In either case a completely unified scheme would not be possible. The observed superluminal velocity would not be a unique function of flux (which would have to depend on intrinsic parameters), and the fraction of objects of a given flux exhibiting apparent velocities in excess of v_o would be $\sim (c/v_o)$ for the cylindrical bullet, and $\sim (c/v_o)^2$ for the modified spherical bullet.

ii) The End of a Shock Tube

We have seen that flow with curved shocks are both plausible and sufficiently flexible to explain almost any observations of superluminal motion. There exists, however, a second equally plausible class of flow models that Scheuer, in his delightful (1984) review, named 'computer-controlled Christmas-trees with beamed lights.' In these models, emitting fluid elements in an initially plane pulse are made to travel relativistically along diverging trajectories. A distant observer sees a bright spot at the projected position of the elements which are moving directly towards him. As the emitting surface expands and distorts, the spot will move. Superluminal velocities are visible from a very wide range of angles, which mitigates the problem of the excessive deprojected sizes of superluminal sources (Schilizzi and de Bruyn 1983). If a variation in the central engine sends a relativistic shock up a pre-existing pressure-confined jet that becomes free at some radius, then when the shock reaches this point it will rapidly balloon outwards, and a 'computer-controlled Christmas-tree' will have been born.

Given our ignorance of the detailed structure of the flow of plasma in compact radio sources, we can conclude only that curved relativistic shocks are likely to be present, and that they can plausibly explain almost any statistical statement about fluxes and the incidence of superluminal motion. Progress requires better observational diagnostics. One of the best is polarization, especially when coupled with high-resolution mapping.

VIII. POLARIZATION —SYSTEMATIC OR STOCHASTIC?

a) The Facts

The polarization of a source, being a mapping from a line (time) onto a plane [the Stokes' parameters $(Q(t), U(t))$], contains infinitely more information than its intensity, which is merely a mapping from a line (time) onto a line $[I(t)]$. It is an important diagnostic of anisotropy in sources (or components of sources) which we are not yet able to resolve.

The efforts of Rudnick, Jones and collaborators (Rudnick *et al.* 1985) have at last provided, for more than a dozen compact sources, multi-frequency observations of all three Stokes' parameters well-sampled in time. The sources are linearly polarized, with polarizations of a few percent.* In most core-dominated sources the headless polarization vector is the sum of a random component and a steady component. The steady component is usually perpendicular to the source major axis seen on VLBI maps (which axis is only poorly correlated with the source axis on the 10kpc scales resolved by the VLA). The root-mean-square length of the random component of the polarization vector is comparable to the length of the steady component.

Recent advances in observational technology have made it possible to make VLBI maps of polarized as well as total flux. Preliminary results for two objects —3C454.3 (an OVV quasar; Cotton *et al.* 1984) and OJ 287 (a BL Lac object; Roberts *et al.* 1984) indicate that the source is resolved into a low-polarization flat-spectrum core and a more highly polarized steep-spectrum "jet." In the core the polarization **E** vector is parallel to the source major

---

* Sporadic reports of circular polarization at the level of 0.3% have not been universally confirmed. Recent measurements of circular polarization are reported by Komesaroff *et al.* 1984, who also discuss its standard interpretations. A convincing measurement of *large* circular polarization at high frequency would indicate the presence of coherent radiation mechanisms.

axis; in the "jet" it is perpendicular. This is qualitatively what one would expect near the photosphere of a synchrotron source with its magnetic field predominantly along the source axis: the jet is above the photosphere, so the source is optically thin and the radiated **E** vector is perpendicular to **B**; the core below the photosphere is optically thick, so the radiated **E** vector is *parallel* to **B** (since this polarization component has a much longer mean free path to absorption). There are, however, quantitative difficulties with this explanation, so there may be a real difference in the field structure between core and jet. Improved observations will be of great interest.

The results tend to confirm the expectation that most of the polarized flux from flat-spectrum cores comes from that (outer) part of the source which is optically thin at the observing frequency.

The time dependence of the polarization in most sources most of the time seems best described as a random walk in the $Q - U$ plane (Moore *et al.* 1982; Rudnick *et al.* 1985; Jones *et al.* 1985). The picture is confused by a few isolated events (of which the cleanest is still the famous outburst of AO 0235+164 —Ledden and Aller 1978) in which the polarization position angle changes smoothly and monotonically.

b) The Pictures

The aberration of light causes an accelerating fluid element to appear to rotate as seen by a distant observer (Terrell 1959). If the observer's line of sight makes an angle θ with its direction of motion, then for $\gamma < \operatorname{cosec} \theta$ the observer will be looking at the front side of the element; for $\gamma = \operatorname{cosec} \theta$, she will see it as if perpendicular to its direction of motion; for $\gamma > \operatorname{cosec} \theta$ she will see the back side. If the fluid element has a magnetic field which is symmetric (though this may be only in a turbulent way —*cf.* Laing 1980) about some axis which is *not* parallel to the direction of motion, then the rotation in viewing angle due to the acceleration will cause the **E** vector of the polarized radiation to rotate. The total angle of rotation can evidently not exceed π. Blandford and Königl (1979) proposed this phenomenon as an explanation of the smoothest part of the rotation in position angle seen during the outburst of AO 0235+164. The total rotation in this event (as in a few other reported cases: Aller *et al.* 1981) exceeded π, however, so the relevance of the explanation is questionable.

A second physically interesting mechanism can explain rotations in PA exceeding π. A helix is formed by uniform translation of a uniformly rotating vector. A shock propagating down a jet's axis will illuminate successive cross-sections. *If* the largest component of a jet's magnetic field were to be a simple global helical field, and a shock were sent down its axis, then to an observer whose line of sight made an angle $\theta \ll 1/\gamma$ to this axis, the electric vector of synchrotron radiation from particles near the shock would appear to rotate smoothly as the shock propagated down the helical field. A specific example of this idea has been worked through by Königl and Chaudhuri (1985). Notice that an observer will see a rotation only if her (aberrated) line of sight lies inside the cone defined by the pitch angle of the helix.

Such smooth rotations as that in AO 0235+164's outburst seem, however, to be very infrequent, and even in this otherwise well-behaved event the intensity of the polarized flux varied wildly while its position angle changed smoothly. As discussed in the previous subsection, the polarization more commonly performs a seemingly random walk in the $Q - U$ plane. Since a random walk can occasionally and accidentally behave regularly, infrequent regularities in the polarization might be suspect.

The polarization would be expected to make a random walk in the $Q - U$ plane if the observed flux came from several subregions whose relative intensities changed in an uncorrelated way (Moore *et al.* 1982). The intensity changes could be caused either by actual changes in the emissivity of the subregions, or by the beaming of their radiation in different directions as their (relativistic) velocity varied. Accelerating a blob whose magnetic field is neither turbulently nor truly symmetric about a preferred axis causes similar behaviour (Björnsson 1982). The regularities in the otherwise chaotic sea of polarizations are potentially of such great physical importance that it would be comforting to know that they cannot be mere statistical flukes. Jones *et al.* (1985) have made a first attempt at determining the frequency of rotations in random walks. Their work inspired the author to make a slightly more detailed investigation. It is hoped that it will in turn inspire someone with a large body of observational data to determine the statistical significance of 'rotation events.'

c) Drunken Lucidity

The polarization 'vector' is not a vector but an indirection (a headless vector; see Kendall and Young 1984 for the coinage). The essential features of the statistics of indirections were recognized only a few years ago (Kendall and Young 1984; Kendall 1984).

To simplify the topology, we work not with the position angle χ, but with the angle $\theta = 2\chi$ in the $Q-U$ Stokes' parameter plane. A 180° swing in PA thus corresponds to a rotation of 360° about the origin of the $Q-U$ plane. We define a PA swing through an angle χ_{rot} as a rotation event if θ rotates "almost monotonically" through an angle $\Theta_{rot} = 2\chi_{rot}$. "Almost monotonically" means that a temporary change in the direction of swing of the vector should not carry it back by more than some predetermined angle Θ_{al} (which an observer might take to be of order the measurement error or some subjectively allowed 'background jitter'). We say that the swing is 'smooth' if between observations θ does not change in *either* direction by more than Θ_{al}.

Our hypothesis is that the polarization of the source is the sum of some large number N of random vectors whose directions change randomly on a timescale T. The lengths of the vectors are assumed constant, but the results are not significantly different if the lengths are chosen from some distribution with a non-

TABLE 1

Probabilities of Rotation Events

Θ_{rot}	Θ_{al}	P_{sim}	P_{pred}
360°	90°	0.05	0.08
360	60	0.025	0.03
360	45	0.013	0.010
360	30	0.0012	0.0009
720	90	0.002	0.005

zero mean. We ask: after a time t, how many events will have been observed in which the polarization vector rotates smoothly and almost monotonically through an angle Θ_{rot}? To order of magnitude, this is equivalent to asking for the probability that in $n = \Theta_{rot}/\Theta_{al}$ coin tosses we obtain either all heads (clockwise rotation) or all tails (counterclockwise) —namely $2^{-(n-1)}$. The time between coin tosses is of order $\Theta_{al}T$. Hence in time t, we will see about

$$2(t/T)\Theta_{al}^{-1}2^{-(\Theta_{rot}/\Theta_{al})} \tag{19}$$

events. The essential correctness of this result has been verified by Monte-Carlo simulation. Representative results are summarized in Table 1, which gives the probability P_{sim} of a rotation event per unit polarization decorrelation time T. P_{pred} is the probability predicted by the simple argument (VIII.1), which works surprisingly well. Recall that Θ_{rot} and Θ_{al} are *twice* the corresponding PA's.

Ledden and Aller's observations of AO 0235+164 have errors in PA of the order of 15°, so $\Theta_{al} \lesssim 30°$. Such events, if accidental in a random walk, should occupy only 0.12% of the monitoring time. The event lasted about a month. Thus, if subsequent well-sampled monitoring showed that similar events occurred with a frequency much higher than once every 50 years, there would be a convincing case for their physical origin (especially if the rotations always coincided with flux outbursts!). The probability of accidental rotation events becomes exponentially small as Θ_{al} decreases. If the events remained smooth and monotonic with observational precisions of 5° in PA, little doubt could remain.

The data required for such a statistical test may already exist. By way of encouragement, we point out that at the midpoint of the polarization swing during the outburst of AO 0235+164 (Ledden and Aller 1978) the polarized flux suddenly peaked. A pessimist would note that the first (and only examined) of 49 successful simulated swings (in 40,000 correlation times) with $\Theta_{al} < 30°$ shows a very similar feature. An optimist would note that this is what would be expected if the emission came from the bow shock upstream of an obstacle being accelerated by the jet (the turbulent magnetic field having been there compressed into a two-dimensional sheet). As the quality of VLBI polarization maps improves (Cotton *et al.* 1984), they will become a powerful diagnostic of events in compact radio sources. If the optimist is correct, these may have easily legible signatures.

IX. THE FUTURE

Two decades of hard work have taught us painfully little about the physical nature of central radio sources. The phenomenology is now much richer; simple toy models can be ruled out. Yet we remain woefully ignorant of the processes that cause the radio sources to appear as they do. Almost none of the ingredients required for a quantitative model have yet been assembled. Still, even without a detailed understanding of their structure, central radio sources can be used as probes of conditions in the nuclei of galaxies, and as indicators of violent transformations of jets. For this reason, the greatest progress in the next decade will probably be in understanding the physical differences between radio cores. These can be due both to differences in luminosity and velocity between jets, and to differences in the density and distribution of gas in the nuclear regions. Already there are indications that these depend upon galaxy type and upon redshift (§II).

As regards the subject of this review: the actual structure of the central radio sources, the future seems less rosy. There are, however, a number of well-defined observational programs which would help to clarify our murky view:

- Observations of polarization at low frequencies. It is possible (§III) that low frequency variability is due entirely to refractive lensing by irregularities in the local interstellar medium. Such lensing cannot alter the direction of polarization of radiation from a single point source. A simple source should therefore preserve its polarization PA while its intensity varies (Blandford, private communication). Unfortunately we already know (§VIII) that sources are made up of at least two components with orthogonal polarization, only one of which is small enough to be lensed. In this case lensing will cause the angle of total polarization to change. The observational test is thus not entirely clean, but would still be of interest to try.

- VLBI at high resolution and high dynamic range (using QUASAT and the VLBA) will probably reveal source structure as complicated as that seen by the VLA in extended radio sources. Regularities could be diagnostic. If the flux outbursts are caused by obstacles entering the jet, one would expect the new component to have a sharp edge on the side closest to the nucleus (as seen in VLA maps of Cen A on a scale of 700pc —Burns *et al.* 1985). If the outbursts are due to increases in the jet's velocity (i.e. to shock waves propagating down the jet), the new component would have a sharp edge on the side furthest from the nucleus (like the sharp edges on the lobes of extended double radio sources).

- VLBI mapping in polarized flux will identify regions of large shear and help to define streamlines. Large-scale radio sources are static, but central radio sources vary in our life-times. With the aid of this additional dimension, it may be possible to use polarization observations to deduce viewing angles and thus the three-dimensional velocities —something we are still unable to do for extended radio sources! Mapping in polarized light should also clarify

- Swings in polarization angle. One of the few regularities in a sea of chaos, their statistical significance in still unclear. Their reality will be proven if they can be shown to be both smooth and common (§VIII). Their interpretation will depend upon whether they are correlated with flux outbursts, and upon how the percentage polarization varies as its PA swings (models here make quite definite predictions). High resolution mapping, in both polarized and unpolarized flux, would identify the moving parts.

- Multifrequency observations and mapping of a large sample of quasars selected by their optical emission lines (e.g. all those in a given redshift and magnitude range) are necessary to determine to what extent there are physical differences between their radio cores. Correlations between radio, X-ray, and optical line properties are a further (but not unambiguous) indicator.

The structure of central radio sources is probably complicated and rather uninteresting. The sources are of interest not so much *per se* as for what they represent: relativistic motion and the traumatic interaction of a jet with the interstellar medium of a young galaxy.

I am indebted to R.D. Blandford, J.B. Hutchings, D.L. Jones, T.W. Jones, Å Sandqvist, and especially R.W. Porcas for generously providing information in advance of publication. For their hospitality, I thank C.F. McKee and the Berkeley astronomy department, where substantial portions of this review were written. I thank also the Caltech Theoretical Astrophysics group for its patience during the hectic week when the review was completed.

This work was supported in part by NSF grant PHY–84–40263.

APPENDIX
GALACTIC WEATHER FORCASTING

It is often stated —especially in funding requests and observing proposals— that further observations of radio sources or emission lines will reveal the secrets of the "central engines" which power active galaxies. This is no more likely to be true than the statement that further study of the earth's weather will suggest a solution to the solar neutrino problem.

Of course, radio sources and emission lines would not exist without the central engine; neither would the earth have weather without the sun. The things to calculate in cloud and jet models are the velocities and mass fluxes; everyone wishes that meteorological models would predict the wind velocity and the mass flux of condensed water in the neighborhood of their world lines.

Yet in gross average, the latter are easy to compute: a fraction f (of order unity) of the solar flux (~ 2 calories cm^{-2} min^{-1} at earth) is absorbed in the atmosphere, in the topsoil (which heats the air by conduction) and in evaporating water (which releases its heat when it condenses). The power dissipated per unit area by a large turbulent eddy of characteristic wind velocity v_w is $\rho_{air} v_w^3$. This power cascades through smaller and smaller scales until molecular viscosity converts it into heat. The heat is radiated into space by collisionally excited molecular rotation transitions. In steady state the heat lost must balance the power absorbed. Hence $v_w \sim (fF/\rho)^{1/3} \sim 14 f^{1/3}$mph, as observed. Likewise, the latent heat $L = 590$ cal gm^{-1} released by the condensation of evaporated water must in steady state be replaced by the flux of solar energy absorbed by evaporating water $\lesssim (1-a)(.75)(.25)F$, where $a = 0.32$ is the albedo of the earth, 0.75 is the fraction of the surface covered by water, and the factor $0.25 = \frac{\pi r^2}{4\pi r^2}$ accounts for the fact that the sun shines only during daytime, while rain can fall at all hours. Hence the globally averaged rate of precipitation should be $\lesssim 0.125 F/L \simeq 90$ inches yr^{-1}, also in reasonable accord with observation.

These results —charming confirmation that the sun is indeed the central engine driving the earth's weather— are diagnostic of nothing but the solar constant F and the density of the earth's atmosphere —as emission-line clouds are diagnostic of nothing but the ionizing flux and the cloud densities. To learn something else about the sun (or central engine) one must look elsewhere —for example, at the tides (or line profiles). Since the moon's effect on the tides is twice as great as the sun's, yet they have exactly the same angular size, one can immediately deduce that the mean density of the sun is half that of the moon —rather as one might use (with less physical justification) the virial theorem to deduce the mean density interior to a line-emitting region.

It may be instructive and humiliating for those confident that we can understand the two-phase equilibria of line-emitting clouds or the state of the non-thermal gas in radio jets to contemplate the problem of calculating the phase equilibrium of H_2O on a planet with atmospheric pressure 10^6 dyne cm^{-2} illuminated by a body ("sun") with $T_{eff} = 5900°\mathrm{K}$ and angular diameter $1/2°$. If the planet were flat, non-rotating, black, insulating and normal to the "sun," it would have a temperature of 390 K, and the water would all be vapor. If the planet were spherical, black and rapidly rotating, it would have a temperature of 276 K, and the water would be mostly liquid, with some vapor. If the planet were spherical with an albedo of 0.32 and rapidly rotating, it would have a temperature of 250 K and the water would mostly be ice. If this latter planet had an atmosphere of molecules transparent to radiation with a color temperature of 5900 K, but with a Kramers' optical depth ~ 0.5 to radiation with a color temperature of 300 K

($\lambda \sim 10\mu$), it would have a temperature of 300 K, and the water would be liquid. On the other hand, dust grains with radii $\sim 1\mu$ would take a time $\sim (r/1\mu)^{-2}$yr (computed from Stokes' formula for viscous drag on a sphere on density 2 gm cm^{-3}) to settle out of the stratosphere. On a planet with radius 6700 km, only 1.5×10^9 tons ($= 1$ km^3, packed) of such dust would form a screen opaque to $5900°$K radiation, but transparent to $300°$K radiation, thus reducing the temperature of the planet to well below the freezing point of water. To lift the dust would require only $Mgh \sim 150(h/40$ km) Megatons of energy; keeping it continually suspended would require a mere 3×10^{-8} of the solar constant F.

To an observer on a planet orbiting α Centauri, the earth would have a magnitude at 10μ of ~ 23, comparable to that of a faint quasar. He could, from spectroscopy, deduce the pressure and composition of the earth's atmosphere. But would he predict the presence of liquid water (or for that matter, can *we*? Things were different in 1816; they may have been different for the dinosaurs; they may change again in our lifetimes)? And would he understand the strange non-thermal radio-emission; the occasional bursts of γ-rays?

No meteorologist would claim that study of El Niño, clear air turbulence or the growth of snowflakes will teach us anything about the solar interior. Yet the earth's weather is a fascinating subject; laymen love to talk about it, despite the fact that the underlying physics is so difficult and subtle as to have attracted —and stumped— many of the greatest minds in classical physics. We should take the phenomenology of active galaxies in the same spirit.

REFERENCES

Achterberg, A. 1984, preprint.

Aller, H.D., Hodge, P.E. and Aller, M.F. 1981, *Ap. J.*, **248**, L5.

Bartel, N. *et al.* 1984a, *Ap. J.*, **279**, 116.

Bartel, N.H., Ratner, M.I., Shapiro, I.I., Herring, T.A. and Corey, B.E. 1984b in *VLBI and Compact Radio Sources*, IAU Symposium No. 110, R. Fanti, K. Kellerman and G. Setti, eds. (Reidel: Dordrecht), p. 113.

Begelman, M.C., Blandford, R.D. and Rees, M.J. 1984, *Rev. Mod. Phys*, **56**, 255.

Beichman, C.A. *et al*, 1981, *Nature*, **293**, 711.

Bell, A.R. 1978, *M.N.R.A.S.*, **182**, 147.

Björnson, C.-I, 1982, *Ap. J.*, **260**, 855.

Blandford, R.D. 1984, in *VLBI and Compact Radio Sources*, IAU Symposium No. 110, R. Fanti, K. Kellerman and G. Setti, eds. (Reidel:Dordrecht), p. 215.

Blandford, R.D. and Königl, A. 1979, *Ap. J.*, **232**, 34.

Blandford, R.D., McKee, C.F. and Rees, M.J. 1977, *Nature*, **267**, 211.

Blandford, R.D. and Narayan, R. 1985, *M.N.R.A.S.*, in press.

Bregman, J.N. *et al.* 1981, *Nature*, **293**, 714.

Browne, I.W.A. it et al. 1982, *M.N.R.A.S.*, **198**, 673.

_____ . 1982b. *Nature*, **299**, 788.

Burns, J.O., Clarke, D., Feigelson, E.D. and Schreier, E.J. 1985, in *Physics of Energy Transport in Extragalactic Radio Sources*, A.H. Bridle and J.A. Eilek, eds. (NRAO).

Coles, W.A. and Filice, J.P. 1984, *Nature*, **312**, 251.

Condon, J.J., O'Dell, S.L., Puschell, J.J. and Stein, W.A. 1981, *Ap. J.*, **246**, 624.

Cotton, W.D. *et al*, 1980, **238**, L123.

Cotton, W.D., Geldzahler, B.J., Marcaide, J.M., Shapiro, I.I., Sanromá, M. and Ruis, A. 1984, *Ap. J.*, **286**, 503.

Cotton, W.D., and Spangler, S.R., eds. 1982. *Low Frequency Variability of Extragalactic Radio Sources,* (NRAO: Green Bank)

Drury, L. O'C. 1983, *Rep. Prog. Phys.*, **46**, 973.

Fanti, C. *et al.* 1975, *Astron. Ap. Supp.*, **19**, 143.

Fanti, R., Padfrielli, L., and Salvati, M. 1982, in *Extragalactic Radio Sources*, IAU Symnposium No. 97, D.S. Heechen and C.M. Wade, eds. (Reidel:Dordrecht), p. 317.

Goodman, J. and Narayan, R. 1985, preprint.

Heeschen, D.S. 1984, *A. J.*, **89**, 1111.

Hine, R.G. and Scheuer, P.A.G. 1980, *M.N.R.A.S.*, **193**, 285.

Hoyle, F., Burbidge, G.R., and Sargent, W.L.W. 1966, *Nature*, **209**, 751.

Jones, D.L. *et al*, 1985, preprint.

Jones, T.W., O'Dell, S.L. and Stein, W.A. 1974, *Ap. J.*, **192**, 261.

Jones, T.W., Rudnick, L., Aller, H.D., Aller, M.F., Hodge, P.E., Fiedler, R.L. 1985, *Ap. J.*, in press.

Kellerman, K.I. and Pauliny-Toth, I.I.K. 1981, *Ann. Rev. Astron. Ap.*, **19**, 373.

Kendall, D.G. 1984, *Q. Jl. R.A.S.*, **25**, 147.

Kendall, D.G. and Young, G.A. 1984, *M.N.R.A.S.*, **207**, 637.

Koomesaroff, M.M., Roberts, J.A., Milne, D.K., Rayner, P.T. and Cooke, D.J. 1984, *M.N.R.A.S.*, **208**, 409.

Königl, A. 1981, *Ap. J.*, **243**, 700.

Königl, A. and Choudhuri, A. Rai 1985, *Ap. J.*, **289**, 188.

Laing, R.A. 1980, *M.N.R.A.S.*, **193**, 439.

Laing, R.A., Riley, J.M. and Longair, M.S. 1983, *M.N.R.A.S.*, **204**, 151.

Ledden, J.E. and Aller, H.D. 1978, in *Pittsburgh Conference on BL Lac Objects*, A.M. Wolfe, ed. (Univ. of Pittsburgh), p. 60.

Lind, K.R. and Blandford, R.D. 1985, preprint.

Marcaide, J.M. and Shapiro, I.I. 1984, *Ap. J.*, **276**, 56.

Marscher, A.P. 1980, *Ap. J.*, **235**, 386.

Menon, T.K. 1983, *Ap. J.*, **88**, 598.

Mitchell, K.J., Warnock, A. and Usher, P.D. 1984, *Ap. J.*, **287**, L3.

Moore, R.L. *et al.* 1982, *Ap. J.*, **260**, 415.

Norman, M.L., Winkler, K.-H.A., and Smarr, L.L. 1983, in *Astrophysical Jets*, A. Ferrari and A.G. Pacholszyk, eds. (Reidel: Dordrecht), p. 227.

Orr, M.J.L., and Browne, I.W.A. 1982, *M.N.R.A.S.*, **200**, 1067.

Peacock, J.A., and Wall, J.V. 1982, *MD.N.R.A.S.*, **198**, 843.

Pearson, T.J., Perley, R.A. and Readhead, A.C.S. 1984, preprint.

Perley, R.A. 1982, *A. J.*, **87**, 859.

Perley, R.A., Fomalong, E.B. and Johnston, K.J. 1982, *Ap. J.*, **255**, L93.

Phillips, R.B. and Mutel, R. L. 1982, *Astr. Ap.*, **106**, 21.

Readhead, A.C.S., Pearson, T.J. and Unwin, S.C. 1984, in *VLBI and Compact Radio Sources* IAU Symposium No. 110, R. Fanti, K. Kellerman, and G. Setti, eds. (Reidel: Dordrecht), p. 131.

Rees, M.J., *M.N.R.A.S.*, **135**, 345.

Reynolds, S.P. and McKee, C.F. 1980, *Ap. J.*, **239**, 893.

Rickett, B.J., Coles, W.A., and Bourgois, G. 1984, *Astron. Ap.*, **134**, 390.

Roberts, D.H., Potash, R.I., Wardle, J.F.C., Rogers, A.E.E. and Burke, B.F. 1984, in *VLBI and Compact Radio Sources*, IAU Symposium No. 110, R. Fanti, K. Kellerman, and G. Setti, eds. (Reidel: Dordrecht), p. 35.

Rudnick, L. *et al.* 1985, *Ap. J. Supp.*, in press.

Ryle, M. and Longair, M.S. 1967, *M.N.R.A.S.*, **136**, 123.

Scheuer, P.A.G. 1984, in *VLBI and Compact Radio Sources*, IAU Symposium No. 110, R. Fanti, K. Kellerman and G. Setti, eds. (Reidel: Dordrecht), p. 197.

Scheuer, P.A.G. and Readhead, A.C.S. 1979, *Nature*, **277**, 182.

Schilizzi, R.T. and de Bruyn, A.G. 1983, *Nature*, **303**, 26.

Shaffer, D.B. 1984, in *VLBI and Compact Radio Sources*, IAU Symposium No. 110, R. Fanti, KI. Kellerman, and G. Setti, eds. (Reidel: Dordrecht), p. 135.

Sieber, W. 1982, *Astr. Ap.*, **113**, 311.

Simon, R.S. 1983. Ph.D. Thesis, California Institute of Technology.

Strittmatter, P.A., Hill, P., Pauliny-Toth, I.I.K., Steppe, H. and Witzel, A. 1980, *Astr. Ap.*, **88**, L12.

Terrel, J. 1959, *Phys. Rev.*, **116**, 1041.

Ulvestad, J., Johnston, K., Perley, R. and Fomalont, E. 1981, *Ap. J.*, **86**, 1010.

Unwin, S.C. *et al.* 1983, *Ap. J.*, **271**, 536.

Wilson, A.S. and Ulvestad, J.S. 1983, *Ap. J.*, **275**, 8.

van Breugel, W. 1984, in *VLBI and Compacgt Radio Sources*, IAU Symposium No. 110, R. Fanti, K. Kellerman, and G. Setti, eds. (Reidel: Dordrecht), p. 59.

van Breugel, W., Heckman, T., Butcher, H. and Miley, G. 1984, *Ap. J.*, **277**, 82.

Wittels, J.J., Shapiro, I.I. and Cotton, W.D. 1982, *Ap. J.*, **262**, L27.

Wright, A.E. 1983, in *Quasars and Gravitational Lenses*, 24th Liège Astrophysical Colloquium, (Institut d'Astrophysique), p. 53.

Zensus, J.A., Porcas, R.W. and Pauliny-Toth, I.I.K. 1984, *Astr. Ap.*, **133**, 27.

EVOLUTION OF ACTIVE GALACTIC NUCLEI AND QUASARS

Daniel W. Weedman

Department of Astronomy

The Pennsylvania State University

University Park, PA

ABSTRACT

A summary analysis is made of many recent optical surveys for quasars, ranging from studies of low luminosity objects in nearby galactic nuclei to high-luminosity quasars at large redshifts. It is found that all data are consistent with pure luminosity evolution, scaled such that quasars at $z \sim 2.2$ are typically 100 times more luminous than quasars within local galaxies.

I. INTRODUCTION

Quasars change. There are many nearby objects in the local universe that have all the characteristics of quasars seen in the early universe, except that the local objects are less luminous by factors exceeding 100. This observation is the empirical evidence for quasar evolution. For the present, quasars are the only objects in the universe for which it is possible to observe changes in some property as a function of the age of the universe. It is not yet clear whether studying these changes will teach us more about quasars, or about the universe.

While it is reasonably assumed that galaxies have also undergone dramatic evolution, and that evidence of such evolution will someday be clearly observable, that evidence has not been found yet. So it is for now only in quasar astronomy that we have the opportunity to treat our data with the application of evolution parameters. The complexities that result from this were discussed in several presentations at the Workshop, and have been summarized in the recent literature by Marshall *et al.* (1983a), Schmidt and Green (1983), and Maccacaro *et al.* (1984). An unrelated comment of relevance was once made by Mark Twain, in reference to a watch of his that persisted in running either very fast or very slow. "For a watch," remarked Twain, "a correct average is not a particularly commendable virtue." So it now is with quasars. It is well established that these are the most concentrated sources of luminosity in the universe, but utilizing an "average" luminosity in a model is no longer particularly commendable. We know that quasars were once very bright and are now dimmer. No quasar explanation is complete without accounting for this.

Historically, observed data for quasars have been interpreted within two alternative scenarios for the evolution (Schmidt 1972). One is density evolution. This means that all quasars of all luminosities scale up in numbers as we observe to higher redshift. A natural consequence of pure density evolution is that the absolute number of quasars per unit volume at a given luminosity increases with redshift. Not surprisingly, more high luminosity quasars are seen, therefore, at high redshift. The alternative is luminosity evolution. In this alternative, the number of quasars per unit volume does not change, but their luminosity systematically increases with redshift, making more distant examples relatively easier to see. Various parameterizations and combinations of density and luminosity evolution may be applied to quasar samples. The difficulty in choosing the best fit comes because the intrinsically faint quasars at high redshift cannot be seen. Until it is known if the luminous quasars at high redshift are accompanied by fainter quasars in the necessary amount, an unambiguous choice cannot be made between density and luminosity evolution. Yet, a great deal has been learned in the past few years, much of which was reviewed at this Workshop. When preparing the present summary, I found that all of these new data lead to a self-consistent description of quasar evolution, encompassing local galactic nuclei as well as the highest redshift quasars. This synthesis of the recent results is presented below.

II. DENSITY vs. LUMINOSITY EVOLUTION

Many results discussed elsewhere in this volume indirectly lead to a meaningful answer regarding the basic nature of evolution. This answer is that quasar evolution must be primarily luminosity evolution. These results are those which confirm the arguments that quasars are events in the nuclei of galaxies, and which trace these events in nearby galaxies to low luminosity examples. Many recent imaging observations were summarized for us that show galactic envelopes around quasars, or that find quasars within clusters of galaxies. These data have mostly been published by the people who discussed them (Hutchings *et al.* 1984; Gehren *et al.* 1984; Yee and Green 1984; Malkan *et al.* 1984). In several cases, these faint surrounding galaxies have been observed spectroscopically, showing that the "galactic" disks imaged around quasars are indeed just that (Boroson and Oke 1984).

Simultaneously, observations have accumulated that demonstrate over broad spectral regions the similarities between quasars and the nuclei of some local galaxies, particularly the Seyfert 1 galaxies (Kriss and Canizares 1982; Wu *et al.* 1983; Yee 1981; Cruz-Gonzales 1984). Keeping in mind that the original spectroscopic indicator was the presence of broad permitted lines, the observation that many other quasar indicators correlate with the presence of a broad line region makes the observer's life a bit easier. It means that we can consider any nucleus showing even one broad Balmer line to be a low-luminosity quasar. This gives an easy distinction from other active nuclei, such as starburst objects and, perhaps, some Seyfert 2 galaxies. As spectroscopic techniques improved, such low-luminosity quasars have been seen in the centers of many galaxies. At this Workshop in 1978, Tim Heckman introduced the liners, which was the first systematic category of low luminosity active nuclei. Many liners, perhaps even all, can now be considered as mini-Seyferts, because they seem to be photoionized by non-thermal continua and often have weak broad line regions (Filippenko and Sargent 1984).

Systematic results for many examples are summarized in Keel's chapter of this volume. Discussions with Bill Keel and Alex Filippenko led me to believe that 10% to 15% of all spirals have broad line regions detectable to optical spectroscopists. This is only a minimum to the actual number of mini-quasars within nearby galaxies. Many infrared and radio indicators of quasar-like activity are detectable in nuclei showing no obvious optical quasar tracer. We were reminded of this by George Rieke and Jim Condon, who have emphasized all along that lots of exciting things may be occurring that are obscured to optical observations. And so it may be. The IRAS results, as yet undigested in this context, should help decide. It should be recalled, however, that X-ray surveys did not turn up large fractions of quasars of Seyfert 1 galaxies that would not have been detected with conventional optical techniques (Piccinotti *et al.* 1982; Osmer 1982; Stocke *et al.* 1983).

The issue of whether Seyfert 2 galaxies do or do not harbor unseen broad line regions, as implied by Osterbrock's scheme for unifying the Seyfert picture (e.g., Osterbrock 1979, 1984), was extensively discussed but not resolved. Conflicting testimony from X-ray, radio, and optical results was given by Andrew Lawrence (Lawrence and Elvis 1982), Andrew Wilson (Meurs and Wilson 1984), Ross Cohen, and Joe Miller (Miller and Antonucci 1984). I was particularly impressed by Cohen's review of evidence that some Seyfert 2 galaxies have changed to Seyfert 1, and by various observers' reports that NGC 4151 may now be changing to a Seyfert 2.

Fortunately for the topic at issue, classification chauvinism does not have a major impact. The point is simply that we now know that many galaxies, at least 10%, have observable little quasars in them. Maybe a lot more do. Maybe all do. At any rate, not much room is left for density evolution, as long as all quasars have to occur in galaxies. Using the minimum estimate, we could only scale up the number of quasars by a factor of 10 back to the early universe, without running out of galaxies. Adopting density evolution more than this factor would require the existence of galaxies then that are not visible today. This factor of ten is far smaller than what is needed by density evolution models for quasars. Herman Marshall pointed out, for example, that the best fit density evolution to his data could require an evolution factor of $(1+z)^{8.7}$, or a factor of 1.4×10^4 at $z = 2$!

The reasoning presented leads me to dismiss density evolution as a significant part of the quasar evolution description. It gives a justification for proceeding with the discussion only in the context of pure luminosity evolution. Initially, the best we can hope for is a meaningful result describing empirically the form of quasar evolution required to fit all available data. More ambitiously, an astrophysical explanation for that evolution can be sought in context of the physics of quasars, an effort such as that discussed by Vagnetti and published by Cavaliere *et al.* (1984).

III. LOCAL AND HIGH REDSHIFT LUMINOSITY FUNCTIONS

If we wish a scheme unifying all objects from the faintest local nuclei with broad line regions to the most luminous, highest redshift quasars, a lot of data must be considered. I am going to proceed by incorporating primarily those data which were discussed at this Workshop, although that includes most recent results relevant to the problem. There are three essentially independent categories of results from optical surveys alone: a) the luminosity function for local galactic nuclei that have broad line regions, including Seyfert 1 and the lower luminosity analogues; b) surveys for quasars that encompass all redshifts, primarily the Palomar Bright Quasar Survey and the Braccesi quasars; c) luminosity function for high redshift quasars determined from surveys sensitive primarily to quasars showing Ly α emission. Other samples are provided from surveys that use the X-ray properties to define detection criteria. I will proceed by discussing the results from the optical samples, and subsequently explain how the X-ray samples fit within the interpretations deduced.

Selection effects abound. We should not be ashamed of them. After all, the ability to understand selection effects is the distinction of the astronomer. Understanding them is not difficult, actually, but explaining them is. The uncertainties imposed by selection effects will dominate the uncertainty in the nature of quasar evolution. By emphasizing this, I hope to demonstrate that it is meaningless to overinterpret the results, to the extent of sophisticated tuning of the evolution parameterization. At present, simple forms of evolution can fit the data within the uncertainties of the selection effects, so simple forms will be used.

The first task is to determine a local luminosity function for quasars, which I equate to such a function for the nuclei that have broad line regions. Even after neglecting those that are not seen simply because of obscuration, other obfuscations remain. Measured magnitudes for Seyfert 1 galaxies, for example, usually are known only for all or large parts of the galaxy. This is not a problem for very bright nuclei, which contribute most of the total galaxian luminosity seen. For fainter nuclei, however, simply defining their magnitude or continuum flux, free from contamination by the surrounding galaxy, is troublesome. Yet, we must restrict the luminosity function to the nuclei alone if it is really the quasar component under analysis. Evert Meurs mentioned efforts he has underway to do this by using small aperture photometry synthesized from CCD images. This will be progress, although some contamination by the galaxy remains unavoidable. The only sure way to measure the pure quasar would be to use as a luminosity indicator the broad Balmer lines, preferably Hα. Such fluxes are not available for the majority of nuclei, however. For now, we are almost forced to deal with continuum magnitudes anyway to compare with the higher redshift quasar samples, for which there are virtually no line flux measures.

The largest single sample of Seyfert 1 galaxies remains that derived from Markarian galaxies. The entire Markarian survey, including 1500 galaxies, is now complete. A summary of available data on these is given by Balzano and Mazzarella (1984). Most of the Seyfert classifications arose from work by Osterbrock and collaborators, and I summarize in Table 1 all Markarian-Seyfert 1 galaxies now known brighter than magnitude 15.5 (Zwicky magnitudes). For this purpose, any Seyfert with a broad line region is considered a Seyfert 1, although some are formally classified 1.5, etc. The magnitude limit is chosen as being the approximate completeness limit of the Markarian survey. From this list alone, a luminosity function can be determined using the simple technique described by Huchra and Sargent (1973); the only improvement I offer is the inclusion of more galaxies. The absolute magnitude of each galaxy is determined; using that with the limiting magnitude yields the distance to which that galaxy could have been seen, and the volume corresponding to that distance is then the volume of the universe containing a galaxy of that particular absolute magnitude. Summing volumes within absolute magnitude bins yields the space densities for each absolute magnitude interval. The biggest uncertainty in this procedure is the adopted limiting magnitude. I illustrate this uncertainty by showing how the results change if completeness corrections are included as done by Meurs and Wilson (1984), compared to my calculation that did not include them. Meurs and Wilson suggest a correction factor of 3 at a magnitude 15.5, which accounts for the difference between these two results in Figure 1.

A similar determination can be made using another recent source of bright Seyfert 1 galaxies: the low redshift objects among the Palomar Bright Quasar Survey (Schmidt and Green 1983). This is an especially useful supplement to Markarian galaxies for the brighter nuclei, because it was a search for starlike objects. Several previously known Seyfert 1 galaxies with very bright nuclei were rediscovered. By contrast, Markarian wanted to see a surrounding galaxy, so may have overlooked the very brightest nuclei. Table 2 contains the PBQS objects with z < 0.1, an arbitrary cutoff for separating "Seyfert galaxies" from "quasars" but

TABLE 1

Markarian #	Z	Mag	Markarian #	Z	Mag
6	0.0189	14.8	590	0.0263	14.0
9	0.0390	15.2	609	0.0342	14.5
10	0.0290	14.0	618	0.0362	14.5
42	0.0240	15.2	662	0.0553	15.5
50	0.0234	15.5	699	0.0342	15.4
141	0.0390	14.5	744	0.0090	13.5
231	0.0410	14.1	766	0.0129	13.7
279	0.0305	14.5	771	0.0630	15.1
290	0.0301	15.0	841	0.0364	14.0
291	0.0352	15.0	883	0.0380	15.2
304	0.0657	14.6	885	0.0250	15.0
315	0.0388	14.8	915	0.0239	15.0
335	0.0258	14.0	975	0.0491	15.0
352	0.0155	14.8	1018	0.0424	14.6
358	0.0454	15.0	1034	0.0350	14.9
372	0.0308	15.0	1040	0.0164	13.9
382	0.0340	15.5	1044	0.0163	15.5
423	0.0319	14.9	1095	0.0330	14.6
471	0.0342	14.5	1098	0.0353	15.5
474	0.0391	15.3	1126	0.0103	14.5
478	0.0790	15.0	1146	0.0386	15.5
486	0.0390	15.2	1152	0.0527	15.5
493	0.0315	14.9	1187	0.0449	15.5
506	0.0431	15.3	1218	0.0286	14.8
509	0.0340	14.5	1239	0.0194	14.5
516	0.0285	15.4	1243	0.0352	14.5
530	0.0293	14.4	1347	0.0503	15.4
541	0.0395	15.5	1383	0.0862	15.0
584	0.0788	14.0	1400	0.0293	15.5

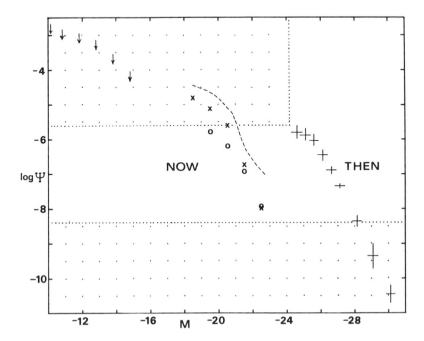

Figure 1: The luminosity function for local nuclei with broad line regions (NOW) and for quasars with 2.0 <z< 2.5 (THEN). ψ is the number of objects Mpc^{-3} with absolute magnitudes brighter than M. Arrows are upper limits from Keel's results for low luminosity nuclei, x are Markarian galaxies in Table 1, o are PBQS objects from Table 2, curve is luminosity function for Seyfert 1 from Meurs and Wilson (1984), adjusted to $H_o = 75$ km s^{-1} Mpc^{-1}. Crosses represent the high redshift luminosity function using magnitude distribution for $2 < z < 2.5$ in Weedman (1984); vertical extent represents uncertainty in counts and horizontal extent represents uncertainty introduced by assuming spectral indices of -0.5 and -1.0 for relating observed magnitudes of high redshift quasars to local nuclei. Dotted zone at top is region invisible at high redshift because magnitudes would be fainter than 22. Dotted zone at bottom is region within which less than one local quasar would be expected within entire volume having $z < 0.1$.

TABLE 2

PBQS #	Z	Mag.	PBQS #	Z	Mag.
0003+199[a]	0.025	13.75	1310−108	0.035	15.55
0007+106	0.089	16.11	1341+258	0.087	15.93
0049+171	0.064	15.88	1351+236[b]	0.055	15.87
0050+124	0.061	14.39	1351+640	0.087	15.42
0119+229	0.053	15.41	1404+226	0.098	15.82
0844+349	0.064	14.00	1411+442	0.089	14.99
0921+525	0.035	15.62	1426+015[c]	0.086	15.05
0923+129	0.029	14.93	1440+356[d]	0.077	15.00
0934+013	0.050	16.29	1448+273	0.065	15.01
1011−040	0.058	15.49	1501+106[e]	0.036	15.09
1022+519	0.045	16.12	1534+580[f]	0.030	15.54
1119+120	0.049	14.65	1535+547	0.038	15.31
1126−041	0.060	15.43	2130+099	0.061	14.62
1149−110	0.049	15.46	2209+184	0.070	15.86
1211+143	0.085	14.63	2214+139[g]	0.067	14.98
1229+204	0.064	14.65	2304+042	0.042	15.44
1244+026	0.048	16.15			

[a] 0003+199 = MKN 335

[b] 1351+236 = MKN 662

[c] 1426+015 = MKN 1383

[d] 1440+356 = MKN 478

[e] 1501+106 = MKN 841

[f] 1534+580 = MKN 290

[g] 2214+139 = MKN 304

one chosen so as not to intrude into epochs at which evolution becomes significant. These galaxies are also used to calculate a luminosity function, shown in Figure 1. The agreement at higher luminosities between the PBQS and the uncorrected Markarian sample implies to me that the Meurs-Wilson correction is too much for M < −22.

Finally, we must tack on the very lowest luminosity nuclei. A luminosity function for them in units of [NII] λ6584 luminosity was attempted by Keel (1983), from his complete sample of spiral galaxy nuclei. He distinguished "low-ionization" nuclei attributable to the non-thermal processes associated with Seyferts, and treated them separately from starburst (or "H II region" nuclei). How can we transform from his units to the magnitude units for quasars? Here is one example of a juncture where treatment of selection effects becomes highly arbitrary. Keel states that [NII] and Hα luminosities are comparable in these nuclei, and I assume that these will scale with the nuclear continuum magnitude the same as in more luminous nuclei. Then, the Hβ fluxes in Yee (1980) are compared with the magnitudes in Table 1 for 18 objects in common to determine a transformation. Making the further assumption that Hα/Hβ = 4 in Sy 1 broad lines, the empirical result is M = -2.5log L(Hα) + 84.70. This transformation makes it possible to add Keel's low luminosity function to Figure 1, thereby producing a summary of the local quasar luminosity function over a range of 13 absolute magnitudes. Since we cannot be sure that all of Keel's nuclei are weak Seyfert 1, those results are more appropriately upper limits and displayed as such in Figure 1.

We can next ask how the local luminosity function compared to empirical results for quasars somewhere else in the universe. An epoch where an evolution-independent snapshot of the luminosity function exists is claimed by me to be z ~ 2.2, because of the large number of quasars discoverable there using low dispersion spectroscopic surveys. I can use the apparent magnitude distribution that I discussed at the Workshop (Weedman 1984) for 2.0 < z < 2.5 to transform to a luminosity function, if cos-

mological assumptions are imposed. The procedure is similar to
that in Gaston (1983), just with a larger sample. Even after H_o
and q_o are assumed, the cosmological equations are not simple.
One must also be arbitrary, the concensus on cosmological models
having reached an inflection point about a decade ago and now
diversing. When considering quasar evolution, the form of evolution is independent of H_o, so the controversy about its value is
relevant only to time scales and actual luminosities. The evolution
form is weakly dependent on q_o for Freidmann cosmologies with
q_o between 0 and 0.5. Given the many uncertainties already in
selection effects, this additional cosmological flexibility is not of
great concern. The methodology can be used for any q_o, but I will
present equations only for $q_o = 0$, because they have been discussed and used in many places (e.g., Carswell and Smith 1978).
All calculations assume $H_o = 75$ km s^{-1} Mpc^{-1}. With these assumptions, the volume of the universe in a unit area of the sky
within a redshift interval dz is

$$dv(z) =$$
$$2.43 \times 10^6 [2(1+z) + 2(1+z)^{-3} - 4(1+z)^{-1}] dz \ Mpc^3 \ deg^{-2}.$$

The absolute magnitude M desired at all redshifts represents the quasar continuum luminosity at a rest wavelength of
4500A. Then,

$$M(z) = m - 5log(c/H_o) - 5log[z(1+z/2)]$$
$$- 25 + 2.5(1+\alpha)log(1+z),$$

where α is the spectral index for $f_\nu \propto \nu^\alpha$. Alternative values of α
will be used in the relevant calculations.

With these equations, the apparent magnitude distribution for $2.0 < z < 2.5$ yields the luminosity function within that
volume. This is shown in Figure 1 as the THEN curve.

The result to the moment, therefore, is two luminosity
functions, one for local quasars and the other for $z + 2.25$, an

epoch about two thirds of the way back to the beginning of the universe, an epoch beyond which our knowledge of quasars is as yet insufficient to trace their behavior. Comparing these functions in Figure 1 shows the difference that must be accounted for by a quasar evolution parameter. If the functions have the same shape at both epochs, requiring the same scaling at all luminosities to go from one curve to the other, then the evolution factor is luminosity independent. That is, if the "THEN" curve can be overlaid onto the "NOW" curve simply by sliding to the left, the same change in luminosity applies to all parts of the curve. My contention is that, within the uncertainties, this is the case. The problem in gaining a definitive answer by comparing the two functions is the limited densities at which they can be compared. The local function cannot exist below the point at which quasar numbers fall below unity for the total volume within z < 0.1. The high redshift function is not yet observable beyond 22 mag. We are then left with the limited range shown within which to overlay the curves.

IV. FORM OF EVOLUTION
FOR OPTICALLY SELECTED QUASARS

The procedure now will be to determine an evolution parameter that transforms high redshift to local quasars, and then check to see if that same parameter can account for other available quasar samples, those from Schmidt and Green (1983) and Marshall *et al.* (1983a). What should be the form of the evolution parameter? Historically, evolution has been considered in terms of (1+z), since this reflects scale length changes, or in terms of the look-back time, expecting that time is a reasonable physical parameter to which any evolution must relate. Various analyses have utilized different parameterizations (e.g., Wills and Lynds 1978). It is to be expected that no unique solution will be found, and the parameterization will reflect the taste of the parameterizer. My taste runs to exponential decay, but solutions equivalent to that which follows could be found for alternative forms. This simple form of quasar evolution has the characteristic luminosity of quasars scaling as $\exp(\beta z/1+z)$. This form arises because $z/1+z$ is a measure of look-back time to the quasar. For $q_o = 0$, the look-back time t in years is $t = (H_o^{-1})z/1+z$. The free parameter to fit is β. In Figure 1, it appears that the low and high redshift functions are separated by 4 to 5 magnitudes. For this amount of luminosity evolution between $z = 0$ (now) and $z = 2.25$ (then), it is straightforward that $5.3 < \beta < 6.7$.

This conclusion does not require that the same quasar has existed since $z = 2.5$, decaying all the while by $\exp(6z/1+z)$, until becoming a Seyfert 1 galaxy today. It is equally allowable that lifetimes as visible quasars are very short, and we see only characteristic quasar luminosities at different epochs., Quasars could then come and go within various galaxies, at arbitrary times, constrained only by having their representative luminosities scale with epoch by $\exp(6z/1+z)$. These are drastically different alternatives, bearing upon the question of whether every galaxy harbors a quasar corpse. Physical models for the quasar ignition process are required to choose between them, as discussed by Cavaliere *et al.* (1984). These models may eventually be sufficiently constrained by an empirical description of the form of evolution to help in this decision.

Herman Marshall reported on his data for faint Braccesi quasars, from which he used the redshifts and magnitudes to deconvolve both a power law luminosity function and an evolution parameter. He concluded that the best fit for pure luminosity evolution is $L \propto (1+z)^{3.5}$. Note that this parameter is in reasonable agreement with what was deduced with the exponential evolution; the latter requires luminosity increase of ~20 by $z = 1$, compared to 11 for Marshall's form, and factors of 55 and 47, respectively, at $z = 2$. That these independent quasar samples normalize well is shown below by fitting Marshall's observed redshift distribution.

Now that we have deduced the parameter needed to go from local to high redshift quasars, what about the route be-

tween? Can this simple luminosity evolution also account for all
other quasars known with redshifts between $z = 0.1$ and $z = 2.5$?
Specifically, can the conclusions reached so far also fit the surveys
by Marshall and by Schmidt and Green, which have nicely defined magnitude limits and cover all redshifts to $z \sim 2.2$? Starting
with the luminosity function defined at $z = 2.25$ in Figure 1, this
function can be progressively transformed with the evolution parameter deduced to see if the other samples are fit. Every quasar
within this luminosity function must have $L(z) \propto \exp(\beta/1+z)$, so
at any z, the absolute magnitude is

$$M(z) = M(2.25) - 2.5 log\{exp[\beta(z/1+z-.692)]\}.$$

The luminosity function $\psi[M(z)]$ at any redshift can
thereby be determined at any redshift using $\psi[M(2.25)]$ from Figure 1. Then, the number of quasars observed $\deg^{-2}$ to limiting
magnitude m, and within a redshift interval dz, is

$$dN(z) = \psi[M(z)] \; dv(z).$$

The luminosity function at $z = 2.25$ in Figure 1 is evolved
in this way to predict the redshift distribution which should be
observed for different limiting magnitudes. The choices of m are
16, to match the PBQS, and 18.25, to match the brighter sample
in Marshall *et al.* (1983b). Results, showing quite pleasing fits for
$\beta = 6$, are in Figures 2 and 3.

It is clear from examining these fits that the uncertainties in the continuous spectral shapes prevent a precise fit for the
evolution parameter. The relevant spectra need to be described
between rest wavelengths of 1300A and 4500A, to cover $0 < z <$
2.5, and quasar continua are not really simple power laws within
this interval. The "blue bump" is of varying strength from object to object, although it may rest on an underlying power law.
By illustrating how the results change for different α, I wish to

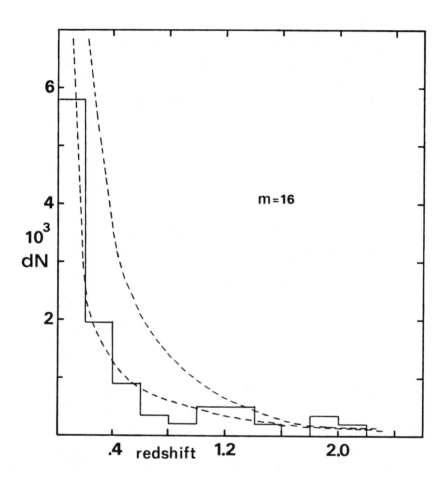

Figure 2: Expectations from the luminosity function and evolution described compared to observations from the Palomar Bright Quasar Survey. dN has units of number deg^{-2} per redshift interval of 0.2 (scale is magnified by 10^3). Histogram shows observed quasars in Schmidt and Green (1983). Upper curve is expectation to limiting magnitude 16 for luminosity evolution of form $\exp(6z/1+z)$ and continuum power law index -1.0; lower curve is same except with power law index -0.5.

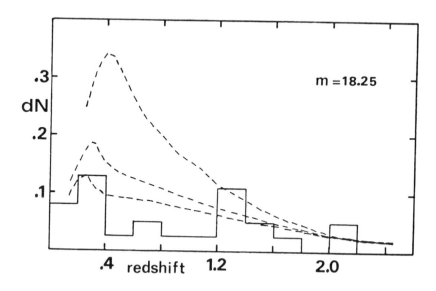

Figure 3: Expectations from the luminosity function and evolution described compared to observations of Braccesi quasars by Marshall *et al.* (1983b). dN has units of number deg^{-2} per redshift interval of 0.2. Histogram shows observations of the Braccesi sample with m < 18.25. Upper curve is expectation to limiting magnitude 18.25 for luminosity evolution of form exp(6z/1+z) and continuum power law index -1.0; intermediate curve is same but the power law index -0.5; lower curve has luminosity evolution of form exp(6.5z/1+z) and power law index -0.5.

demonstrate why there is still so much room for choice in picking an evolution parameter.

V. RESULTS FOR OTHER SAMPLES

What has been found with the preceding analysis is a self-consistent description of quasar evolution as seen by the optical observer. Here is a big hitch. What we really want is quasar evolution described in units of bolometric luminosity. The X-ray results demonstrate that the optical continuum does not contain the same fraction of total quasar radiated power for quasars of all luminosity. This is shown in several ways and by many studies (e.g., Tananbaum *et al.* 1983, Reichert *et al.* 1982). Discussions at this meeting, based upon work still underway, were led by Claude Canizares and John Stocke. What has been found is that the ratio of X-ray to optical luminosity changes with optical luminosity. This can be expressed as $L_x \propto L_{opt}^{0.7}$, or with the parameter α_{ox}, defined as the slope needed to connect flux at 2 keV and 2500A. The α_{ox} is ~ 1.2 for low luminosity quasars and Seyfert 1 galaxies but ~ 1.6 for higher redshift quasars, according to the summary by Canizares. Observationally, the effect is that X-ray based quasar surveys reveal systematically lower redshifts than optical surveys, because the preferential gain in luminosity is not as great at high redshifts (i.e., high observed luminosity). Naturally, therefore, different conclusions will be reached about the form of evolution if only X-ray luminosities are considered. The best fits give $L_x \propto \exp(4.5z/1+z)$ (Maccacaro *et al.* 1984). Presumably, an evolution parameter describing bolometric luminosity would lie in between that for optical and X-ray. That quasars redistribute their radiation as a function of luminosity is an important clue for physical models (e.g., Tucker 1983), but a distressing proof to the observer of how our perception of quasar evolution depends upon the tools of the beholder.

Radio astronomers have not been idle in determining quasar fluxes. Unfortunately, most quasars discoverable by optical and X-ray techniques are not detectable radio sources. The radio, luminosity function of Seyfert galaxies has received attention, and was summarized nicely by both Evert Meurs and Andrew Wilson (Meurs and Wilson 1984). This determination represents a major accomplishment, providing an important local benchmark. Richard Green reviewed the efforts by him, K. Kellermann, R. Sramek, D. Shaffer and M. Schmidt to observe all 118 PBQS objects with the VLA. By pushing to 1σ limits of 250 μJy, 60% of the objects brighter than 16 mag. were detected, but these quasars are very bright by most optical standards.

The hazards of pushing the VLA too far in searching for quasar fluxes were demonstrated by Jim Condon. He pointed out that the disk emission from a normal 15 mag spiral galaxy would be at least 100 μJy, so radio detections at that level could not be attributed to an active nucleus. His very deep radio maps show primarily spiral galaxies fainter than 500 μJy. To the extraordinary limit of 13 μJy (1σ), he was able to find about 1000 sources deg^{-2} in the two fields mapped so deeply. Yet, very few of these sources are quasars. He summarized by saying, "When we beat down VLA limits, we are not seeing further into space, we are just seeing the dregs of the universe."

Not surprisingly, we still do not have adequate radio data on high redshift quasars to undertake a discussion of their evolution, analogous to what was done for the optical sources. Conclusions about the evolution of radio properties of quasars still have to be drawn from the very small fraction of quasars that are radio-bright. Determining the extent to which these are representative of the entire quasar sample provides a continuing challenge for radio observers.

VI. EXPECTATIONS AT VERY HIGH REDSHIFTS

I see the next big step in trading quasar evolution optically to be at redshifts beyond 2.5. It is already very obvious that quasars cannot be found in the numbers expected (if the evolution deduced for lower redshifts extends to z of $\sim$ 4 (Osmer 1982; Schneider *et al.* 1983). There were early hints that this was the case, although the apparent deficiency of very high redshift quasars was marginally accountable (Carswell and Smith 1978; Lewis *et al.* 1979). For convenience in future comparisons, the expectations of quasar numbers based upon the luminosity function and evolution deduced above are shown in Figure 4 for 2 < z < 4. The high z cutoff is chosen so that the blue magnitude does not fall below the Lyman limit. The lower redshifts in this interval have already been probed by photographic surveys for Ly α quasars, and CCD-based surveys can extend almost to z = 5. No survey so far shows the expected number of quasars with z > ~ 2.5. Much work remains in calibrating magnitudes and spectrum shapes. It can be seen in Figure 4 that the shape of the expected redshift distribution changes significantly with limiting magnitude. Somewhere in

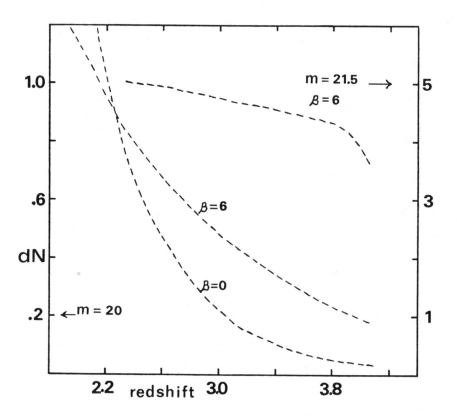

Figure 4. Redshift distributions expected for 2 < z < 4, based on luminosity function and evolution discussed. dN has units of number deg^{-2} per redshift interval of 0.2. From top to bottom, curves are for limiting magnitude of 21.5 (scale on right) with evolution of form $\exp(6z/1+z)$ and continuum spectra of power law slope -0.5; for limiting magnitude of 20 (scale on left) with evolution of form $\exp(6z/1+z)$ and continuum slope -0.5; for limiting magnitude of 20 (scale on left) with no evolution of the luminosity function in this redshift interval and continuum slope -0.5.

this redshift interval, I think near z = 2.5, a significant alteration occurs in the parameter describing evolution for optical quasars. Tracking down this alteration precisely is an exciting and realistic project.

Once it is defined observationally, the interpretation challenge can be undertaken. What actually happened to very high redshift quasars? The key issue will be whether luminosity evolution in units of bolometric luminosity underwent the same change as seen in optical luminosity, or whether we are looking to an epoch at which the optical spectrum is obscured. One way occurs to me of setting at this answer, and that is to look for signs that obscuring material becomes more common for z > ∼ 2.5. Do the broad absorption line quasars, for example, increase in proportion at such redshifts? Answering questions like this requires large samples of quasars, most of which can be accumulated from the ground with existing telescopes. The challenge of describing the real development of quasars in the early universe promises to keep quasar observers busy for quite some time.

My research on these issues and attendance at the UCSC Workshop has been supported by the National Science Foundation. I thank many participants, not just those mentioned above, for useful discussions on the problems of quasar evolution. Also, I thank S. Huels and S. Donnell for helping with some of the numerical calculations.

REFERENCES

Balzano, V.A., and Mazzarella, J.M. 1984, *Ap. J. Suppl.*, submitted.

Boroson, T.A., and Oke, J.B. 1984, *Ap. J.*, **281**, 535.

Carswell, R.F., and Smith, M.G. 1978, *M.N.R.A.S.*, **185**, 381.

Cavaliere, A., Giallongo, E., and Vagnetti, F. 1984, preprint.

Cruz-Gonzales, I. 1984, Thesis, Harvard University.

Filippenko, A.V., and Sargent, W.L.W. 1984, *Ap. J. Suppl.*, in press.

Gaston, R. 1983, *Ap.J.*, **272**, 411.

Gehren, T., Fried, J., Wehinger, P.A., and Wyckoff, S. 1984, *Ap. J.*, **278**, 11.

Huchra, J., and Sargent, W.L.W. 1973, *Ap. J.*, **186**, 433.

Hutchings, J.B., Crampton, D., Campbell, B., Duncan, D., and Glendenning, B. 1984, *Ap. J. Suppl.*, **55**, 319.

Keel, W. 1983, *Ap. J. Suppl.*, **52**, 229.

Kriss, G.A., and Canizares, C.R. 1982, *Ap. J.*, **261**, 51.

Lawrence, A., and Elvis, M. 1982, *Ap. J.*, **256**, 410.

Lewis, D.W., MacAlpine, G.M., and Weedman, D.W. 1979, *Ap. J.*, **233**, 787.

Maccacaro, T., Gioia, T.M., and Stocke J. 1984, *Ap. J.*, **283**, in press.

Malkan, M.A., Margon, B., and Chanan, G.A. 1984, *Ap. J.*, **280**, 66.

Marshall, H.L., Avni, Y., Tananbaum, H., and Zamorani, G. 1983a, *Ap. J.*, **269**, 35.

Marshall, H.L., Tananbaum, H., Zamorani, G., Huchra, J.P., Braccesi, A., and Zitelli, V. 1983b, *Ap. J.*, **269**, 42.

Meurs, E.J.A., and Wilson, A.S. 1984, *Astr. Ap.*, submitted.

Miller, J.S., and Antonucci, R.R.J. 1983, *Ap.J. (Letters)*, **271**, L7.

Osmer, P.S. 1982, *Ap. J.*, **253**, 28.

Osterbrock, D.E. 1979, *A.J.*, **84**, 901.

——————— 1984, *Q.J.R.A.S.*, **25**, 1.

Piccinotti, G., Mushotzky, R.F., Boldt, E.A., Holt, S.S., Marshall, F.E., Serlemitsos, P.J. and Shafer, R.A. 1982, *Ap. J.*, **253**, 485.

Reichert, G.A., Mason, K.O., Thorstensen, J.R., and Bowyer, S. 1982, *Ap. J.*, **260**,. 437.

Schmidt, M. 1972, *Ap. J.*, **176**, 273.

Schmidt, M., and Green, R.F. 1983, *Ap. J.*, **269**, 352.

Schneider, D., Schmidt, M., and Gunn, J. 1983, it B.A.A.S., **15**, 957.

Stocke, J.T., Liebert, J., Gioia, I., Griffiths, R.E., Maccacaro, T., Danziger, I.J., Kunth, D., and Lub, J. 1983, *Ap. J.*, **273**, 458.

Tananbaum, H., Wardle, J., Zanorani, G., and Avni, Y. 1983, *Ap. J.*, 268, 60.

Tucker, W.H. 1983, *Ap. J.*, **271**, 531.

Wills, D., and Lynds, R. 1978, *Ap. J. Suppl.*, **36**, 317.

Weedman, D.W. 1984, *Ap. J. Suppl.*, submitted.

Wu, C.-C., Boggess, A., and Gull, T.R. 1983, *Ap. J.*, **266**, 28.

Yee, H.K.C. 1981, *Ap. J.*, **241**, 894.

Yee, H.K.C., and Green, R.F. 1984, *Ap. J.*, **280**, 79.